D0268152

Being Sarah

Written by Sarah Horton
Edited by Fiona Shaw
Graphic design by Ken Ashcroft
Proofreading by Judy Tasker
Printed and bound by Lulu.com

All photos by Ronnie Hughes, excep[t]
Sarah and Ronnie on page iii by Kar[...]

ISBN: 978-0-9566344-1-2

© Sarah Horton
Sarah Horton is hereby identified as the author of this work
in accordance with section 77 of the copyright, design and
patents act 1988.

First published in October 2010 by
Wordscapes
Metal @ Edge Hill Station
Tunnel Road
Liverpool L7 6ND

www.beingsarah.com

Author's Note: This is a book about my own experience.
It is not intended to replace the advice of your doctors for
any medical condition. If, however, my experiences help
you to ask more questions, then I believe that will be a
good thing.

FOR RONNIE

Ronnie says:

"*Sarah graciously offered to dedicate this book to me. Thinking about it, I declined the offer. I helped – obviously. But what you will read here is the story of Sarah – her determination, what she did. It has been a privilege to live with such an opinionated woman through this story and for all this time.*

This is Sarah's book."

June 2010 - Ronnie Hughes and Sarah Horton. Sefton Park, Liverpool.

"I had known the pain, and survived it. It only remained for me to give it a voice, to share it for use, that the pain not be wasted."

Audre Lorde, The Cancer Journals [1]

Introduction

She's asking me to put the pink t-shirt on. Pink, the colour of hope. 'OK,' I say, knowing instinctively, somehow, that I don't really want to. 'It's for the photos, for the calendar, we're all doing it,' she says, encouragingly.

So I do. But it's the only time. The only time I ever wear pink for breast cancer. Because I know I have to find my own way through this.

My own way of being me.

part **one**
The day
everything changed

February 2007 - At home the day after diagnosis.
'I wake the next morning and briefly, just briefly, I forget.'

CHAPTER ONE

Disaster

I am staring hard at the carpet. I think I might faint. I've never fainted so don't know what it feels like. I've just been told I have breast cancer. I am 43 years old. This isn't supposed to happen. All I can think about is dying. I hear enough to recognise the word 'mastectomy'. This can't be happening to me. How did I get here?

I am Sarah Horton. I am an artist, a film-maker, a knitter, a gardener, a quilter, a runner. I live in Liverpool in England with my partner Ronnie, and it is just coming up to our tenth wedding anniversary. We think we might go to Amsterdam.

We've run our own business together for 11 years. We left our jobs so we could spend more time with each other, and we have. We've worked all over the country with groups of people helping them create new futures, an unusual personality-led business. We are good with people. We bring the best out of groups.

We also started to make films about six years ago. I am tenacious about learning new media, and we have a growing reputation for doing short films with meaning and passion, capturing the spirit of the places and the people we work with. We have just finished the story of a community-led building in Bradford which was built by the determination of the feisty residents of the estate. And we have also just sent off a job for duplication of 20,000 DVDs with subtitling in six languages, for the council tenants of Liverpool. We are proud of our work, of giving real people voices. It is January 2007, we have both worked hard on these projects. I am happy, fulfilled. Life is good.

Then, at the beginning of February when I'm putting my bra on I feel a lump in my right breast. And I mean a lump. It's enormous. At least it feels like it to me, and it wasn't there the day before, it's just appeared from nowhere. I am a bit concerned. My period is late, my breasts are in their usual premenstrual tender and uncomfortable state, and I'm very tired. Normal for me to be tired before my period. But this lump is definitely *not normal*. I make an appointment at my doctor's the soonest I am able to, which is over a week away.

My period arrives. The lump does not go away, as I had hoped. Now I am more concerned. So I go to an emergency surgery at the doctor's. The very pleasant female doctor I see says she will refer me to the breast clinic. What? She hasn't even examined me yet. I am now *very* concerned. She is very patient with me. She doesn't give me any opinion about what she thinks it might be.

'You should be seen at a breast clinic. There is a lump, you are over 35, you are a priority. You will get an appointment within a fortnight.'

I go home and tell Ronnie. He says it's best to get it checked.

All the rest of the week I convince myself that this is a hormonal change, and it is a cyst. I even convince myself that the lump has become smaller. But I think I'm not really convincing myself very well. I keep telling myself that nine out of ten lumps are nothing and it's best to get it checked out.

We carry on with our work, we both have filming projects to complete. I set up lights and microphones, and all the time I am trying not to think about the lump and concentrate on work.

It is the weekend before my appointment at the breast unit and I don't have work to distract me anymore. We drive up to the beach at Crosby where Anthony Gormley's cast iron sculptures of men stare out to sea. I want to be distracted. We drive around, I am listless. I am finding it impossible to think of anything else other than the lump.

In the middle of one night I get up to go to the toilet. I catch sight of myself in the mirror. I think, if I have to lose a breast that will be the worst possible thing that can happen to me.

R⁊Ø

Then it is the day for the breast clinic, it is now three weeks since I found the lump. The appointment is at 8.45 am, so we are up early and I am at my worst this time of the morning. Ronnie tries to be cheerful as we walk to the taxi rank. We decide to get a taxi as it's difficult to park near the hospital. It's looking like it's going to be a nice day. I can feel spring arriving. The third week in February. It's lighter than it has been for weeks. Ronnie asks where I'd like to go for lunch after the appointment.

'I'm sure it's a cyst, I'm sure it is,' I say.

I'm not up to having a proper conversation.

We sit in the ordinary waiting room. Everyone there looks vaguely terrified, most people are with someone else. When my name is called Ronnie stands up and follows me. But at the double doors which go through to the next area the nurse says he can't come.

'It's the gowns,' she says.

'What?'

'Well, there are ladies here and they are only wearing gowns.'

This is my first sense that something isn't right, the gowns aren't right. So Ronnie goes back to his waiting, alone. And I go through the double doors into the unknown.

I am given a shopping basket, a wire one, to put my things in and given a gown to put on after I have undressed, 'top half only'. So this is where the wire supermarket baskets have gone. They are in breast units being used to carry your clothes around as you are shunted between the different bits of checking. It seems incongruous and I suppose I might even have found it funny if I wasn't there under these particular circumstances.

I change into the gown. It is blue and white, a horrible utilitarian pattern. It opens at the front and there is no way of fastening it. Great. No wonder I have seen all these women clutching the gowns across them as they sit there, looking terrified. Fortunately I am wearing a brooch on my knitted linen jacket, so I take it off and put it on the horrible gown. At least it keeps it closed and I can use my hands to knit. Except just now I can't even contemplate knitting. I am sitting in a tiny screened-off area. On the screens there are cards from grateful patients, thanking the nurses for looking after them. I do not want to be here. Then my name is called.

It starts with a mammogram, the unconcerned nurse shoves my breasts one at a time between these flat cold plates, and takes x-rays from the top and from the side of each breast. And then the waiting starts. I have my knitting with me. I am knitting a baby's cardigan in purple cotton. But I still can't knit. Another room, and I then have a case history taken by a nurse practitioner. It doesn't take very long, I don't have a case history, I've never been ill. Had my tonsils out and that's about it.

More waiting. I text Ronnie, 'ultrasound next'. He is still out in the waiting room, not knowing what is happening. I have no idea what he is thinking or why it is taking so long. I start knitting. I am knitting the collar now, on the jacket, it is the first time I have done short rows, it's quite complicated. Then I am called in for ultrasound.

In the ultrasound room it's dark and the blinds are drawn. It's actually relaxing and pleasant, and the staff are friendly. They ask what I am knitting, the baby garment, they think I am pregnant. So I tell them about Ellie, Ronnie's granddaughter. The cardigan is for Ellie, age seven months. I don't know my life is minutes away from being turned upside down.

The radiographer puts some cold gel on me and then spends ages and ages going over the lump with a probe, and then into my armpit. It's very quiet in the room. Peaceful. I am trying to relax, waiting for the moment that I can leave this place and get back to my life. The radiographer seems concerned, and tells me that all her work is checked by a doctor. Even I don't believe this and I have my first slight sense that things aren't as they should be. Does she not want to alarm me by sending for a second opinion?

The doctor comes in and they both peer at the screen together. The doctor takes over and spends an age back and forth over the lump with the probe, staring at the screen. I'm craning my neck trying to look at what they can see on the screen. It's a grey picture of my breast with a big orange shape where the lump is.

'Is it a cyst?' I ask.

'It doesn't look like a cyst.'

'So is it cancer?'

A pause.

'We don't know.'

Still lying where I am they arrange the next test. A fine needle aspiration. If I thought the mammogram was unpleasant then this one's a bit worse. My breast is clamped and a long fine needle is inserted into the lump. Actually, I don't know how long the needle is, as by this time I am looking away frantically counting backwards from 101 in sevens, as recommended by my friend as a diversionary tactic when pain might be involved. 94, 87, 80,

73, 66, 59. Is it over yet? 52, 45, 38. Then I am told to get dressed and wait for half an hour. I can see from the look on all their faces that they think it is serious. Shit.

I get off the bed but I can barely stand. A nurse helps me walk back to the changing cubicle and carries my clothes in the wire basket for me.

'Are you OK?' she asks.

Well, I could say, yes I'm perfectly fine, or I could say, no I'm shit scared. But in fact I can't even speak because I am terrified. I am shaking. She tries to be positive. I mean, let's face it, I'm probably just about to find out I've got breast cancer. She looks at me and smiles.

'You know they can do wonderful things these days. There's lots of choices.'

I have no idea what she is talking about. I still want to entertain the possibility that this isn't cancer. I glare at her. She stops smiling.

'I'll get your husband. What's his name?'

'It's Ronnie. Hughes. Not Horton. Hughes.'

She smiles at me.

I think I have a reasonably instinctive feeling at this point that I have breast cancer. This is the point when things start to swim a bit. This is the point when I would like to have woken up and realised it was just a bad dream. I get dressed, leave the cubicle and the nurse is hovering in the corridor and I am shown into the 'quiet room', rather than the waiting room. It must be bad. A few minutes later Ronnie joins me. He looks worried. I can't speak, so the nurse tells him.

'Well, we've done some tests and we need to find out whether this is cancerous. We're just waiting for the result back from the lab now. Then we'll know.'

She leaves us alone. I can't speak. Time stretches like elastic as we wait for the half hour to pass.

After 15 minutes there is a knock. The nurse comes back and apologises. The test was inconclusive. Would I mind if we did the needle test again? No friendly chit chat this time. I follow her back to the consultation room. Top off, needle in, then back to the room with Ronnie. More waiting. It's a blue sky, almost spring-like day outside. We are in a bubble suspended in a quiet room looking out of the back of the hospital at the air vents and the traffic moving slowly. Ronnie says there's always a traffic jam on Hall Lane. He is hopeful, thinks the repeat test might mean it's negative. I so want it to be.

A knock on the door. A new nurse. She says the doctor wants to look at me again. Back to an examination room, with Ronnie this time. He hadn't been allowed 'in' before so I suppose it is serious now. The doctor introduces herself as a surgeon and has a very thorough feel of my breast. I feel completely detached from my breast now. I have the sensation that I am drowning.

I go to the toilet. I want the floor to open up and swallow me. I throw some water on my face. I can't believe this is happening to me, that this day has turned out so badly. Back out in the corridor I see the surgeon who has just examined me, and some other staff. They look tense. I go back to the quiet room and wait for the news. The world is spiralling off its axis as the surgeon bursts through the door and immediately says I have breast cancer and I need to have a mastectomy. She is accompanied by another nurse, who is not in uniform, a breast care nurse, who looks like she is wearing a mask as there is no expression on her face.

I am leaning forward, wringing my hands and I'm now fully immersed in the nightmare. But it can't really be me. This isn't happening to me. But, oh yes it is. I am looking down at the carpet now. Grey with flecks of maroon and blue. Ronnie asking sensible questions and I can only stare at the carpet, wondering if this is what it feels like before you faint.

A black diary is produced and pored over. The surgeon tells me I will have a mastectomy on Friday 16 March, just over three weeks away. I probably look like I haven't heard her. She says again, 'You have breast cancer and you need a mastectomy. This lump is six centimetres.'

Six centimetres? *What*? How did that happen.

Just to make sure I fully understand exactly what this means she draws a diagram of my right breast. Then she draws the lump, which is actually three lumps, and it takes up almost all of the lower part of my breast. I'm sort of getting the picture now. She carries on.

'We don't think it is in your lymph nodes.'

'Is that good?' I ask, I can barely hear my voice, it is a whisper.

I am so ignorant. I know nothing about cancer. Well, apart from the fact that you definitely die. I don't know that tumours outgrow their primary sites and start spreading to the rest of your body. I don't know that with breast cancer they can start doing this by spreading to your lymph nodes.

'Well, we can't tell for sure, but we will remove all your lymph nodes to check.'

I think to myself, I wonder if they put them back in if they are OK? I'm being stupid aren't I? I don't know what I should be asking. I look blank.

The surgeon, having delivered this news, leaves the room and we are alone with the breast care nurse, who tells me she will be my friend through this.

'Any questions?' she says.

Yes, thousands, millions. No, just one actually.

'Will I die?'

I am so shocked I can't even cry. I am numb.

I manage to regain enough of myself to say, 'You should have a bar in here, because as a rule I don't drink in the day, but I feel like a drink now.' My new friend, the breast care nurse, smiles at me. I think she feels sorry for me. I wonder if she has heard all this before.

'I can't have a mastectomy. I just can't,' I say. 'These are my best assets.'

I am a 38FF. I've always had large breasts. It's never been a problem to me. I like them. A lot.

Ronnie puts his arm around me and says, 'but you are your best asset, really.'

He does mean it. It doesn't make me feel any better.

We spend some time with the breast care nurse and she arranges to visit us at home in a few days when we can talk further. I have more tests, first a core biopsy on my breast under local anaesthetic, where some samples of the tumour are taken. We can now officially call it a tumour, my lump, now we know it is cancer. The surgeon who does the biopsy cheerfully waves the sample bottle at me and says, 'We're going to have a really good look at these and do lots of tests.'

'Oh, do all the tests you like, I'm getting out of here.'

'Oh you'll be back,' she says. 'We'll be getting to see a lot of each other over the next ten years.'

What? What did she mean, ten years? Ten years? I'm sort of starting to realise that this is serious.

Then I go for blood tests. And then a chest x-ray. I leave Ronnie in yet another waiting room and go through to the next waiting area. I change into the white flimsy gown that has been washed a million times and feels like it should be thrown away. I sit on the utilitarian grey moulded plastic chair with the metal legs, and I look down at the floor. And the floor is that sort of 'hospital' colour, you know that mixture of white, grey and beige, washed a million times, just like the gown, and devoid of colour.

In this instant I realise I am going to spend so much time in places like this. Waiting, getting undressed, having tests. I really don't feel like doing this for the next year or however long it will take. That really pisses me off. And I lean over and start to sob.

An older woman in the waiting room, another patient, looks across at me. She asks me what's wrong. I tell her I have just found out I have breast cancer and will be having a mastectomy. She comes and sits next to me, being sympathetic and sisterly. She says her friend, who is also young, like me, has had breast cancer but she's had reconstructive surgery and now you can't tell. Oh, that's OK then is it? I think, I bet her friend can tell herself, I bet she knows she had a mastectomy. But I don't say anything. I will sound rude. I do not want to hear this. I do not want to be jollied. I do not want people trying to tell me that this isn't a fucking disaster.

I have my x-ray done in tears. The nurse thrusts a handful of tissues at me. She can read. It says 'breast cancer' on the chitty. She doesn't try and say anything nice. Shit, shit, shit.

Finally we emerge. We are outside the hospital. We have been in there for six hours. It feels cold after the stifling heat of the hospital clinics. Why are they always too warm? Ronnie looks worried and concerned.

'What do you want to do now?' he asks.

'I was serious about that drink,' I say.

Taxi to wine bar. One large Pinot Grigio coming up.

CHAPTER TWO

Alison

Sitting in the wine bar with my drink in front of me I am simply stunned. I am looking, staring, out of the window at the road outside. It is like the world has gone into slow motion. It is a normal day for everyone who passes, for everyone in the cars and the buses that pass by. A normal day. But for me it is quite simply the shittiest day of my whole life. I look at the condensation on the outside of the wine glass and wipe it with my finger. I am so exhausted I can't speak. I just drink.

Back at home I ring a friend, who knew I was going for the tests. I tell her the news. It is surreal. I feel like I am having an out of body experience, completely detached from what I am telling her. And she is as shocked as I am, there don't seem to be any appropriate words. I really want to talk to someone who knows what this feels like.

I have been given a leaflet at the hospital about a national mentor service where you can talk on the phone to someone your age, and breast size if you want, who has been through what you are about to go through. I ring them, and give my details. They say they will put my details in their database and match me up, and then tell me someone will call me in the next couple of days. Amazingly, my mentor, a woman my age, rings me that evening. I have many, many questions, and she calmly answers them honestly and directly. I say, 'So, can you still have sex with one breast?' We both burst out laughing. I didn't think I'd have a laugh today.

Several glasses of wine later and evening dissolves into early morning. Ronnie sits with me as I bawl my eyes out at three o'clock in the morning, convinced that I will die. Soon. My head is going to explode with all the things I want to know. And some of them are too uncertain anyway, no-one can know if the cancer will spread. And I am going to spend so much time in hospitals. This was just not what I had planned on doing with my life. Finally we go to bed and fall asleep, completely drained. And drunk.

I wake the next morning and briefly, just briefly, I forget. Or I don't remember. I think about what day it is, Thursday; what I am doing? Hairdresser; and then I remember. I was diagnosed with breast cancer yesterday. That wasn't in the diary.

Even though my new friend, the breast care nurse, told me not to go on the internet - well, except for two approved sites - I have of course been all over it. I found out that a number of people refer to breast cancer as a journey. Well, yesterday certainly didn't feel like that, it felt like a nightmare, but the sort of nightmare that would end eventually and I would emerge blinking and things would be 'normal' again. But I don't think there will be normal again. I have breast cancer and I am due to have my right breast removed in three weeks.

When I was told I would have a mastectomy I really didn't want one. That was yesterday. Now, already, I really do. It's such a strange sensation. Actually wanting to have part of my body cut off. This lump feels like a foreigner in my breast and my body, and I just want it removed. I will be a real Amazon now.

My life has changed in a moment and is turned upside down. And it seems like the lump has immediately taken over, that everything is because of it, the lump is the priority. I cannot believe how there can be a date in the diary for a mastectomy. I couldn't even imagine that a week ago.

The next day, Friday, is like a 'normal' day. The kitchen roof is leaking. A lot. We don't need this. We're busy having one crisis, breast cancer, we don't want another one as well. It doesn't seem fair. Unbelievably, we are working that afternoon. Filming some interviews for, of all things, a comedy film. This is not our usual style, but this is a fun piece we are doing for a retirement party. Fun? Yeah, just how I feel right now. It feels surreal, doing this, knowing that we have this news that's like a bomb. I feel disorientated, distracted. Somehow we get through.

On Saturday I go running in the morning, as usual, with my running pals, a group of women I have been running with for a few years. They are all upset. I tell you, they can't be as upset as I am, except I still think I might wake up and it's a bad dream. I keep hoping I will. Each morning the same, a brief moment when I have forgotten. Then I remember. Shit. Life has changed.

I now put myself on a crash course on learning about breast cancer. Using the internet, obviously. My new friend, the breast care nurse, will be cross because I am going to have a thousand questions for her when she comes to see us. Ronnie and I also go and buy every book they have in Waterstone's about breast cancer. And I buy pyjamas for going into hospital. Ronnie says there is no situation that I can't find a reason to shop for. So mastectomy as shopping excuse. That would seem a bit extreme.

I have this sense that I am about to go on holiday. I feel like I am getting ready. Holiday? Some fucking holiday this is going to be. Bet this is the holiday no-one else wanted so I got it at a discount price. But I have a sense of wanting to put things in order before 'It' starts. Don't even know what 'It' is, I just feel that it's going to be quite a ride.

I've not had children, by choice, but I've seen women doing that nesting thing. Where they tidy up, you know, wash the pavement outside the house, clean things you didn't even know needed cleaning. And that's what happens to me. I am tidying drawers and shelves. What's happening to me? Am I going mad?

In between my cleaning I start to read the cancer books. This is the first day I have actually felt scared. Scared that I have cancer everywhere and nothing will save me. This is when instead of waking up in the morning and forgetting, I start waking at 5 am. I am now convinced I am going to die.

Would it be better if I didn't read the books? Perhaps if I didn't know the possibilities then I couldn't be frightened of them? Maybe. I am very scared. But I still think being informed is better. It's just so frightening, and the fact is that I have this lump inside me, potentially spreading and putting seeds all over my body.

My new friend, the breast care nurse, arrives at the appointed time after the weekend. She asks how I am doing and then hugs me. She didn't look like the hugging kind when I met her last week, but not to worry, she never hugged me again.

She spends several hours with us going through all my questions. She has some items in her bag to show us. A drain. Hum, OK so that's what they look like. A clear plastic bottle with measurements down one side attached to a long clear plastic tube. She tells me when I wake after surgery I will have several of these in my wound to drain the fluid. It seems meaningless to me, it doesn't really go in at all. Then she produces a silicone prosthesis, a false breast. She passes it to me. It's heavy and cold. I don't like it. I'm not really sure how to react so I laugh and throw it to Ronnie, who catches it. It's horrible.

'I will never wear one of them,' I say.

She just smiles, as though she knows better.

We do talk about bras. I am worried about what I will wear after surgery. She says she'll get some catalogues for me. She doesn't seem to think that there will be any problem. After she leaves I feel sort of empty, like I'm not sure what's going to happen. It's not even a week since diagnosis and already I feel engulfed by medical-ness. I don't like it. Can't we go back? Please?

My research continues. Supplements. Bras. Benefits. Financial advice. Are cosmetics dangerous? Do they contain chemicals that cause breast cancer? Can I go swimming after surgery? What will I wear anyway? And, of course, most importantly I need to clean under the kitchen sink, for some reason.

It's a week and one day since diagnosis and I can't believe where time has gone. Gone into a fog of shock. A new landscape, a place we've never been before, we can't see it for the fog.

At the end of the week it's time for results. Or, rather, my initial results. Results will start to become a normal part of my life, I don't realise that at the time. I get up and have a bath. Then I cut my finger nails. They are growing fine and I think, how can I possibly be ill when my body seems so perfectly healthy? I put my best bra on, my red lace one, and we go to the hospital for our first cancer patient appointment.

We are in the consulting rooms for the first time. I will become very familiar with all these places. The car park. Crossing the main road. Past all the smokers outside the entrance to the hospital. The walk through the main hospital, along the linoleum corridors, out the back door, past the smokers next to the 'No Smoking' sign. Up the steps to the breast unit. The glass door. The café on the ground floor run by volunteers. The reception desk no-one uses. Up in the lift to the second floor. Outpatients. Grey carpet. Pink vinyl padded chairs. Waiting. And then being called through to one of the consulting rooms which cluster around a central office where the consultants and other medical staff congregate.

I hear her before I meet her. Alison Waghorn, breast surgeon and endocrine consultant. She is not the surgeon I met on diagnosis day. She is talking loudly in the central office with the breast care nurse, and referring to my notes.

'Yes, I see, OK then well let's go and meet her then,' she is saying.

The door opens forcefully, she bounds in and thrusts her hand at me.

'Alison Waghorn. Nice to meet you.'

She is tall, angular. She has blonde hair, it looks natural. It is straight, shoulder length with a fringe. She wears a plain black trouser suit with a white t-shirt underneath. She is not wearing make-up and looks the picture of health. She is radiant.

She sits down in the chair next to me and my new friend perches on the bed, wearing the same expressionless mask she had on when I was diagnosed. I can see she thinks that Alison is being too friendly. Alison uses her first name, unlike any doctor I have ever met, and she is young, about my age. I am surprised, I thought consultants were older, mature. I don't think of myself as mature. Alison is chatty, friendly, and direct. She tells me the result of the biopsy I had last week. I have a hormone positive cancer. I'm not really fully aware of the implications of this yet. She says it is a grade two tumour, on a scale of one to three, with three being the more aggressive. But she also points out that this result can change when they have the mastectomy results, it could go up, it is unlikely to go down. She tells me, again, that it doesn't look like cancer is present in the lymph nodes. And all of this is presented to me like good news. Which is a bit of an achievement considering the nature of what she is telling me. I like her. A lot.

And, of course, the inevitable examination. Which Alison handles really well.

'Would you mind if I had a look?' she says, giving me a kind look.

I don't feel quite so prodded as I did on diagnosis day. She even compliments my lovely breasts. I am touched. She obviously likes her patients. I get dressed again. I know I am in the right hands.

We have drawn up a list of many questions, which Ronnie has written down. Alison peers over Ronnie's shoulder and starts reading ahead, pre-empting them.

When I ask her what causes breast cancer she sighs and says, 'Well, we don't know. It might be hormones in our food, from meat or dairy, or chemicals in the environment, but really we just don't know.'

An honest answer I suppose. We move on to my treatment.

I have already asked my breast care nurse about one thing I've found on the internet. I want to have a sentinel node biopsy before mastectomy. This is an operation done under general anaesthetic which removes some lymph nodes, the 'sentinel' node and some random ones. The sentinel node is the first node in the ladder of nodes in the armpit, there is usually one but sometimes two. If they are unaffected by cancer then it probably hasn't spread to the lymphatic system. If it has spread here, then it could have started to travel to other parts of my body. Breast cancer favours the bones, lungs, brain and liver, and can form secondary cancers in those parts. You probably didn't want to know that. I know I didn't.

The alternative, which is to remove all the lymph nodes, can result in an increased risk of lymphoedema, fluid retention which causes swelling in the arm and hand which restricts the use of the arm. Mastectomy affects the arm, shoulder and armpit anyway and some stiffness is normal, but I am told it is temporary. I am right-handed and this will affect my right arm. When I think about having the lymph nodes removed all I can think about is how will I possibly still manage to use my camera and earn a living. So I'd like to try and keep them. Alison is in agreement to the sentinel node biopsy. It can be done at the same time as mastectomy, but if it is positive it would mean going back to surgery for more lymph nodes to be removed. So, Alison says it is better to arrange to have it done separately before the mastectomy surgery.

Alison says she will arrange this, but warns me anyway, 'You know with a tumour this size it's a 50:50 chance that it will be in the lymph nodes. But, of course, we can check anyway.' She gives Ronnie a look.

'Well, I'm 43 and I have breast cancer. I'm not feeling that lucky, but let's see,' I say.

My breast care nurse, the one who is my friend remember, reminds me, 'It does mean you have another general anaesthetic though.' Is she warning me against this procedure? I am very sure it is what I want.

A bustle of paperwork as Alison barks instructions at my breast care nurse and the operation is organised for the following week by another surgeon, as Alison is already booked up. Alison is in complete control.

About the other surgeon, she says, 'Oh, she won't mind, I'll just give her secretary a ring.'

My breast care nurse reminds Alison that I will need a 'pre-op', a pre-operative assessment to check I am OK to have surgery, to have a general anaesthetic. She seems determined to be putting up barriers to this surgery. Alison doesn't think this is problem.

'Well, let's get the house doctor in and do it now. Then Sarah won't have to come back and they can go on holiday.' And she beams at me.

Ronnie has suggested that we go away before the mastectomy, to give us both a break. We're planning on going to Cornwall. Alison doesn't seem to think we should miss out on this.

'Is there anything else then?' she asks.

'A sick note?' I ask, even though I'm not sick and am not employed so I've no idea what will happen to my income.

Alison scribbles a sick note.

'I'm just going to write *breast surgery* here,' she says. 'They can make their own minds up about what that means.' She hands me the note. It's for six months. Six. Months. What? I'm going to be sick for *six months*? I'm too confused to say anything, just dumbly staring at this piece of paper that says six months. I have never been sick for more than a week. What's happening to me?

Alison leaves us with her sign-off, which I will get to hear many many times.

'OK, so any more questions then?'

And off she goes.

A house doctor is summoned and my medical history is taken. It's very short. No major health issues. Only had my tonsils removed.

We leave the hospital in a good mood. I feel happy. All things considered.

❧

The world seems to have speeded up. Medical appointments dominate. Before the sentinel node biopsy I need to have an isotope injection. Wow. They will inject me with a radioactive substance into my breast, and when I am in theatre they will use a Geiger counter, at least that's what I imagine, to locate where the radioactive substance has drained into my lymph nodes. That will show them the first lymph node, the sentinel node. I have images of my surgical team all suited up like something in a nuclear power station disaster movie, with me lying on the bed, anesthetised and blissfully unaware of the chaos around me.

So it's back to the hospital to the nuclear medicine department. The same routine, the car park, the smokers, the big entrance, the linoleum corridors, following the signs. Nuclear Medicine. It is located at the far end of the hospital. I suppose you don't want anything to leak out of this department do you? There are those big yellow caution signs as we enter, and it all feels a bit surreal. There is no changing room so the nurse shows me into a storage room and I change into a gown looking around at boxes of medical things that I have no idea what they're for. I am in a completely alien environment. Hospital. It's not my place.

I'm trying my best to be positive. To be nice to the staff, to not make this feel like the ordeal that it obviously is. I am shown to a bed and the curtains are drawn. A nurse, who must be related to my breast care nurse because she has no expression, comes in with a cardboard dish containing a small syringe. I smile. She looks blank and says, 'Sarah Horton?'

'Yes,' I say.

'Date of birth?'

'Twenty-four, nine, sixty-three.'

'Right breast?'

'Yes.'

'OK then, could you take your gown off please?'

The injection is administered. It's painless and quick.

'Well,' I say, 'let's hope the mastectomy goes that well.'

I am trying to be funny, to make light of this, even though it's not funny at all. The nurse is not sure how to take my comment.

'You do understand, don't you, that you are having your breast removed?'

God, as if I didn't know that. Does she have no sense of humour?

Back in the store room I get changed. Another nurse comes in while I am still just wearing my bra, she didn't realise I was in there.

'That's a nice bra,' she says. I am wearing my red bra again.

'Thank you, it's my favourite. But if you're the same size as me you can have it, because I'm having a mastectomy next week so won't need it anymore.'

She at least does have a sense of humour. Thank God.

I am exhausted. The information just keeps coming. I am overloaded. I can't deal with this. I keep reading about cancer and coping. Coping? I don't want to cope, I want to get better. Everything just keeps happening and it doesn't feel like it's going to stop any time soon.

I am sleeping badly now, regularly waking around 4.30 in the morning. Finally getting back to sleep around 7.30, and managing to get up around 10 o'clock. Those nights always leave me feeling groggy.

My life has turned into a list in the last two weeks since diagnosis. Things to do, things to find out. All the information doesn't make me feel better, all those statistics. Statistics about survival. That means dying. Shit, shit, shit.

Sentinel node biopsy today. We are at the hospital at 7.30 in the morning. I am not expecting to stay overnight but have some food with me for my breakfast after surgery. I am lucky, first on the list, so I change into my gown straight away. I meet my surgeon very briefly, a woman even younger than Alison. Very professional. She draws a star above my breast on my right side using a thick black pen. I am reassured that they won't operate on the wrong side. Then the anaesthetist comes to see me. He is also very young. Maybe I have got older if I think everyone is young. I think he can sense my anxiety. It's just that during my 43 years I have barely been in a hospital. It's the last place I want to be. He says that sometimes you have to let go and put your trust in the medical staff. He has lovely brown eyes.

And then I am wheeled to theatre on a trolley. I feel like a fraud, I am not sick, I don't need to be treated like a sick person. It's an alien environment to me. The clean floors, the metal rails on the beds, the tubes, the monitors, the oxygen, the amount of people around in the pre-theatre room, the hair nets. I am glad when the anaesthetic starts to work, I am drifting away, letting go.

I am back up from surgery and eating my breakfast at 11.30. The other patients on my ward ask if I've had a general anaesthetic, they think I seem so well and energetic. But I am realising that I'm glad I was out running last night. Being fit is going to help me recover quicker.

But this hospital thing, it is really teaching me patience already. Is that why we are called patients? All the sitting around, the waiting and everything done for the convenience of the medical staff. This feels like the start of a getting well adventure, even though I'm not even aware of being ill.

The other women on my ward talk to me a bit. I tell them I have breast cancer. I tell them this very matter of factly. There doesn't really seem any other way to tell it. They ask about reconstructive surgery. That means recreating a breast shape on my chest using an implant or my own tissue, skin and fat from another part of my body, like my stomach or buttock. I just have no opinion about this. I honestly do not care. I just don't want to have cancer. They are talking about breasts, I am thinking about saving my life.

It's time to go home. I've done the qualifiers, had a wee and a poo, and had something to eat so I'm OK. I draw the curtains round the bed and I look down at myself before I get dressed. Mesh knickers, they look ridiculous, are they supposed to preserve my dignity? The white knee-length stockings to stop blood clots, with my toes poking out. And no toe polish. The nurses asked me to take it off because they use a machine to check oxygen levels in the blood while I am under anaesthetic, and the monitor is attached to a toe. Nail polish can give a false reading. I had only put it on last night, bright red, clinging on to my glamour whilst in hospital for the first time. And my poor bruised breast. It is not painful but the bruise developed in the days after the core biopsy I had on diagnosis day, the lower half is now almost a complete solid purple bruise.

And now, just to top it off, the nipple and the skin around it is bright blue. They did warn me about this, the blue nipple. In order to locate the sentinel node they use a blue dye, in addition to the radioactive injection. But the dye stays in the system for a while. Look out for blue wee they said. Yes, had that. But the breast is going anyway, next week, so the blue nipple doesn't bother me that much. And, finally, to complete the look, a dressing under my armpit, still too soon after surgery to feel sore.

This is just the start, I think, and look at me. It does not feel like my own body, already, and I was only diagnosed two weeks ago.

I don't know myself sometimes. I feel like I am standing outside my body and have allowed the person that I want to be to come through. I am calmly telling people I am about to have a mastectomy. It still feels wrong. But I have no choice. The strong person who very confidently said to the two other women on my ward today, that my main concern is not to have cancer, is that really me? Not having two breasts is not my primary worry right now. I am glad my resilience seems to have returned in full. I need this.

Back at home I lie on my chaise longue. Bliss to be home. Safe. Letting go has never felt easier. The only things that feel meaningful are Ronnie and silence and rest and laughter. Deep joy. Today is the first day I've actually been anything you could describe as 'ill' and I feel completely indulged. Rest is a wonderful thing.

I instinctively feel I have a big challenge ahead of me.

Our holiday has started. We are in Chipping Campden, stopped here on the way to Cornwall. I am dozy, still full of anaesthetic. My right arm is tingly and numb. I don't feel comfortable sitting for hours in the car. I am full of worries. I haven't had a general anaesthetic for over 15 years and I don't know how I might react.

I am generally just full of worries. Oh, and I really, really do not want to lose my right breast. We are having a lovely time in one of our favourite places but none of this makes me accept what is about to happen to me. It still feels wrong.

The next day I pass the time in the passenger seat driving to Cornwall finishing the purple baby cardigan for Ellie. The knitting is done but it has eyelets around the hem and cuffs and each one is embroidered with a yellow daisy. I am sewing them in the car.

We arrive in Cornwall. It is sunny. I feel better. We are in St Ives. I go running on Porthmeor Beach. Acres of sand. Delightful. A magical start to a magical day. The most beautiful light, golden sand, turquoise sea. This was a good idea. We are relaxed and strong and ready for the next stage of this unforeseen adventure.

Back in Liverpool and it is the day before mastectomy. It has come too soon. We are seeing Alison to talk about the results of my sentinel node biopsy and decide what my surgery will involve. She apologises, because the results are not back from the lab.

'Hold on, I'll ring them,' she says.

We look surprised.

'It's OK, I know them,' and she smiles her beaming smile and disappears.

We sit in the consulting room. Alison has gone into the office and is on the phone to the lab. We can hear some of her conversation, even though the door is shut. She is talking very loudly.

'Look,' she says, 'we're doing these sentinel node biopsies now *before* mastectomy, not at the same time. So I really need the result tomorrow before I operate.'

We can hear Alison shouting down the phone, telling the lab that she has the patient with her, ready for surgery tomorrow. I know she will sort this out.

She comes back in and says the node slicer has broken. It sounds bad.

'My node is broken?' I ask.

'No, it's just the machine they use to do the analysis. They will get it fixed and get the result tomorrow morning.'

She then moves my surgery time the next day from the morning to the afternoon, and says she will come and see me with the results before I go to theatre. I just know that this will happen. I completely trust her. She is like your best friend at school, but also happens to be Head Girl too. We talk through the options.

Alison says, 'I was thinking about this last night.' And I am amazed. I didn't know surgeons thought about their patients. She obviously has though.

If the nodes are all negative then no more nodes will be removed. If one is positive then she suggests we do a full clearance, or remove a sample and have radiotherapy after surgery. If two or more are positive then do a full clearance. Alison makes it sound straightforward. It doesn't sound like dying or anything to do with death. Secondary cancer? No, that's not mentioned.

She reassures me that we will have the result tomorrow and that we'll take it from there. It feels good, it feels proper. Just as well Head Girl was here to sort it all out.

She examines me again, says she is sure that mastectomy is the best surgery, rather than lumpectomy which will just remove the lump. If the lump is removed then I will be left with part of a breast and will lose symmetry. She casually mentions my future options, reconstructive surgery. She does not know what I think about this. She looks at me and says that if I have enough fat on my stomach I can use that to recreate a new breast.

'Then you get a tummy tuck on the NHS,' she says.

I know she's trying to make it sound positive. I'm still overwhelmed by the fact that I'm going to have my breast cut off. I can't think further than that.

CHAPTER THREE

Mastectomy

How can I sign a consent form to have my breast cut off? How can I not? I know enough now to be terrified that this tumour in my breast will behave badly and send out seeds all over my body waiting to grow into more tumours that will kill me. Horrible.

I am on the afternoon surgery list so I can have my breakfast at home at 8 o'clock. And then wait to go to the hospital.

It is a strange morning. I have toast with Marmite and peppermint tea. Have a bath. Ronnie takes a photograph of me sitting on the bed, wearing a red sheer silk top I made myself. Always liked the way it draped over my breasts. Me with two breasts. Strange. Very strange.

Ronnie drives us to the hospital, the Women's hospital in Liverpool. Not the same place where I have had my other appointments so far. The breast surgery is done at a different hospital to the clinics. Ronnie gets my bag out of the car and we go in. Up in the lift and find the ward.

The ward is very quiet. My bed is in the corner. Ronnie sits on the chair, and I sit on the bed. I get my knitting out. I am knitting a pair of mittens for Ellie. In pink cotton.

The anaesthetist comes to see me. He doesn't have my results. I still don't know if I am having my lymph nodes removed. He says Alison will see me herself in a bit. More waiting. A nurse comes and asks me to change into a gown. She has one, folded neatly, which she puts on the bed and says, 'Opening at the back.' Then she is gone. I change, sit back on the bed and continue my knitting.

Alison arrives on the ward. Again I can hear her before I see her. She is talking loudly and rushing down the corridor. She comes in like a whirlwind in her theatre outfit. She is wearing those shapeless green surgery trousers and gown, but on her it looks stylish. She has those plastic holey shoes in white, and a green theatre hat with her mask pushed up over it. A strand of hair has come loose and falls across her cheek. She is pulling the curtains around the bed and smiling at me. She looks lovely.

'Good news!' she says.

She sits on the bed and slaps down the sheet of paper with the results on. She is obviously delighted, and tells me that all my lymph nodes are clear. No evidence of cancer. So no more are to be removed.

'So my chance of secondary cancer is reduced?' I ask.

'Yes.' She beams at me.

'Oh.' I don't know what to say, what to think. Alison is gushing.

'This could be it, Sarah, this could be it.'

I'm too shocked and happy to know what she means by this. *This could be it.* I reflect later that maybe she means that the mastectomy could be the extent of my 'treatment' for breast cancer.

I feel lucky and massively relieved. I suppose if you could be in a good mood before a mastectomy this is about as good as it gets. Alison whips out her black pen and draws a line on me across the top of my right breast. Ready for theatre.

Alison flies off to get on with her first patient, leaving me happily knitting. The mitts for Ellie. I always think of them as the mastectomy mitts.

❧

When it is time for me to go to theatre a nurse comes and collects me. Together with Ronnie we walk to the theatre. It is just along the corridor on the same floor as the ward. Ronnie hugs me and I am really conscious of the fact that the next time we hug it won't feel the same, I will only have one breast. Then he leaves.

The nurse settles me on a trolley bed and takes my dressing gown and slippers back to the ward. I am left with a new set of staff, all wearing those green shapeless theatre outfits. The pre-theatre checks all take place. What is my name? Date of birth? Am I wearing false teeth? Do I have a pacemaker? Everyone is so nice, they can probably see I am upset. I am wheeled through into the anaesthetic room. Machinery everywhere, lines hooked up to me and monitors and screens and needles and so many people. I am overwhelmed by it all. There's no going back now I think.

I am lying on my bed feeling completely helpless. All the staff are doing their jobs. Monitors are stuck on my chest and back. The first needle goes in, tape is put on. The green oxygen mask is strapped to my face. Abject terror is replaced by anaesthetic and the next thing I know I'm in the recovery room. I am shivering with cold and a nurse puts a blanket on me. I hear a familiar voice.

'Hello Sarah, do you want to see Ronnie now?'

It's Alison. She grabs my notes from the rack at the end of the bed to get the phone number, and goes to the telephone. She rings Ronnie, and I can hear her telling him I'm OK and that he can come and see me. Then she is gone.

I am back on the ward when Ronnie visits me. It is evening now. I am still in shock, clutching the oxygen mask. Ronnie brings me home-made juice, apple and lime, my favourite. I drink some with the straw and then I go back to sleep.

In the night I call the nurse, ask if I can use the toilet. She unties my drains from the side of the bed and helps me get up. I can walk OK so she lets me go alone to the toilet, carrying the two drains that are attached to my wound. I lock the door, then put the drains down on the floor. Then I cautiously pull the front of my operating gown forward so I can look down. There is only one breast. The missing one is covered with a dressing. It doesn't look too bad. I am surprised at how unemotional I am.

The next morning I get up and change from the gown into my pyjamas, and sit in bed knitting. I have finished the pink cotton mitts for Ellie, and am now making a pair of fingerless gloves for me, they are stripey in green, orange, pink and cream. It's Saturday but Alison comes in to see me, on her day off. She comes to see all her new patients, to see how they are doing. I can hear her barking at nurses as she strides down the corridor, her black coat flying out behind her. She says she is very pleased with my progress.

Days in hospital seem to just pass. Other people have lots of visitors it seems, whole families. My visitors are few. Mostly just Ronnie. He is all I want, even though I send him home early because I want to sleep.

The next day I wash my hair and paint my toe nails. I am so determined to do this, even though I have to sit on the floor and stretch forward to paint them. I feel bare without my toe nails painted. They are red to match my dressing gown. I had planned my hospital look. I am trying my best to keep up my standards of grooming and appearance.

I have one drain removed, which feels horrible. The plastic pipe is sticking out of the wound under my arm. The stitch that is holding it in place is cut and then it is dragged across the inside of the scar. Oooh. Blood runs out down my side and onto my pyjama bottoms. But I am much more comfortable without it. The other drain will come out in a few days.

I talk to the woman in the bed opposite, Jane, who has had a double mastectomy. She says she remembers me from the diagnosis clinic. Well, remembers Ronnie, actually. She has had expanders put in underneath her mastectomy scars. These are like flat balloons which will gradually be pumped up with saline solution every few weeks, allowing the skin to stretch. When the stretching is complete the expanders are removed and replaced with silicone implants. At visiting time she always has a group of people round her bed.

I stay in hospital for three nights. On the Monday morning Alison comes round early, about 8.30 am. Whenever she is around I feel like smiling. She's that sort of doctor, she has that effect on me. She says again that she is impressed with my progress and I can go home.

I pack my belongings. I have the bottle changed on the remaining drain, and am given a chart which the district nurse will fill in each day, showing how much fluid is being collected, until it is ready to be removed.

Before I leave I am seen by the sister on the ward in a private room and she sorts out a foam 'softie' breast for me. This is a triangular flesh coloured breast-shaped thing, which is filled with some sort of substance resembling kapok. I try it in a sports bra, which is the only bra I have that doesn't have wires in. Ronnie has brought the bra in for me, especially for this purpose, no-one thought to ask me beforehand to bring a bra with me. Anyhow, the bra is too tight as I am wearing it over the drain tube. The mirror in the room which is above the sink is also too high, it's intended for someone's face not breasts. I stand on tiptoe and try and peer at my breasts. It looks the right sort of size anyway. Sort of. The nurse gives me two, one to wear and one in the wash. They are in square white boxes, like cake boxes. I already know I don't like them.

So I go home with a drain in and start my new life with one breast. The removed breast is sent to the lab for analysis, I'll get the results in two weeks. When I put the seatbelt on in the car there is nothing in the way, it's just flat.

This adventure, this complete removal of the life you were gently living. It's a whirlwind.

When I talk about my breast I point to where it should be, and I expect it to be there, and it feels odd that there's a space there now. When I lie down on the chaise longue with a cup of tea I find I don't have a shelf for my saucer. It's different.

I can't sleep on my right side as the scar and drain are in the way. I lie on my back, frustrated about how difficult it is to move. My body is asking for rest. I spend long periods of time in bed during the day.

I wake the next morning and I am in a bad mood. A couple of weeks before my mastectomy I had a persistent toothache. I went to the dentist and had a large filling replaced. After my first surgery, the sentinel node biopsy, it started hurting again. One of my nurses said it could have been because of clenching my teeth or the trauma of the anaesthetic. It seemed to settle down, but it is back again after this anaesthetic. I will need to arrange to see the dentist.

The district nurse visits me each day. The first one who came is very friendly, after just a few minutes said I was positive and strong. How am I projecting that? She doesn't know me. What is it that other people see? Can't they see I am *terrified*? That I don't like any of this?

After a couple of visits from the nurses the drain is removed. This one doesn't feel as bad as the first one when it is taken out, but this nurse had a good technique which involves me breathing out at the same time. It works. It feels great not to have to walk everywhere with a small pouch containing my body's excess fluids.

I have been home two days now, have no drains, and I have a shower and wash my hair. I can't manage to bend over so don't bother to shave my legs. My standards are slipping already. I'm worried that I will become bed-bound, will be unable to wash my hair, or to wear lipstick. That I will slip down some imaginary hole and vanish.

I do not like the foam thing they gave me. The thing that is supposed to be a breast. I try wearing it pinned in a vest. I feel silly. I feel like I am playing dressing up, like I did as a child, stuffing socks inside my top, trying to imagine what having breasts would be like. So what am I going to wear now? I use the internet and find some style advice from Dina Rabinovitch, the journalist who writes in the Guardian about her own experience with breast cancer. She does not like the foam thing either. So it's not just me. She suggests wrap-around tops which drape in the space where the breast was.

Resourceful as ever, I decide to go shopping to buy a sewing pattern for a wrap top. This means I will have to leave the house, so I get one of my older bras, a white cotton one, and cut out the wire in the right breast. I put the foam thing in and try it on. It looks OK. I go shopping. Everything hurts. My scar, my back, my arm, my hand. I find a sewing pattern. But then I need to go home and lie down.

The next day my scar under my arm is swollen. I am worried. Although the hospital staff did warn me that this could happen, the swelling. They say it is called a seroma, it is just fluid and it can be drained.

Alison told us that there is a clinic at the hospital every day. If we have any problems we can always be seen. So we ring my breast care nurse. We get the answerphone, which says that they may not return the call the same day. Great. What am I supposed to do meanwhile? Sit and wait?

So Ronnie rings reception at the breast clinic, and tells the receptionist that we can't get a response from the breast care nurses and that Alison had said there would always be someone to see me. This seems to trigger off a minor revolution in the breast unit, but we are told we can come into clinic that afternoon.

We go back to the hospital and wait in the clinic to see Alison. I hope it isn't an infection. She is in her usual good mood.

'Are you growing your breast back?' she asks laughingly from behind the curtain. She's trying to make light of it. I'm not feeling very light.

She pulls the curtain back and has a look, touches me gently with her expert fingers.

'Oh, OK, nothing to worry about,' she says. 'Just some excess fluid. I'm not going to drain it because it's very close to the axilla.'

'Axilla?'

'Yes, it's a big nerve going down your back. Best to leave it alone, it will settle. How did it happen?'

'I was wearing a bra.'

'Hmm.'

'Should I not wear a bra?' I feel a bit dismayed about this.

'Well, only if you really feel you need to.'

So, that's it then, is it? The end of bras? They didn't tell me this would happen.

But I am determined. I think there must be a bra solution. I go back to the internet. Yes, there are post-surgery bras. Soft bras that you can wear after breast surgery. But there isn't much choice. Like white or black, or - if you are really lucky - a flesh-coloured one. I order a selection from the very small choice I have for my size.

The bras arrive. But I am too tired to try them, taking them out of the packaging felt like enough. They are horrible anyway, I know I will never wear them. Massive horrible bras with wide straps. My life is disappearing. No more sexy underwear. I am bereft.

We have only told a few close friends about my diagnosis. I just don't want to go public with the news yet, plus I have so much to do, so many medical appointments. So Ronnie is responding to my emails and phone calls. I don't seem to have the energy right now to engage with anyone.

❧

I have been told about a support centre for women going through breast cancer. It is in north Liverpool, off my radar as I am firmly based in the south of the city. But it is well spoken of by the people who tell me about it. So off we go. I am only two weeks post-mastectomy so am unable to drive, Ronnie drives me. It is a drop-in session. I am welcomed and sit with a group of women who are eating pork pies and cake. Many women there are much older than me, in fact a lot older than me.

They offer me tea, but I don't drink caffeine. I'm wondering what to say to them. Then I am greeted by the founder members. They are friendly. They even invite me to play bingo. Oh. My. God. Bingo. I don't have anything against bingo - well I've never played it actually - but I just didn't expect to be playing bingo when I was 43. I thought it was something for older people.

I had a brief chat with their benefits adviser. I am worried. It sounds like I might never work again. Will I? The women say their 'affected' arms are still not the same as before, many years after surgery. That I won't be able to wash my windows as well. Actually, that's not something I do very often.

I think there and then, I will not become a victim.

This is one of my worse days. The mastectomy bras and the bingo. Perhaps I should just go outside and get myself run over. I am seriously not happy.

❦

Next, my worst day? Another one? Results. I know that Alison is away at a conference, she told me. So I see a nurse practitioner for my results, two weeks after mastectomy. My breast care nurse has told me that this is an important day. That the information in the results will be used to decide what further treatment, if any, I will have. She is here today, and once again it looks like she is wearing a mask. No emotions are visible. I thought she was supposed to be my friend.

I am told that my tumour was in three pieces, totalling just over six centimetres, in a larger area of cells showing pre-cancerous changes, called DCIS which means ductal carcinoma in situ. The nurse practitioner is very careful to point out that this means that mastectomy was the right choice, as just removing the tumour would have left pre-cancerous cells behind. It is a grade three tumour, not two as the initial biopsy reported. And it is oestrogen and progesterone positive. And HER-2 negative.

I look bewildered. I look to my friend for some sort of explanation.

'That's good,' says the breast care nurse, nodding wisely, but offers no further information.

I have been reading my books, I have questions. The answers are good. Well, good is relative, but reasonably good under the circumstances. There is no lymphovascular involvement, that means no cancer evident in the surrounding tissues. And the margins are clear, that means that there were no stray cancer cells left in the tissue beyond the breast. As far as we can tell at this point.

The nurse practitioner says it has been decided I will have chemotherapy, radiotherapy and hormone treatment. I am not given a choice, it is not discussed. It is a statement. This information has been decided, without me, at a multi-disciplinary team meeting, the MDT, where several medics look at my case. They call it an 'individual treatment plan'. I am not so sure.

They look at my scar, say it is healing well. The breast care nurse gives me some catalogues for bras. When I look at them at home I wonder if she even opened them, the largest bra is a DD cup. I am a FF, I had told her.

I leave the hospital. I am drained. I am given an appointment the following week with an oncologist.

My scar is sore. I am tired. I can't find any bra to wear. I didn't expect to be so sore. The scar is very very sensitive, everything rubs it. I try again to wear the softie they gave me pinned in a camisole vest without a bra, but it rubs the scar. Why am I even wearing it? Am I trying to recreate an image of myself for other people? So that other people can look at me and I appear 'normal'? I am happy with my one breast, because it means I don't have cancer, and it feels easier to wear no bra now. Perhaps this is how it will be for me now?

Before my surgery I rang a mastectomy lingerie specialist and asked about bras for FF cups. That is bras without a wire in, suitable to wear after surgery. I was quite surprised by the response.

'Mmm. Oh dear,' she said. 'Not nice.'

'What?'

'Well there's only really one non-underwired bra in that size, and it's a bit, well you know, matronly.'

Great. But she was right. There are no bras for me now.

A week later, now three weeks after mastectomy, I have an appointment with the oncologist. They did not tell me it was going to take place in a chemotherapy clinic. I was not prepared for this. I walk in and there are people sitting around wearing headscarves, covering their bald heads. I go to the reception desk and there are people in chairs hooked up to drips of clear fluid. So that's what it looks like, chemotherapy. I did not know that. I have a realisation that it will soon be me here. No hair and on a drip.

The clinic is running hours late. We are sitting waiting in a row of chairs down a corridor. There is no space. People and chairs everywhere. My life is disappearing in hospital corridors. Ronnie has made us a packed lunch and a flask of tea. I didn't know that my life would now be days out in a hospital. Nobody told me that would happen. I have a bad cold. My eyes are streaming. I am not crying. I am in an extremely bad mood.

Finally we go in to see the oncologist. She is young. Well, younger than me. I hope she will be like Alison, I want her to be. She is petite, almost prim, and her dark hair is very neatly tied back, no loose strands. She has large brown eyes and I think she is going to be sympathetic. After all I don't imagine she gets that many young people here, now that I am called young all the time, young to have breast cancer that is. I am wrong though, she is nothing like Alison.

Her first question is, 'Can you tell me why you are here?' It's a sad attempt to see how much I understand about this cancer, and I feel like a child in school, reporting back on my homework. I have learned my results and can recite them in full. I can also tell her that I have been told I will have chemotherapy and radiotherapy, with hormone treatment at the end.

I tell her I'm still not sure what the chemotherapy is for as there is no evidence of the cancer having spread, either in my lymph nodes or in the blood or tissue around the tumour. I also ask for the gain figures. These are the figures that tell me how much, in percentage terms, I can expect to 'gain' from a particular treatment. That means gain in terms of less chance of dying. She says she can't give me gain figures because my tumour is 'multi-focal', meaning three tumours not one. She calls it multi-focal, but it was explained to me as one tumour in three sections, not three separate tumours. The oncologist is adamant that the figures don't apply to me. How am I supposed to make a decision then?

She goes on to tell me about the chemotherapy regime she recommends for me. It is called Epi-CMF chemotherapy which lasts seven months. This is a standard chemotherapy regime for breast cancer, four sessions of epirubicin, followed by four cycles of CMF, a cocktail of chemo drugs. Then she tells me there is also a *choice*. Great, a choice.

So, the choice is I can have this chemotherapy as outlined, the standard way of doing it. Or, I can opt to go on a trial to see if doing the chemotherapy in a shorter time is of any benefit, or whether the side effects will be even worse. So, it's chemotherapy or chemotherapy, basically. She gives me a leaflet to read about the trial so I can think about it. I know that we can only improve medicine by trying out different ways of doing things.

But really? A trial? I am sick now so I am someone else's property, I have become a guinea pig have I?

I am thinking all this, my mind is miles away. The doctor is still talking. She says radiotherapy may be offered at the end of chemotherapy to burn possible stray cancer cells on the chest, but this is only a possibility.

But she then says I might want to think about having another mastectomy to reduce the risk of getting breast cancer again. I'm wondering here if I just landed in the wrong place by mistake. As well as feeling bewildered I'm beginning to feel the sharp edges of rage, even though I don't know what the feeling is at the time. It just all feels wrong.

I am given a week to think about things.

We leave the room. I feel empty. I don't feel cared for or treated like an individual. I feel like I am on a conveyor belt.

Jane, who was in the bed opposite me in the ward, is in the waiting room. She had a double mastectomy. Ronnie has been waiting to crack his joke. We had expected to see Jane at results clinic, but missed her. So Ronnie gives the results now.

'Two, one,' he says.

That's two breasts Jane has lost and one that I have lost. She and her sister laugh out loud. It's a Liverpool thing I think.

Jane is here to see the oncologist. I ring her that evening and she has been offered exactly the same as me. She thinks it's good. I'm not so sure.

And on that afternoon, after the hours in the oncology department, we have an appointment with Alison. This is the first time I have seen her since I left hospital after the mastectomy. She again tells me that mastectomy was the right surgery for me. I don't need convincing about that, I have accepted that.

I show her the chemotherapy information. I tell Alison I am not sure, that I have reservations. I tell her I am finding it hard to make this decision when I don't have the gain figures. The oncologist has given me a copy of my histology report, only because I asked. It says that I have a tumour which appears multi-focal. *Appears*. Not *is*. Alison points this out and says that I have in effect a tumour which is larger than five centimetres, not a multi-focal tumour. This is the first time I have seen the doctors disagree.

So, she goes off and puts my information into the database which they use to get the gain figures. It takes a short while, and we sit in the consulting room feeling cheated. Cheated by the oncologist who would not do this for us. Give us information to help us make a decision.

When Alison comes back she is her usual chatty self. She tells me that because breast cancer is so common there is lots of data available about survival. That's the good news. The bad news is that for my particular results, if I have no further treatment, the chance of me still being alive in ten years is 60%. Or if you look at it the other way, the chance of me being dead in ten years' time is 40%. Well, even I can see that that's not far off 50:50.

A long pause.

Alison can see I am a bit shocked by this.

'So you see, Sarah, we don't know which of the statistics you will be in. That's why we offer you treatment, to try and increase those figures.'

Alison points at the bar chart on the sheet she has printed out. I could be in the black bit, the 'alive' people, but I could be in the white bit, the 'dead' people.

'Maybe they died of something else?' I am trying to be hopeful.

'No, these are the cancer figures here, these figures here are other deaths.'

These figures don't even register on the bar chart, they are so small. The main figures are about cancer. Shit.

I'm starting to get it now, what they actually mean by 'gain'. I'd rather be anywhere else but in this room just at this moment. I really don't want to hear this.

'OK, so what's the gain?' I ask.

The gain for chemotherapy is just under 10%, the gain for hormone treatment is just over 10%. If you do both of them the gain is not simply the figure of adding up the two statistics, it's a new figure of less than 20%.

Another long pause.

So the biggest gain, and there is no guarantee of it, is just under 20%, so if you add that to 60% then the chance of me being alive in ten years is roughly 80%.

80%. Or eight in ten. Or four in five.

I'm very shocked by this.

'Is that all?' I say.

Now I can see why not everyone wants to know the figures. They are fucking scary, that's why.

Plus there's no guarantee I'll be in the 80% anyway. I could fall into the 20% who are dead.

But I am still questioning the chemotherapy. Alison is being really honest and telling me that when used as a precaution it does have gain, but they don't really know exactly why.

I don't feel ready to do this. I am not afraid of the treatment, but something in me says it is wrong. Plus, I am still bothered by the persistent toothache, I need to get that sorted out. So I ask Alison if it would be OK to get the dental work done first, before chemo starts. She says that doing it by the book would be to start chemotherapy six weeks after surgery, but if I want to postpone that until eight weeks she doesn't think it will make any difference.

Shit. Shit. Shit. I could postpone chemo for another two weeks. Or I could choose to refuse it. Could I? Can a cancer patient say no? What will happen? An impossible decision. How on earth do I live with myself if I make the wrong decision? Well, I won't have to. I'll be dead.

I go home feeling a bit down, to say the least.

I am thinking about my prognosis. Even though I have no lymph node involvement, I am being offered chemotherapy as a precaution. I feel very uncomfortable about such a toxic treatment. It's not the fact that I will lose my hair or that I will be sick, but destroying a healthy immune system just feels wrong. It's an intuitive feeling I have.

What I do know is that my particular breast cancer is oestrogen positive. This means that although oestrogen did not cause my tumour, it fuelled the growth. So as I am still menstruating, having clockwork regular periods, and therefore still producing oestrogen then I could be at risk of further cancer, either a recurrence somewhere else or a new primary tumour. Oestrogen is now known to play a part in some cancers, and the oestrogen status of a tumour can be measured. Mine is 90% positive. So I will be offered a hormone blocking treatment at the end of chemotherapy to protect me from oestrogen, for five years.

When I reflect on this I think about my hormones. When I was an adolescent my parents' favourite phrase was, 'It's your hormones.' Everything was my hormones. Then I started my periods. More hormones. Causing havoc. Then I was a slave to premenstrual syndrome throughout my 20s, half the month savaged by my fluctuating moods. When my periods finally settled down in my late 30s I assumed my hormones were finally calming down. Little did I know they were actually quietly behaving badly behind the scenes, fuelling this tumour in my breast. Doctors disagree about the length of time that it might take to grow a six-centimetre tumour, but it could be as long as eight years. So all the time I've been thinking I'm in perfect health but I've actually got cancer.

I look at my histology report. It is three pages long. I read every word. My right breast weighed 1,430 grams. That's just over three pounds. It says, 'The breast is sliced into 13 slices from lateral to medial.' My breast cut into slices and analysed. This seems bad enough. How on earth do I decide what to do next?

A week later I go back to the oncologist and sign the consent form for chemotherapy. We agree a start date of 10 May. That will be eight weeks after mastectomy. I feel like I have won a minor victory, getting it delayed by two weeks. But everything feels wrong.

R⅔ჿ

I'm travelling at 100 miles an hour on a train with no brakes. It's time to press the red 'stop' button. Quick. I need to get off.

part **two**
Things that are
lost forever

March 2007 – Porthgwidden beach, St Ives; a short break before mastectomy.
'This was a good idea.'

CHAPTER FOUR

Research

I feel completely out of control. Am I doing the right thing? How on earth do I know? I don't feel I have a choice about any of this. It is all feeling completely out of control.

We go to the wig shop which, as it turns out, is just round the corner from where we live. I had noticed this shop before, never believing or even thinking it would be conceivable that I might actually go in.

I try a variety of wigs. This is in preparation for losing my hair when I start chemotherapy. I feel like I am watching someone else trying on wigs, laughing about them. It's like it is not happening to me. I am trying to make this fun, but in fact there's nothing fun about this at all. The NHS will give me a financial contribution for one wig, but if I want others then I will have to pay for them. I try a neat headscarf which has a fringe sewn into the front, it looks very realistic.

And there are tons of headscarves on eBay. I buy a Missoni silk scarf; actually I buy two. These are the scarves that Dina Rabinovitch recommended in her Vogue article about breast cancer and style. They drape and shimmer in brilliant jewel colours.

This is going to be an adventure. At this stage I believe I will be a fighter. I have swallowed the terminology that is used for cancer. Fighting?

My toothache continues. And I have to find a new dentist. My previous dentist is not returning my calls. He has been my dentist for over ten years, removed all my mercury fillings and replaced them with non-toxic substances. And he has corrected my bite and improved the way my jaw sits. But now, now I have breast cancer and we have rung and asked for an emergency appointment, he has not called back.

So I need to find a new dentist. One dentist I speak to says they won't treat me once I have started chemotherapy, I'm not sure why. Increased risk of infection maybe? So I try someone else and find a dentist who can fit me in. But because of the time it takes to arrange all this, I decide to postpone the start date of my chemo by two weeks – so I will start treatment with my teeth sorted out.

And in that extra time, it's like the fog lifts. I become clear headed. I don't know whether it is the two anaesthetics finally leaving my system but I just feel I haven't got enough information about my treatment and that there is more research to be done.

A friend has suggested that I go and see another doctor, a private doctor. Initially, I am reluctant. It will be expensive, I will have to travel. I have my team here at the hospital, surely they are looking after me in the best possible way? Why do I need to see someone else?

But my friend has just been on a seminar about integrated approaches to treating cancer, and is recommending this doctor, Dr Rosy Daniel, the founder of Health Creation. Dr Daniel also worked for many years at the Bristol Cancer Centre, now called the Penny Brohn Centre, which pioneered the idea of treating cancer patients holistically. This means developing an integrated, individual treatment plan for each patient, using whatever treatments the patient is happy to have. It doesn't mean being told what you will have. And it doesn't mean ditching conventional medical treatment either.

I decide that I will go and see her, just to see what she has to say. I have my treatment arranged to start in May, the chemotherapy, so this appointment with her will just be to talk about getting the right support to minimise side effects, and discuss what other treatments might be available to me. I have never seen a private doctor in my life. Why would I? I have the NHS.

I ring Dr Daniel's clinic in Bath and ask what normally happens. They say that I can have a telephone consultation, but for the first appointment it is better if I come to the clinic.

'But it's in Bath,' I say.

'We can recommend somewhere for you to stay.'

I pause and think. OK, so now it's turned into a holiday has it?

'So how much is the consultation?' I ask.

They tell me.

Another pause.

'Sorry, how much? For *one* hour?' I am shocked.

Why am I surprised? I had no idea what a private doctor would cost. I think they can tell I am a bit gobsmacked at the fee. The person at Dr Daniel's clinic is trying to be helpful.

'If you are having financial difficulties then we can help you,' she says.

'OK, well it's just that I'm not working right now.'

'I'll send you details of Yes to Life, they are a charity that may be able to help you.'

I book the appointment anyway, thinking that I can worry later about paying for it.

My life is full-time breast cancer now. There is no space for anything else. Researching treatments mainly, and thinking a lot. I find a new dentist, 40 miles from home, and have several dentist appointments. I have lymphatic drainage to help the swelling and stiffness around my mastectomy scar. I have days in bed. I look for a breast cancer group in south Liverpool, where they don't play bingo. I can't find one. Buy a mastectomy swimming costume. Despair about bras. Shove all mine in a bag and put them in the back of the wardrobe. I can't bring myself to throw them away. Preparing for chemo. Looking for clothes for one breast. Wrap round tops. Get my long hair cut shorter, a bob just above my shoulders, in preparation for hair loss. Where did my life go? I feel down. How can I recover a sense of me, a sense of pleasure and things that aren't cancer related?

I feel the whole diagnosis is over. It's time for treatment now. And side effects. But not just yet.

We travel to Bath to see Dr Rosy Daniel. Yes to Life did come up with the money to cover the cost of the consultation, so I'm thinking, well if this woman is a quack then at least we're not paying for it, and we'll just have a nice break. Ronnie finds us a serviced apartment to rent in the city centre in a Georgian terrace. He books us in for two nights so we can enjoy ourselves. Bath is actually one of our favourite places and we've been there many times before and so we are looking forward to a short break, despite the circumstances.

On the morning of the appointment we walk up to Dr Rosy Daniel's clinic. It's spring now and buds are starting to open, coming into flower.

We walk through a park, which is next to the botanic garden. I want to explore it. Ronnie says we can go after the appointment, we don't have time now. It is blossom time. There is pink blossom everywhere, it is gorgeous. Life bursting out everywhere. Spring. My favourite season.

Rosy's clinic is in a large Georgian building which is on the north side of Bath. There is an osteopathic clinic in the same building. We sit in the waiting room and I'm really not sure what to expect.

A curvy woman dressed in black wearing a lacey top comes in and says hello to me. She has a big presence in the room, and she is looking directly at me.

'Are you Rosy?' I ask.

She smiles her lovely smile and says yes. She has lovely twinkly eyes.

We follow her upstairs. She is wearing kitten heels, black stockings. She is perfectly glamorous. Imagine, a glamorous doctor.

We sit down in her cosy chairs. She settles down like she's about to have a friendly chat, not a medical consultation. Rosy is the right name for her. She gives out a lovely glow and it is comforting just to be in the same room as her. Rosy is compassionate. She's met lots of people facing cancer. She asks me what's been happening and I feel completely at ease. She smiles reassuringly and nods as I start to tell her what has happened since diagnosis in February, which was only eight weeks ago. I say that I would have described myself as being in perfect health, as fit, that I looked after myself. And I don't know how I've landed up here.

After we have talked about me and my diagnosis, she explains her approach. She believes that nutrition is very important, as well as the right supplements to maintain health, so she gives me information about them. She also thinks it would be useful for me to get a second opinion from an oncologist about the statistics. And she points out that with a highly oestrogen positive cancer the most gain is actually achieved by using hormone treatments, not chemotherapy. I haven't really done much research about hormone treatments, I don't actually understand the term. I just think that my hormones had done enough damage and it's probably best to leave them alone. But Rosy points out that the thing that will most likely cause a recurrence of cancer is actually oestrogen, and I am nowhere near the menopause, so I have lots of it.

In addition, Rosy tells me that there are detailed blood tests that are available, privately, which can tell how many malignant cells, if any, I have in my blood. This would be indicative of the possibility of recurrence. This seems like a good idea.

She goes to her computer and prepares her report, prints it off and gives me two sheets of information summing up what we have talked about. I look through it. I am clear about the first page, but on the second page there are some treatments we haven't discussed. One says, 'Iscador for immune stimulation'.

'What are these?' I ask.

'Well, they are treatments you might want to consider if you aren't having chemotherapy. But I can see that you have made your choice about that so they don't apply to you.'

'I have made my choice?' I say, bemused. 'Did I have a choice?'

She looks directly at me. 'It's up to you.'

This is why I am here isn't it? This is the moment. I can just feel it. We have reached the end of the consultation, and we are all standing up ready to leave. I am reluctant. I feel that if I could just stay here then everything, somehow, will be all right. Rosy seems to sense this, and she says, 'You know Sarah that your *spirit* will see you through this.'

Then she shows us out. I am clutching my sheets of paper. I think I just might actually finally have a choice.

We walk back down the hill to Bath, back through the botanic garden. Every spring flower is smiling at me.

'What do you think?' I say to Ronnie.

He doesn't say anything.

'No chemotherapy?' I suggest.

The next day we go to Westonbirt arboretum. It is on the way back home. We enjoy the bluebells and spring trees. The azaleas are all out in shades of pink and red and orange. It is magical. I feel like I have been reprieved from the death sentence. I feel I have a choice.

Over the weekend I think about this. A lot. I make a very big decision. I decide I am going to take a month to pause, while I have a look at other treatment options and decide which is the best for me. I will take the whole of May. Finally, I feel back in control of my life.

Back in Liverpool I ring my oncologist's secretary and I cancel my chemotherapy which is due to start two weeks later. She is very worried.

'Well, I won't cancel it just yet, I'll wait until you've seen Miss Waghorn again,' she says. Because obviously, she must be thinking, as I am *only* a patient I can't possibly have made this decision on my own.

Miss Waghorn is Alison. I'm going to see her to tell her what I've decided to do. I don't need her approval to make this decision, to cancel.

'That won't be necessary,' I say, 'I won't be there on 10 May, so please give the appointment to someone else.'

She can tell I am serious. This isn't me getting cold feet. This is me taking control. And it feels great.

I have already agreed to go to a 'scarf tying' class at the hospital in preparation for chemo and losing my hair. Jane, who shared the ward with me, had suggested we go together. So, even though I have 'postponed' my chemo, I still go. I say 'postponed' because this is what I am telling people. I know they will be shocked if I say I have cancelled it. But it's still possible that I will decide to have it, so I suppose postponed is the right term.

Jane is waiting for me on the ground floor of the hospital. She has had her first chemo and already her hair is thinning. I tell her about going to Bath, seeing a private doctor, and my decision. She says I think too much and ask too many questions. I guess we just have different approaches to life.

The class is only for us two, run by two friendly volunteers. I enjoy it, even though I sort of feel like a fraud, like I shouldn't be there because really deep down I know I won't have chemotherapy.

In the afternoon, again at Jane's suggestion, we are on a workshop for women having cancer treatment. I assumed it would be about generally looking after yourself and about confidence. Turns out it's about make-up.

I am shown to a small room where there is a large table with five chairs around it, each place set with a small round mirror on a stand. I am one of five women here today and we all look at each other nervously, not quite sure what to expect.

We are then proudly presented with a white zippered bag containing a selection of expensive skin care and make-up. The collections of products are fair, medium or dark, depending on your complexion. I have a terrible feeling in the pit of my stomach.

'Right ladies, you can open your bags now,' we are instructed by the white-coated woman who is leading the event.

Oohs and aahs from everyone, except me, as the 'ladies' discover the goodies in their bags. Yes, there are expensive and branded products in the bag, lots of them.

Oh no. I was right to have the terrible feeling in my stomach.

During my internet research I have found out that most personal care products and cosmetics use parabens as a preservative. This is found as ethylparaben, methylparaben, propylparaben or butylparaben. Go on, have a look at anything in your bathroom cabinet, see how widespread they are. There is growing controversy about the use of these chemicals because they have weak oestrogen activity, and *may* contribute to tumour growth, especially in breast cancer.[2] I am 43, I have been diagnosed with oestrogen positive breast cancer, I want to avoid a recurrence. Do you think I trust these chemicals? I have been clearing out all my personal care products and finding 'safe' alternatives, which do exist. In fact enough 'safe' natural products exist to make me feel that there must be some validity in the claims that the chemical ones are toxic. And then a bag full of them turns up in front of me.

I'm thinking, shit, shit, shit, why am I here? Did I not get to this point in life anyway without learning how to look after my skin and apply make-up? I don't think a bag of make-up begins to make me feel any better about having had a mastectomy, or an uncertain future regarding my health.

The class begins and the woman in the white coat, like someone from behind those counters on the ground floor of department stores, tells us all to get a cotton wool pad and make-up remover. I am paralysed. I can see one of the helpers approaching me, as I stare blankly at the table in front of me, at the cotton wool balls. I am paralysed, my hands frozen in my lap. And I can feel this panic rising in my chest, and I have the most terrible urge to leave the room or I will suffocate.

I think I say, 'I need to go outside,' and rush to the door. I throw myself out and onto the nearest chair, outside the blood test room. I bend forward over my knees and sob. I can't feel anything else except the lack of a life. Is this what it's come to? A make-up class.

Where did my life go? I am in free fall.

I feel a hand on my back, and the woman who did the scarf tying class has come out to me. A nurse from the blood tests looks anxiously at me sobbing and opens the staff room door. Someone says, 'Put her in here, out of the way.'

So I need to be *out of the way* now? I am crying in a cancer treatment centre, not really so unlikely is it? And yet it can't be seen.

I try and explain, but I am so, so angry. Make-up so I can cover up and not show my face or my emotions. I am so upset, but even in my distress I feel I don't want to upset them, to tell them how angry I feel, for them to think I am not grateful for them trying to do something for me. But the something I need just right now is *not* a make-up class. Actually.

This is not self-pity, no, this is a deep raw rage. All my confidence has gone. I try and explain to the volunteer from the cancer support office who is with me that everything in my life has gone, that Sarah has disappeared. She is kind and tells me that she still sees a very strong person. 'Please don't pity me,' I want to tell her, but I can only cry.

Ronnie comes to collect me. I go to bed early completely worn out, but wake at 5 am convinced that I will die soon. How crap does it get?

My life is turning into a series of my worst days. This one is a contender for *really* the worst so far. Sixty-nine days after diagnosis and it feels so bad.

⸙

I go back to see Alison. It's funny because now I am a cancer patient I can get appointments with consultants in the NHS just by ringing up their secretary. It is now accessible to me without months of waiting and chasing up appointments. Wow.

She bounces into the room, surprised to see me. I was not due to see her again until the autumn, when I would be in the middle of chemotherapy. She doesn't know why I am here. She looks confused.

I tell her I have been to see Dr Rosy Daniel. Yes, she has heard of her. She doesn't give any opinion. I tell her I'm not sure about the chemotherapy.

She starts to defend it. I tell her that I am not saying 'no' – at least not yet, but would like a second opinion. She says of course I can see the other oncologist in the team.

'But it's highly unlikely her opinion will be different from the first one, if you know what I mean,' she says.

She is being astonishingly honest with me.

'Well, I was actually thinking of another oncologist altogether,' I say.

'Yes, yes, that can be very helpful for people facing difficult decisions.'

I don't think she's quite expecting what I tell her next.

Rosy has suggested I go and see Professor Karol Sikora. He is an oncologist and acknowledged authority on modern management of cancer, and has a practice in Harley Street in London. He's really quite famous.

'Oh, I see. Yes, I have seen him talk,' she says. She seems quite impressed.

She says she will happily do the referral letter. Even though I will be paying to see Professor Sikora, I have to have another doctor refer me to him. For some reason.

I then ask her if she will arrange to have my blood tumour markers measured every three months, as well as oestrogen levels, as Rosy has suggested. The tumour markers are indicative of cancer, but only when they are done regularly so that you have a trend. If the trend goes up then you can look at further tests or investigations. I had asked the oncologist about getting these tests done, she said they weren't useful. I also find out later that they are expensive too. But Alison is happy for us to monitor these, as well as my oestrogen levels; she whips out the coloured forms and plastic bags which she scribbles my name on and gives them to me to take to the blood nurses, the phlebotomists.

'Anything else?' she asks.

She has done everything I asked her. She is a star. I am so determined.

But we are so tired. This has been such hard work, even dealing with reasonable Alison. I so feel there is only one way of doing things here, in this system where they only process you in their way. Not yours. Not unless you ask very persistently.

What I didn't realise was how emotional this whole time would be. I feel angry. I cry a lot. I need to do something. I remember an advert I saw in the independent bookshop in town, News From Nowhere, run by a women's cooperative. The advert was for a female counsellor, so I go back and get her number. I arrange to see her the following week. But I am unsure. I tell her on the phone, 'Would it be OK if I can't make it, I'll ring you.'

This is crazy of course, but I'm finding it difficult to get out of the house. What happened to me?

But I do go and see her. I sit on a large sage green leather settee and tell her what has happened. It feels great, actually, to talk to this woman, a stranger, to tell her what happened to me. I arrange to see her again the following week.

Around the same time, seven weeks after surgery, I start having weekly acupuncture sessions as well. I have known my acupuncturist for about five years. I originally started seeing her for my sinus problems, but felt so much better generally that I carried on seeing her once a month. She is caring and compassionate, I feel safe with her. I feel healing.

I also go back to my yoga class. Even though the thought of it gives me palpitations, I am scared to go out to a new thing, a group of people, somewhere that is not a hospital. Will they notice my one breasted-ness? Does it matter? I always found yoga easy, a joy. I stretched easily, I liked the mind-body connection. In class I used to wonder why sometimes people wouldn't do all the exercises. Now I found out. I can't stretch the same, I feel I have been kicked in the chest. I actually feel like crying when I try some of the stretching. I feel let down by my body. I looked after myself, but somehow I still got this.

And now I qualify for a *proper* prosthesis, the false breast made of silicone. It's going to help with my confidence apparently. I read that it will 'restore my femininity'. So a lump of silicone is going to make everything OK is it? I actually really don't think it is. But I am in this process, this is what they do to mastectomy patients. They think they know how I feel. They can't possibly know that.

My breast care nurse rings me to make the appointment. She says I will have a choice, that I will find something that will work for me. How can she confidently say this? I don't even have a bra I can wear, so how on earth can they find a prosthesis for me? I am so angry really about all this, but I just don't know how to express it. So I ring up and cancel the prosthesis fitting.

But I do it on a Sunday when I know I will get the answerphone, I don't want to talk to anyone about this. I don't feel they will understand me. I feel so lonely. It's just crap.

I don't know whether to expect my breast care nurse to be concerned about this, whether she knows if I have postponed my chemo. What does she know about me? Isn't she supposed to be my friend, my supporter in all this? No, she's far too busy processing the next woman to deal with someone difficult and opinionated like me.

R🙣ℰ

It is 10 May. The day I was going to start chemotherapy. And we are camping in the Lake District. We love camping. It is a new thing for us, discovered in recent years first by hiring camper vans, and then we moved on to owning a tent. It's a lovely tent, our tent. It's a tunnel design, so not unlike a polytunnel with two big hoops making the main frame. It is spacious, apparently a five 'man' tent. So that makes plenty of room for us, and, more importantly, you can stand up in it. I am not going to crawl around trying to get dressed when I am on holiday.

We are doing something 'normal'. Well normal for us. And, more importantly, not about breast cancer. I know that when I get back I will have more appointments, more thinking to do. I will have to make decisions. But just now, just here, I don't have to. I can just be. It feels great. Eskdale is beautiful. I don't mind the rain, I am so glad to be here.

Back in Liverpool my foam swimform has arrived. This is a lightweight breast-shaped piece of foam that can be worn in a pocket in a swimming costume. Unlike the 'everyday' false breast, the silicone prosthesis, this one is not available from my bit of the NHS, I have to buy my own.

I have found a mastectomy swimming costume, with pockets, which is the term for the extra fabric inside the breast area where a prosthesis can be put. It is turquoise. I'm not sure about it, I think it looks odd on my left side, on my left breast, because it has a pocket on both sides, and the pocket wrinkles over my breast. I ring another supplier and ask about getting a costume with only one pocket. She explains to me that I can cut out the pocket on the left side. I feel like she is talking down to me. But please, just tell me, how on earth was I supposed to know this? I feel stupid, like I haven't read the user's manual, but actually there isn't a manual that tells you what to do about any of this. Why didn't someone tell me? Isn't that the sort of thing that the breast care nurse was supposed to be for?

It works a treat anyway, cutting out the pocket I don't need. The foam breast is a success, although it feels strange as it is so lightweight. But I have a contour shape of two breasts. Then I go swimming, at last. I manage six lengths and sit for a long time in the sauna. It feels blissful.

The next day we go to Harley Street to see Professor Karol Sikora for a second opinion on my cancer treatment plan.

I feel odd, other worldly. Going to Harley Street isn't what people like me do. It's for rich people, famous people. Not me. We get off the train at Euston, it is a sunny spring day, so we decide to walk. In Goodge Street we find a café, and stop and have an early lunch. I have a salad, and carrot and spinach juice, freshly made. We sit outside at the pavement tables. I'm not sure what's most unlikely, whether it's that I am about to visit a Harley Street doctor or that I am drinking spinach juice.

We continue on to Harley Street. We pass a newspaper seller. There is a headline in the Daily Mail about the latest drug for early breast cancer, Zoladex. I quickly read the article, I do not want to buy the paper. I have standards. It is claiming that this drug, when used to treat young women - women who have not had the menopause - may be as effective as chemotherapy, but without as many side effects. This sounds good to me.

Harley Street is a long road. The buildings are Georgian. Huge doors and sash windows. Black railings around the front, and steps up to front doors with polished brass knobs and rows and rows of gleaming brass plates packed with doctors' names and qualifications. We find number 81, and go in. There is absolutely no comparison I can make to seeing a doctor in the NHS. The reception room is massive, I mean huge. And fresh flowers in tasteful arrangements on the mantelpiece and the reception desk. Only 17 chairs, but not the sort of utilitarian pushed together too close chairs. Proper armchairs and settees, with side tables, so widely spaced that you have privacy with your partner. Country Life magazines. And, a cold water dispenser, and free hot drinks and biscuits. I give them a minus point for the plastic cups though.

So I settle down with my knitting, a new project which I started while we were camping in the Lakes. It is a loose stylish jacket for me, in a new yarn, spun from bamboo in a gorgeous neutral shade called 'rope'.

I am expecting the usual wait. I have just put my needle in the first stitch of the row, and at 12.30 pm precisely, the time of our appointment, the friendly receptionist calls us to the door, and shows us the way to the third floor for Professor Sikora. We go up to the top floor in a tiny rickety lift, emerge into a small corridor and find a door with a brass plate with his name on it.

He's world-famous and has loads of letters after his name, but he's just a dead nice bloke. He welcomes us and like any famous people I've seen in real life, he's not as tall as you think he will be. He sits down behind his enormous wide expensive desk and smiles. He's friendly. He seems determined to make this a good consultation. He opens my file, it only contains the referral letter from Alison. He smiles good naturedly at me, enquiringly.

'There must be more than this?' he says, expectantly.

I have a copy of my histology report with me which I hand across to him. I also have a letter, a copy of the letter I received after I got my first results. He asks for a moment while he reads it.

The room is quiet. Ronnie and I exchange looks, waiting.

Suddenly Karol Sikora bursts out laughing.

'Are they still writing letters like this in the NHS?' he says.

I look questioningly at him. After all, I think this is the first letter I've had from the NHS, how do I know what to expect?

So he carries on, 'It says here,' and he reads out loud, 'that the multi-disciplinary team have decided you will have chemotherapy, radiotherapy and hormone treatment.'

I am speechless. So?

He repeats, '*You will have.*' And looks straight at me.

Oh, I see, then it dawns on me. He is making the point that the treatment should be *my* decision, *my* choice. I like him. He shakes his head, puts the letter down and moves on the histology report.

'Just give me a moment to read this would you please?'

Ronnie and I sit in silence, glancing sideways at each other, trying to glean any kind of information from the way my histology is being pored over.

Then Karol Sikora gets down to business. First he asks me to undress my top half, behind the screen and then he examines me, very thoroughly, tapping my stomach and listening to my lungs.

When I am dressed I return to the chair beside Ronnie in front of his desk. Karol Sikora puts his elbows on the desk and clasps his hands together. Then he tells me the statistics. So, depending which way you look at it, he tells us again the 60% chance of survival, or the 40% chance of death, if I do nothing. He quotes these gain figures from memory. They are the same as Alison has told me, so I am not shocked. I know them. I know all this. I know he is recommending chemotherapy.

Time for me to start telling him things. He seems stunned at my knowledge and my probing questions.

'Well Karol,' I say 'about chemo and menopause.'

'Well Sarah,' he pauses, looks directly at me. I wonder if I have stepped over some invisible line, using the professor's first name.

I tell him that current thinking for hormone positive breast cancer suggests that chemotherapy is successful in women in their 40s because it usually puts them into menopause. So the protection is coming from the lack of oestrogen. There are other ways to stop me producing oestrogen, instead of chemotherapy. Like Zoladex. I have already read about this, but now I have just seen it on the front page of the Daily Mail. Although that does not mean it is true.

Professor Sikora pauses, and then says I am right. He looks at Ronnie and says, 'She has got all the books hasn't she?'

Ronnie, his timing impeccable, doesn't pause, 'Yes, and she's read them all.'

Karol Sikora laughs. He's not used to such opinionated people I think.

He is straightforward and proceeds to give us exactly what we are there for, his opinion. He tells us that my tumour was 'unusual', because it was in three pieces. This is how he describes it - unusual - and I remember how the oncologist tried to tell me that it was three tumours, or multi-focal. But Alison said it was one tumour in three pieces, in a single area of pre-cancerous cells and they would eventually grow to form a single tumour.

Karol Sikora also says that the tumour was staged as grade three, the most aggressive type of cancer.

He pauses and then looks straight at Ronnie. 'If it were my wife I'd persuade her to have the chemo.'

That wasn't what I wanted to hear. I mean I wanted him to talk to me, which mostly he did. But now he has assumed that Ronnie would persuade me. I have briefly gone off him. What does he know? I am trying to concentrate, to make the most of this very expensive hour that we are paying for, to hear everything, to make sense of it.

OK, so we are talking about chemotherapy then. We then talk about the different types, or cocktails, of chemotherapy drugs and the ones that he would use at his hospital. But really, he says, it doesn't matter what combination is used, they are all effective, it depends on the protocol at my hospital. He would not, of course, try to tell them what to do. It is just his opinion after all.

Turning to hormone treatment he talks about Zoladex. This is the drug I've just seen in the headline of the paper on the way here. Perhaps this is a sign? I am trying to convince myself that there is something, anything, other than chemotherapy. I think he can sense this, although I don't say it out loud. Yes, he says, stopping oestrogen production is important in preventing a recurrence.

He knows that I have come to him because Rosy Daniel suggested it. He says he has respect for her. He goes on to say that he has patients who refuse all treatment, that they want to do everything with 'alternative' treatments. Do I look like an *alternative* type?

We end the consultation by him saying that if I only want to do one treatment I should at least do the hormone treatment. I think he knows what I think about the chemo option. We stand up. My hour is over.

As we turn to leave the room he says, 'You will do well.' This simple statement makes me feel better. After all, he's seen lots of people facing cancer, making these horrible decisions. Can he tell which ones will survive? Does he have some sort of instinct? After all, as well as talking to me, he has done what I will come to recognise as the very thorough physical examination, the cancer check.

On the way out of the door I notice his suit jacket hanging up on the back of it, but not on a hanger. It is a normal dark suit jacket, but the lining is dark blue silk with a repeat pattern of red and white circles, very unusual. Perhaps this is his way of showing that he is a bit different? Is he? Don't all oncologists recommend chemotherapy?

We leave the building. No-one mentions money. I wonder whether I am supposed to go to the reception desk and pay. I suppose they will send me a bill. Or maybe they will feel sorry for me and they aren't going to charge me?

We go out into the sunny traffic-filled day and find a café and sit outside at a table on the pavement. Ronnie says the pendulum is swinging towards chemotherapy. We both start crying. It just feels wrong. Just wrong. I still try and imagine the day I am starting chemotherapy and I can only see myself ripping the needle out of my arm and making a scene. It just doesn't feel right for me.

Back on the train to Liverpool, and I am determined again. As we leave Euston I have a sense of coming out of the corner I felt backed into. I feel my resolve again.

'It is only 18 May. I said I would take the whole month to decide. I still am. This is only one opinion.' Ronnie smiles at me, but I can see that he is anxious.

I am still gathering my knowledge. Then I can make a decision about my treatment plan. But not yet.

Doing all this stuff costs money. Lots. Hundreds of pounds a time, which soon adds up to thousands. Not just the doctors' fees, but the travelling as well. How on earth can I afford this? I put together a list of my expenditure. I know I am going to see another private doctor for blood tests; I don't know what they will cost. I make an estimate. A scary four-figure amount. I need money. What can I do?

I ask Yes to Life for more support. They have been great so far, funding my appointment with Rosy Daniel, and then, unasked, offering me financial support towards my supplements for the next two months. All I have to do is send in receipts.

Robin Daly, the founder of the charity, is really helpful, but only able to make a contribution towards the latest costs. I am not expecting them to fund everything but there are such a lot of expenses. Robin suggests that I set up a website and ask for donations. What? Ask people for money? Is he serious? I can't.

And then I think, 'Well, why not?' I have not told many people about my diagnosis, but I have heard people say, 'If there is anything I can do.....' And then their words seem to vanish, evaporate. What can they really do? So, here is something they can do. They can give me money. What is wrong with that? It's very un-British to ask for money, but I don't really have time right now to worry about that.

But do I know how to make a website? Er, no. Well, it's time to learn then. I am tenacious, determined. I have lots of photographs, Ronnie has been taking pictures of me from day one, at my request. I instinctively had an urge to document this experience, I don't even know why.

Ronnie suggests 'Being Sarah' as a website name. Being Sarah. Being Sarah. Yes, I like that. I am Sarah, but I am going to continue Being Sarah, that's what this is all about.

I sit at my computer and I learn. Very quickly. I finish the site, it is simple and direct, five basic pages telling my story. It is about me and my determination to find a path through this treatment for cancer that will give me the best chance of survival. Yes, we are talking life and death here. And I need money. I put a PayPal button on. It is bright orange and it says 'Donate'.

And then I send the site details to everyone I know. Friends. Clients. Everyone. I write:

> I am writing with some distressing news. I am currently recovering from surgery for breast cancer, and exploring treatments to limit the chances of cancer recurring.
>
> This has been, obviously, an extremely emotional and terrifying time for me. It has also been a time of intense learning and I want to pass on the essence of what I've learnt so it might help others, and tell my story. So I've created a website which you might like to have a look at.
>
> I'm also looking at various treatments, some of which are not funded by the NHS so I'm running a fundraising appeal to help with these. This is on a page on my website called Support Me.

An hour after I have launched the site I receive my first donation. It is a hundred pounds. Wow! This is going to work. I am deeply touched.

To my surprise and delight, my website is a success. The money continues to come in. Some people use the PayPal button, some people send cheques. Some people send good wishes. Some by email, some send cards. Some are praying for me, some are lighting candles for me. All are what I need.

Every message and contact is a tonic. And people send my site details on to others, so I am contacted by strangers. But it feels wonderful. I feel my support is gathering around me.

And people I don't even know are sending me their suggestions. One email reads, 'I hope you don't mind me getting in touch with you but I'm one of those people that have a cure for cancer.' As if it wasn't enough that I am trying to find a way through all this, now I have let other people in and am getting their opinions. Is this what I wanted? Or expected? I don't know, I don't know. What is happening? How many opinions do I want?

But it is an amazing response. One hundred percent positive. Nearly.

I get one letter from someone who was a very close friend, we'd met as students and stayed friends. We'd lost touch. She married a good friend of mine, and I hadn't seen either of them for several years. I recognised her writing on the envelope. I was pleased that she had written back, looked forward to reading her words. The first line of her letter however made me think I wasn't going to enjoy the letter.

'I have received your communication,' she wrote. She then went on to tell me that she didn't know why I was telling her about my breast cancer. Bad things happen to good people, she was sorry. And could I seriously be asking for money? That was, in her opinion, 'grubby'. I ask Ronnie to return the letter to her. I do not want this poison in my life.

***

I am still in this whirlwind of emotion. I am seriously researching treatment options. How do I decide? I still think I'm going to die soon anyway. I talk to Rosy on the telephone. I have so much fear. I am so afraid. So afraid that if I do have chemotherapy it will kill me, that the grim reaper is waiting for me with a message from my dead father. Or that I will have secondary cancer in two years, so even if I don't die now, I will die then. I have fear of leaving Ronnie alone, of dying before I am 50, how painful it will be for him. It is so much to deal with. But my intuition is telling me I don't want chemotherapy as my first treatment.

Rosy talks to me about the alternatives to chemo. Her first suggestion is Iscador. Iscador is a form of immunotherapy treatment. It works on the immune system. It is derived from mistletoe, which is toxic to humans, and has been used since the early 20th century to treat cancer. It is injected regularly into body fat near the site of the primary tumour. Use of Iscador may reduce the incidence of secondary cancer as well as reducing tumour marker levels in the blood. Rosy tells me I can get this treatment on the NHS. I am not so sure.

She says I will walk away from all this, this 'car crash', that it will become the past. Right now, it feels like I'll never feel anything else ever again. Only this fear.

It is the last day of May, 100 days since diagnosis. The last day of my month of research. We are on a train going to Yorkshire to see another doctor about more blood tests, the doctor Rosy recommended. It is a day trip.

So we are on a train. The carriage is full. Somewhere in Yorkshire outside the window it's all so green, so beautiful, rolling and rugged, a dark brown horse flicks his tail. The sun streams in and I look across at the next table. A small boy, maybe eight years old, is doing a crossword helped by his father, obviously off on a day out, as it is half-term. I can barely describe the feeling that comes from nowhere and seizes me. I feel my heart will explode with emotion as I even contemplate the possibility of not seeing Ronnie's beautiful granddaughter, Ellie, reach the same age. My eyes fill with tears. This happens a lot lately.

I reflect how I thought during those weeks of February, before I knew it was cancer, that the worst thing would be that I would lose a breast. I was wrong. Very wrong. It is devastating, horrible, distressing, this loss of a breast. But worse, no much worse, would be dying. I know that now.

Before lunch we go to a church. We light candles. Am I praying? No, but I am hoping that some sort of spiritual message will somehow help me. Help me to not die.

After lunch we get a taxi to go to the practice. I am tired already. I am thinking so much. I say to Ronnie, 'It takes a certain sort of person to do this doesn't it?' I mean all the travelling, the questioning, the research. It would be easier to accept the first treatment offered. Not to ask so many questions.

I reflect, 'Not everyone would do this.'

'But there's two of them in this taxi.'

The next doctor we see, this scientific doctor as Rosy describes him, is not instantly likeable. He doesn't have Alison's engaging personality and confidence, or Rosy's empathy. He launches straight into some facts about breast cancer, about diet and supplements, about the toxicity of mercury fillings, and hormones in animal products. He also tells me there are lots of other treatments that are used intravenously instead of chemo. Lots. This sounds good. I'm starting to warm to him a bit. He has sheaves of paper sorted into clear plastic folders and he rifles through them as he talks to me, passing me long handouts about the information he is talking about.

We move on to talk more about my histology, my particular oestrogen positive cancer. He thinks hormone treatment would be a good route for me. And Iscador. He is very clear about this. He also offers me a blood test, a minimal residual disease test, that can detect malignant cells. Depending on the result we can talk further about chemo or other options. Or if it is appropriate there is further testing that can be done which would test my blood against a variety of chemo drugs, to see which one is the most effective. This seems logical to me, rather than just throw the 'standard' cocktail at the cancer, then this would provide a tailored approach. By the way, all the tests are, you will not be surprised to hear, very expensive.

Even so, I feel ever so slightly excited. That a crack has just opened. That I might finally, at last, have found a *choice*. The choice I feel I've not been offered so far.

The next day, 1 June, is 11 weeks since mastectomy. It is time to decide on my treatment plan. We are going to see Alison to tell her what I have decided.

CHAPTER FIVE

Treatment

Every doctor I have seen who will give me gain figures agrees that the most 'gain' will be from hormone treatment. Some doctors think that chemotherapy will give additional gain. I am still unconvinced at this stage that chemo will be of benefit to me. So my decision is to start hormone treatment, and look at other treatments to support my immune system.

This is what I tell Alison. She says it is my decision. She says that I have been offered the treatment the team has recommended, chemotherapy, as my first treatment. But it is up to me.

I then tell her about Iscador. This is the treatment Rosy discussed with me and recommended, and the scientific doctor also supported this. Alison says she has heard of it, but doesn't know much about it. She says she doesn't think it is used instead of chemotherapy. But she is happy for me to pursue it. It is described as an 'anthroposophic medicine', which means that it attempts to engage the whole person in the healing process.

On the NHS it is prescribed by homeopathic doctors, even though it is not a homeopathic treatment. But there is a homeopathic department in Liverpool, so I ask Alison to refer me to it. She agrees. Of course. She does not refuse any of my requests, as I am coming to find out.

And now we discuss the hormone treatment.

Hormone treatment is, I feel, a confusing description. It actually means hormone suppressant treatment, which will reduce the amount of oestrogen in my body, as I have had an oestrogen positive cancer. The likelihood of further cancer could be fuelled by oestrogen. So the first treatment is a drug taken daily to block oestrogen receptors, and this will be followed by another drug by monthly injections which will stop my ovaries working. Alison says she doesn't start the two together so that we can gauge the side effects. This is the first time I've heard side effects mentioned. I hadn't thought about them before. But I know that not everyone gets them, and Alison explains that individuals vary about how they respond to hormone treatments.

So, tamoxifen first. Tamoxifen is well established for the treatment of hormone positive breast cancer, and at this time, the early 21st century, it is the world's largest selling drug for that purpose.[3] It has been in use for over 20 years so its success is well documented. Trials have proven that tamoxifen saves lives in early breast cancer, that is breast cancer that has not spread elsewhere and become advanced. This drug is taken daily and blocks oestrogen receptors in cells. That is a very simplistic description of the action, but basically that's what it achieves. It is very effective but can have negative side effects.

What I don't know at this point about tamoxifen is that, although it is widely used for breast cancer treatment, it has been classified as a human carcinogen by the World Health Organisation.[4] Tamoxifen is successful, but there are risks associated with it. Some are life-threatening. Such as endometrial cancer, as well as increased chance of stroke and possible increase in cancers of the digestive tract.

I don't know all of this when I decide to start tamoxifen as my first treatment after surgery, although Alison tells me that we'll monitor the side effects carefully, that the chances of them being very serious is unlikely.

Alison explains that after I've taken tamoxifen for a month then I will come back and she will start the Zoladex injections. These are given monthly and will cause my ovaries to stop working. She says that Zoladex is still in its ten-year trial, although coming to the end of it, and early figures look like it has gain somewhere just under 10%, in fact not dissimilar to chemotherapy.[5]

'Well, there you go, you've got your gain after all,' she says. And she smiles at me. I like her even more.

But best of all, because of this decision to start hormone treatment, is that Alison will be my main doctor. She is an endocrine consultant, as well as a breast surgeon. Endocrinology is the study of hormones and that's what we're dealing with, so she is the best person to treat me. I will continue to see her to see how treatment is going. I don't need to get passed on to another doctor or an oncologist.

'OK, so any more questions then?' she asks, smiling at me.

I know she will stay in the room with me for as long as I want her to if I have anything else to talk about. It is a good feeling.

She leaves the room, the curtain next to the examination bed wafts as she slams the door behind her. A minor whirlwind. Alison. Alison is my doctor. Yippee! Ronnie punches the air and cheers when she leaves the room. 'Thank God for Head Girl!'

It is a good day today. I am on my path. We leave the hospital in a good mood.

Now that I have chosen my treatment path, for now anyway, I am finally relaxed. I can finally feel a letting go of the worry that has haunted me since I found the lump four months ago. I am doing the best, in my opinion, to make a recovery. And in this new found peace there is great joy in simply being. We go to the beach twice in one week as summer arrives. I knit, paddle in the shallow water, and Ronnie reads. It is quite simply magical. Summer has arrived and I hadn't noticed. I've been too busy. I notice now.

I start to meditate and finally feel that healing is beginning. At last.

I go back to the clinic in Yorkshire to give a blood sample for the private blood test. Ronnie is working so my friend Bren comes with me. I don't really need someone to come with me. Or do I? I'm still feeling very vulnerable. I feel I need the protection. I feel safer with someone else.

This detailed blood test screens for 'minimal residual disease' which is basically any sign of cancer in my blood showing up as malignant cells. We get an early train so that we can be at the clinic to give the sample before midday, so it can be sent to Greece that afternoon for analysis. The receptionist is friendly, she remembers me from last week, me and Ronnie. Now I am with Bren, and she looks at me and then at Bren, and then back to me.

'So, who's this then?' she asks. A pause. 'Your son?'

Me and Bren exchange a look, and laugh.

'No, not my son, just good friends.'

There is no more time to explain. I am ushered into the room where I saw the scientific doctor the week before, and the nurse has laid out the items he will be using to take the sample. A needle, attached to a flexible small tube that is attached to a much larger syringe. It is a large sample, much larger than any sample I have given. It takes much longer than the blood tests I've had at the hospital. Afterwards he asks me if I want to stay sitting down.

'I'm fine.'

I stand up, and immediately sit down again. I feel woozy. It's weird. I feel drained. I want to escape this. I don't like all this medical stuff. Is this how my life will be now, giving blood samples? I want to leave the room, but stay sitting down anyway.

The tube of my blood is immediately taken away to be packed into a box on ice, and the courier will arrive to take it off somewhere so it arrives in Athens as a fresh sample. I am sitting still, the door is open and I am watching this happen in the corridor outside the room. I am waiting until I feel OK to stand up.

We leave and I am told I will get the result in about a week.

Me and Bren go for lunch and then shopping. We find an excellent leather shop and I buy a pair of purple nubuck leather clogs with wooden soles. We sit outside a pub in the sunshine, drinking like tourists. No-one would mistake us for people on a life and death mission. We saunter to the station to go home.

I think about the test. The doctor has told me that there is also a chemosensitivity test which assesses the response of the blood to an array of standard chemotherapy drugs as well as other treatments, like Iscador which I am trying to get. She also mentions high dose vitamin C which can be given intravenously, and some other options. I really hope that it won't be necessary to have to consider these, but feel reassured that there are options.

The way this disease seems to operate is that there is an unfolding, every test giving a bit more information about what's going on in my body. But every test, and there are now loads of them, means the gnawing anxiety of waiting for results. And I already know the agony and suspense of this is going to test me to my wits' end.

On the train home Bren sleeps. I am sitting next to him, and gaze fondly at him. Grateful to have him with me today. A tender, motherly gaze. Yes, people think he is my son.

He is not my son. He is 17 years younger than me, so could be my son. He met Ronnie before he met me, selling The Big Issue. An affable young Irish person, easily falling into conversation with people, in a way that city people usually don't. He was chatty, got talking, told Ronnie about his background. He had arrived from Ireland, young and alone. He needed some adult support. He needed a lot more than that.

He asked for help. Said he was interested in working outside, and Ronnie suggested my allotment. I told him I knew nothing about the problems in his life. What did I know about homelessness and drugs? How could I help? Well, I found a way through. Spent every Sunday at my allotment together. I learned a lot. Cried a lot. Laughed a lot. Four years on and he still comes to the allotment every Sunday.

Ask Brendan about me, and he'll just say, 'She saved my life.'

Brendan's mother died of breast cancer. I do not want to do this to him again.

Five days later my blood test result arrives. I talk on the phone to the scientific doctor. I have a good result, he says. My risk of developing further disease is low. This is good. After I put the phone down I wonder. Should I feel exuberant, like rejoicing? But I don't. After all, it's still a blood test involving cancer. I feel despondent that I'm even having to have the test and have a conversation about it. And then do it again in three months' time, to monitor this disease.

It's summer now and everywhere I look I see women with two breasts and I find it so depressing. I am only four months since diagnosis and have been through so much already. I have become sick of this subject and yet know that knowledge is power, and I have forced myself to learn, to read the long words, to understand the whole process of what is going on. I have challenged medical opinion, I have looked at death straight on, I have faced really tough decisions, I have travelled the country for opinions, for support, to find compassion.

I have cried in joy at the pleasure of being alive. I have cried in pain over the loss of my breast. I have cried deep into the night, I have lain awake worrying about death, my death. I have felt isolated and alone, I have wept in hospital waiting rooms, I have nervously examined my own blood as it goes off to be tested, wondering if I could see anything wrong with it, how my own body has let me down like this.

I have a good day. June is in full bloom and I love England in the summertime. I spend three hours at my allotment on my own. Fully absorbed in gardening. Delighted to see all these visitors, the plants that 'just grow' and appear uninvited to flower. Purple verbena is everywhere, with its wiry stems and tight clusters of purple flowers; papery white and orange Californian poppies; yellow spires of evening primrose; the blue star flowers of nigella, Love-in-a-mist, with its frothy delicate foliage; and blue geraniums looking better than ever. I briefly find joy and a remembered pleasure in the simple act of connecting with the soil.

But all around my good days are appointments. Every week yoga, acupuncture, my counsellor. My GP for a repeat prescription of tamoxifen. Where is my life going? I am now starting to feel the effects of this medication, tamoxifen. What is this drug doing to me? Well, bad moods, temperature changes, tiredness, nausea. And am I tired? Is it the drug? Or am I just tired?

I see another doctor, the NHS homeopathic doctor. He is the route to Iscador. He is extremely reticent. But asks me lots of strange questions. The way homeopaths do.

'So, what sort of weather don't you like?' he asks.

What on earth can this possibly have to do with breast cancer?

'Cold, damp,' I say.

'And what sort of foods don't you like?'

'Curry, spicy food, chillies, anything hot.'

'And how have you been feeling?'

'Emotional. Tired. Angry.'

'Angry?' He raises his eyebrows.

'Yes. Angry.'

'Angry? What about?'

'Breast cancer,' I say. 'The politics of breast cancer.'

He looks up from the notes he is writing and looks at me. He can see I was serious. He writes this down.

I didn't even know I felt this until I said it. I am angry that my treatment for breast cancer is dictated by the limited range of treatments available on the NHS, that I was told what I would have. That I feel I was supposed to agree, not ask more questions. That I have had to work so hard to get this far. To get a choice. To get some kind of control over my own treatment.

I am angry. And I am angry for all the other women that this is happening to and will happen to. It's not right.

My reticent doctor makes no comment.

He then explains a little about Iscador. Iscador is produced from mistletoe, which is a parasite plant that grows on a number of different host trees. For cancer treatment different types of Iscador are made from mistletoe that grows on apple, oak or pine trees. The different types of Iscador are given for different cancers. The dose, the injection site, the cycle of injections, plus other medical treatments will all vary with every patient. So Iscador is considered a 'highly individualised and comprehensive treatment'.[6]

One major effect of mistletoe extract is that it stimulates the immune system, and that the incidence of secondary cancer may be reduced, blood tests for tumour markers can go down and remain stable. In addition patients report better quality of life, they feel better and stronger. It generally does not cause side effects. He is very careful to point out that none of these results is guaranteed. The doctors didn't guarantee the chemotherapy either.

He says the Iscador will arrive in a few weeks and when it does I should ask my GP surgery to provide me with syringes and show me how to inject myself; he will write to them.

The consultation is over. It is vaguely dissatisfying, but I have the Iscador on the way, which is what I wanted.

Further research tells me that 'the clinical effectiveness of mistletoe is a subject of controversial debate'. That's because double-blind randomised trials would not give suitable results, because the treatment is so individual. But there are plenty of other clinical studies to give significant data to show that Iscador is effective in cancer treatment.[7]

Making tough decisions about treatment was really hard work. I feel like I haven't stopped. It is probably a good time to be going away somewhere quiet. I am in this place of sorrow and hurt. But I have a fear of going away somewhere, I think I will feel stuff that I haven't had time to feel yet.

Before my diagnosis with breast cancer at the beginning of this year I had been feeling a desire to come away, to have a break on my own, as I have often done, most years of my life. I had found a place in south Wales that runs five-day healing breaks; it was bookmarked on my computer. When I return to the page I am amazed to see that it says, 'Are you facing cancer?' Ooh. Did I have some sort of premonition about this place?

I book a five-day break there. Yes to Life give me a donation for half the cost, because, yes, this is about recovery from cancer.

South Wales. A long train journey. But the place is lovely, restful, my room to myself like a sanctuary. I am sharing the house with four other women, all who are here for some kind of break from their lives. All the meals are vegan, and prepared for us, and that is the only time we have structured time together. In between times we have four different therapeutic sessions of our chosen various therapies.

The first evening we talk over our meal, asking each other why we are here. Stress and overwork are the reasons given by the two younger women in the group. I am completely open about the reason I am here, about breast cancer and the mastectomy and feeling like I need some space. Another woman has had a lumpectomy for breast cancer, and has just finished her radiotherapy. She is working again, with a demanding family and wants some time to herself. And the final woman, who is not much older than me, says her husband died a year ago.

'He had cancer.' She looks straight at me and nods, as though having cancer means that you will die. That I too will die. I do not like this.

She goes on to tell us the sad painful time she has experienced as he struggled with chemotherapy. It sounds horrible. Painful and messy. But she has adult children who are close and she does seem like she is coming to terms with her loss.

The mention of cancer is a weight in the group. I go to bed thinking about death. Waking at 3.19 am gripped with fear. What do I think about at these morning wakings? Well, I think about the loneliness of cancer. The people who said they would visit but then smartly stepped out of my life. It's hard not to feel disappointed by this. The people who didn't come. Are they afraid?

I feel deserted. I thought that I would find closer friendships. Now I feel I am forgotten, that I have been ill for 'too long', that there is an expectation for me not to be resting anymore. It is five months since diagnosis. But I'm not really ill anyway, at least not from breast cancer. I am ill from the emotional stress of cancer, and also the treatments to prevent a recurrence. Tiredness and nausea.

The next day I take a walk with the woman whose husband died. She asks me about breast reconstruction. I am learning that this is often the first question other women ask about breast cancer.

'I really don't have an opinion,' I say. This is my honest answer. I am trying to be cancer free, not two breasted.

'Oh, well if it was me, I would,' she says.

'How do you know?' I snap at her.

I am angry, she doesn't know. She has no idea what it would feel like to lose a breast. She has no idea what it would feel like to have a life-threatening illness. She is talking as though she knows, as though she understands. She doesn't. We walk back in silence. I don't talk to her again the whole five days.

Here I have nothing to do. All my meals are made, I don't have to wash up. I should feel glad, pampered. But I am so raw. Coming away like this with strangers has really exposed me. I don't know if it was the right thing. I feel so vulnerable. The last day I take my meals on a tray in my room. Being in a group is not where I wanted to be.

❦

We are back at the hospital for the next drug. Zoladex, the trade name for goserelin. Zoladex will stop my ovaries working. It switches off the signal that tells my ovaries what to do. It is given as a monthly injection, an implant in my abdomen which slowly releases the drug over the next four weeks. We have seen Alison, she says she has ordered the Zoladex for me, but it's not in the consulting rooms, where it should be.

'Sarah, this *is* a hospital, and the drugs *are* in here, well, somewhere. Just not here. I'll go and find out what's happened.'

She storms into the central office, slamming the door behind her. We can hear her talking, very loudly. Very loudly indeed, in fact, nearly sort of shouting. We look at each other, and smirk. Someone is being asked about my Zoladex in no uncertain terms.

She puts her head back round the door, 'Just sorting it out, Sarah, won't be long.'

The door slams shut. More talking and rustling. Next thing Alison is back. She sits down and brushes her hair back from her face.

'OK, it *is* here, but not actually *here*, if you see what I mean.'

She is smiling, in her charming delightful way. Ronnie and I are laughing now.

'It's in the pharmacy, but none of that lot,' she looks at the door, 'has got it. So would you mind terribly, I mean I know it's not the usual arrangement, but would you mind going down to the pharmacy to get it?'

She is so nice, so polite, so apologetic, of course we don't mind at all.

I have got used to the fact now that hospital appointments usually mean a day out. I bring my knitting and a flask of peppermint tea, I get used to the waiting around. We go to the pharmacy. More waiting. But the Zoladex is there, two months supply. We take it back to the breast clinic. Alison says that I should keep hold of the second month's injection and she will get someone to do the first one, and she'll see me in four weeks.

'Is that OK? Any more questions?' And then she is gone.

The nurse who comes to see me is taking the Zoladex out of the box and telling me how wonderful this syringe is, how it has won awards for the ease of use. All I can see is a massive needle, it looks something like a gun you would use to apply sealant round a bath, well perhaps not quite that big, but not far off. The nurse apologises for the size of the needle and says it may hurt a bit. She injects it into my abdomen and swiftly puts a plaster over the injection site. It's done.

What I don't know at the time is that, in drug terms, this is sort of like, well, a sledge hammer. I am about to find out.

CHAPTER SIX

What summer?

e are camping in St Ives in Cornwall. I am lying on the beach. From my vantage point I can look sideways across to the sea. I can see sand, sea, waves rolling in and sky, all as strips of colour. I can see 14 different shades of blue, green and turquoise. It is heavenly. The next day I do the same thing, but this time realise that a whole day has passed and I didn't think about breast cancer. The fear is leaving me.

On the campsite I see an older couple, maybe in their 60s. They are sitting outside their camper van in the early evening sun. She has a glass of white wine and he has a glass of red. I thought, that could be me and Ronnie in 20 years' time. And then I realised I just had a forward thinking moment where I assumed I'd still be alive. I have not done that since diagnosis.

Being away is good. I am letting go. I am with the two people who are my best support. Two men. Ronnie and Bren. Bren has his own small tent that he pitches close to ours. We share meals and it's special, our ability to have fun together. But they are both men. This is a surprise. I had expected women on this journey. But they seem afraid, the women, they have not come with me on this journey so far. And so it is Ronnie and Bren who hold my hands when we walk on cliffs that fall away steeply to the sea and I am afraid.

But my treatment, the first Zoladex injection, is making me nauseous a lot of the time. My period arrives. It's early. My last period? I am only 43, the average age for last period is 51. I didn't ever want my own children. My periods have always been regular like clockwork, and sometimes troublesome. Of course I have always known that one day they would stop. But a perfectly natural biological stopping, when it was the natural time for it to happen. Not by medical intervention. I do feel odd about this, I don't really know what the emotion is. It's strange, I really did not expect to feel any emotion about this. Then when I think about it more I realise that I have stereotypical images of what menopausal women are like. Will the lack of oestrogen make me age quicker. More wrinkles? Grey hair? An old crone? A miserable menopausal grumpy old woman?

Back home in Liverpool and it is straight back into admin for my ongoing treatment. My mastectomy scar is over-healing, becoming red and raised, as well as uncomfortable and tight. Alison has given me a note about some silicone tape I can use to help it settle down. I tried to get this at the hospital when I was there, but no, I have to go to my GP, ask them for a prescription and get it that way. This must be something to do with budgets, that the hospital won't pay for this, but it seems crazy to me because I see the NHS as one provider and it doesn't matter where the money comes from.

I collect the prescription from the GP, and take it to the pharmacy, but the pharmacy's supplier doesn't have it in the size Alison has asked for. So I take the prescription back to my GP, where it is lost. A new one is done but it is too late for the pharmacy to order it until the next day. So all in all it has taken nearly a week. Aaargh. So frustrating. This is typical of the non-patient focused systems that I encounter in the NHS, where an administrator has not actually thought about how it would work for the patient. Frustrating when the really big things are done so well that the little things can be so difficult to negotiate.

My Iscador has arrived. Seven small glass vials in a neat white box. I have two boxes of this first series, a series of low doses which gradually get stronger. I have also received a short letter from my GP, saying they will not show me how to inject myself, even though this is a treatment prescribed on the NHS. So it's back to my reticent homeopathic doctor.

He does the first injection, and shows me the technique. The small glass vial containing clear fluid is opened by pressing the red dot which is the weak bit of the neck of the glass. The top pops off, then the contents are sucked up into syringe and injected into fat on my stomach. I will go back three times this week to repeat, and then I will be able to do it myself.

The first time I do the injection myself I am shaking. I can barely break off the top of the glass vial. When my reticent doctor opens one, he simply flicks his thumb and it pops off, it looks easy. When I do finally get it open I cut my finger, then when I suck up the liquid with the syringe it becomes a foamy mess. I have done it too quickly and sucked too much air into it. My doctor is very patient, shows me how to tap the air bubbles out, and then it's time to stick the needle into myself. I have a generous layer of fat on my abdomen, which I have always tried to get rid of, and now it is coming in useful. Piercing my skin with the syringe. Not as bad as I thought it would be. I'll get used to it.

Iscador is given in increasing strengths until the correct dose is found. Once the correct level is reached I get a local reaction in the injection site on my stomach. This is a small area of inflammation and some skin reddening – it is a sign that my immune system is reponding.

I continue with Iscador injections, three times a week, for four weeks, then a week's break. The treatment is usually continued for five to ten years, with the breaks gradually increased after a period of stable disease. I will see the doctor every three months to review my progress. Even when I go on to six-month check-ups at the breast cancer clinic, I still go every three months to see my Iscador doctor. This makes sure that I am getting a highly individualised treatment, which is how Iscador should be prescribed.

It is only two weeks since my first Zoladex injection and things aren't going well. I am distracted. I feel full of stuff, chemicals. I am tired, quiet, weak, weepy, distracted. Hot and then cold. Strange. My right arm aches. This aching, this tiredness. When will it stop? When will I feel like me again? What a long road this feels like.

I am generally feeling premenstrual and nauseous. My temperature also fluctuates quite wildly. I am tired a lot of the time. I mean *tired*. I keep falling asleep. It must be the Zoladex, my hormones, I have no idea what it is doing to me, I am disorientated, lost. It is the start of a chemically induced menopause. I had no idea what this would actually be like.

And then I have a 'pain' in my right heel. A sensation, a dull ache. I noticed this a few weeks ago, thought it was maybe my new clogs, but it is back and am I imagining it or can I also feel it in my other foot? In my darkest moments I start to worry that this is a secondary breast cancer in my bones and will ask Alison about it. But also hormone treatments interfere with bones. I don't know if it can happen so quickly. Am I paranoid? Will I turn into a hypochondriac, worrying about the slightest thing now?

The combined effects of tamoxifen and Zoladex are that I am dozy all the time, in a chemical fog. I sleep poorly at night and spend lots of days trying to recover and have lots of naps during the day. I can't concentrate on anything and I've forgotten what it feels like to have fun. It's not great. At all. I had no idea just how bad it would be some days. I am so ill. I feel like I am in a bubble. Walking is an effort. I feel sick the whole day and have a headache. So distracting.

So this is my treatment is it? All these side effects. I'm not really ever aware of being 'ill' during my diagnosis with breast cancer and it doesn't hurt at all. So what is 'hurting' is my reaction to the drugs that I am taking to prevent breast cancer recurring. Basically, I feel crap.

❧

I continue with the supplement programme I have agreed with my integrated doctors, Rosy and the scientific doctor. This is a twice daily routine of multi-vitamins and minerals, plus a variety of supplements to support and improve my immune system.

And these supplements cost money, over £100 a month. But Yes to Life continue to help me with the costs. That is what they do – help people who are trying to recover from cancer, while still trying to stay well.

I do feel well, sometimes. When the menopause symptoms ebb, then I realise that I am feeling well, and I certainly look well. I make some changes to my diet. I avoid dairy, because it is often from animals injected with hormones. Same goes for meat, which I never eat now. Most of my food is now organic and freshly prepared. I have freshly made fruit and vegetable juices twice a day. Eating becomes a big focus for us. I don't believe that diet alone will make me well, but it is part of my overall plan to try and stay cancer free.

But it's still very up and down, emotionally and physically. Trying to manage the menopausal symptoms. I read about natural plant oestrogens that can help. But are they dangerous? Is black cohosh safe? It is a herbal remedy used for menopause symptoms, but it is thought that it may act like oestrogen, so not suitable for breast cancer patients. I am awash with information and I don't know.

Summer is slipping away. It is the end of July now, and I can barely tell what day it is sometimes. I sleep a lot. I feel that I am *doing* so much about breast cancer. I want to stop.

I feel all wrung out. I say to Ronnie, 'I want to do absolutely nothing tomorrow.' So I don't go to my yoga class. Stay in bed instead. Have a bath. Sit in the park with Ronnie, and knit. I feel that now. I want to do nothing.

I manage to stop.

I am extremely grateful for this time. This summer of stopping. It feels absolutely right for me. I have managed to achieve now-ness, sometimes. I don't think ahead, I don't worry. I am just me now, healing.

The thing is, I look so well, it seems to confuse people. I've been ignored by people, who walked straight past hoping I wouldn't notice; and then there are those who pat my shoulder and look at me with a sort of pity that seems to imply that I might die soon. Is that what they think?

I have been very hurt by some people's reaction to my cancer, to their emotional reaction. I think they find it easier to stay away. I think it is fear. Their fear. That this has happened to me, it could happen to them. And it makes me lonely.

But I've also been shown things about some friends that I would not have known without cancer. Like Bren, my other closest friend next to Ronnie. And for that I am extremely grateful.

There is another challenge that I had not anticipated. What to wear?

I did not come to the hospital, when invited, to be fitted for a *proper* prosthesis. That means the silicone one that will weigh a ton. I knew when I was shown that one after diagnosis that I would never come to like it. I don't like the fabric things filled with kapok they have given me either. They seem ridiculous to me. I can't wear them. Plus, of course, I can't wear a bra, it's too uncomfortable still.

I wonder what the false breast is for. For me? So I can feel whole again? Is that what it's for? But even if I put on a front for the rest of the world where I appear whole, I know that I'm not. And the whole sham will be unveiled the moment I get undressed. And it's in those moments, those alone moments when my clothes come off, that I see my body in a different way. It has one breast, so it is not symmetrical. Almost all our human features are duplicated. Two arms, two legs, two eyes, two breasts. One looks odd, wrong.

Not all of my previous wardrobe works anymore. Although I possessed a delightful cleavage I didn't really dress to show it, but it's impossible to avoid when you are a 38FF. So I look for clothes that are different. I am no longer symmetrical. Hems don't lie straight, so I find asymmetric clothes. I also find a fabulous open weave linen top which has a twist in the front, and covers the space where my right breast was. I order two more even though they cost £95 each. Wasn't really expecting to have to buy a new wardrobe.

And so over the summer I do find clothes for my new wardrobe, but I also make my own too. Because I can't always find what I want, I end up knitting and sewing my own clothes, for the woman with one breast. And if you knew I had one breast then you would be able to tell, but if not then the clothing solutions I find are a good disguise and I am happy with it. I wonder if there is a market for one-breasted clothes, but it seems that I am the minority here. Mostly it seems that women use a false breast to fill in the space.

Audre Lorde writes about this 'pretense' in her book The Cancer Journals.[8] She was diagnosed with breast cancer in 1979, age 44, and lost her right breast, like me. She died in 1992. Of breast cancer. So although she was a black American lesbian, I feel I can identify with her. She writes that women are encouraged to be the 'same as before' after their mastectomy surgery. To cover up with a prosthesis. Lorde says that this prevents a woman 'assessing herself in the present', in her newly changed body, and that a woman 'must mourn the loss of her breast in secret'. And also, it encouages us to see mastectomy as 'a cosmetic occurrence', but in fact this disease is about death. Surely we should be developing our priorities for 'usage of whatever time' we have left to us?

But whatever I wear, people may say, 'you can't tell'. Well, I can. And I will not hide behind the false breast, the hope of illusion. I cannot fool myself. Why would I fool everyone else with the illusion of two breasts?

It is time to see Alison. Again. I am getting used to these Thursday clinics. Full waiting room. Pink vinyl covered padded chairs. Really horrible in hot weather, the chairs are so uncomfortable and make you sweat. Especially when you are having hot flushes. No air.

When it is my turn I report on my progress with the combination of drugs. It is only two months since I started hormone treatment. I feel crap.

I tell Alison, 'I know this isn't a medical condition but I don't feel myself.'

'Yes, I didn't think you'd like Zoladex. Sorry about that.'

She tells me that people don't usually get used to this if they don't like it initially. So, what are my options?

Alison has already mentioned that at some point in the future, which sounded a long time away, I might want to consider having my ovaries surgically removed. It's called an oophorectomy. When she first mentioned this it just sounded like a remote possibility. Now that I know I don't like Zoladex it's starting to look like my only option. Shit. Do I really want more surgery?

I have a sense of walls crashing in, I mean I didn't feel like this a few months ago, but now I feel backed into a corner. I have been doing research like a maniac to give myself some choices here, but I'm using them all up.

Alison says she will refer me to a gynae surgeon, Mr A, to discuss oophorectomy. She says he is 'really nice', that all her oophorectomy patients go to him. Why are all gynae surgeons men? Why can't there be a 'really nice' female surgeon?

We look at my blood test results. The tumour markers for breast and gut are normal, down from last time, which is good. But my ovary tumour marker is very slightly elevated. Should I be worried? It is 40, and normal is 25, it was 27 at the last test. So, not a massively worrying result. But, all the same. I have a sense that it is different now. Now that I am a cancer patient. Everything has significance. Alison ums and ahs, and says that I can get an ovary scan done when I see Mr A. She doesn't seem worried, but she obviously doesn't want to leave anything that might be something. I feel pissed off that I'm just having more and more medical appointments.

Alison says she will see me in September, in a month's time if I want, but is happy to see me in October. I have been seeing Alison regularly now for five months, it feels odd not to be seeing her again so soon. But I know that I don't need to, and we agree the next appointment will be in October. By then, she says, I will have seen the gynae doctor and will know more.

Back at home my internet research tells me that a slightly elevated value for ovary tumour markers is not necessarily a cause for concern. Elevated means in the hundreds. Not 40 like mine. Phew, so perhaps I'm not just about to find out I have ovarian cancer now.

But it's such a long process. And the constant monitoring. When the results are not good but not bad, but borderline, it's so frustrating. Am I ill? I don't know. I never felt ill at diagnosis, I thought I was enjoying good health.

Nothing can entertain me. All my thoughts are cancer, illness, tests. Death. It's horrible.

CHAPTER SEVEN

Counting

e are in Galway, Ireland for a few days. Just me and Ronnie. Although I can barely speak, I am so drugged. Coming away, being away, it's so symbolic of leaving things behind, all that 'stuff', hospital, appointments, doctors, tests. We need a break. Ronnie suggested Galway for my birthday in September, next month, but I said why wait, why not go now?

So here we are. It is delightful. We have happy memories of previous visits to Galway, it is a good place. Just as I remembered and I am glad we have returned. We fly from Manchester and hire a car. It is a long day. I am exhausted by my own physical behaviour of protecting myself, my scar, I don't want anyone to bump into me. It is so hard to keep that up for hours.

We spend the next day in Galway, just being. We take the open top bus tour around the city. It is six months exactly since diagnosis. We both spent a lot of time reflecting on this and saying that what we most feel now is tired, and, frankly, exhausted. What a long slog. So intense and all consuming. And how lonely too. A very strange six months.

The following day we drive north to Westport and drive back through Connemara. The hedgerows are bursting with vivid colour, pink fuchsias, orange-red crocosmia with acid green leaves, purple loosestrife and some yellow flowers I don't know the names of. And the kniphofia, red hot pokers, look like burning orange sparklers, punctuating the sky. It is simply intoxicating. The light is golden, simply gorgeous. It is the sort of place that defies capture. It's just so beautiful to be here. The translucence of it. So much sky and water.

We stop at the coral beach, where we have been before. The 'sand' on this beach is actually made up of tiny particles of broken white coral. Heavenly. Then we stop at Roundstone for our tea, reluctantly leave as the light is fading and we still have a long drive back to Galway. I sleep in the car, dreaming of the magical colours I've seen today. Repeating our favourite days out, what's wrong with that?

And the next day another translucent day in county Clare. So lovely. I am easily satisfied. We spend half an hour on the Burren and I am happy to leave. I don't want to be late like yesterday. I am getting tired so easily.

Now it is time to go home. Yesterday I wanted to go home. I've had enough of being away, although the trip has been great. But today as we pull into the airport car park I'm trying not to cry. Because I don't want to go home. I love home. It's not home I don't want to go back to, it's the admin of illness. Getting my next Zoladex injection organised, more blood tests, bone density test, tumour marker tests, seeing Rosy in Bath, and so it goes on. And none of these things is bad, but just seem to occupy so much of my life.

When do I get my life back?

ℛ ✣

I am becoming too familiar with 6.19 am in the morning. This is when I have been waking. Tossing and turning for the next hour, alternately hot and cold, a hormone-induced side effect of my treatment, and falling back into troubled sleep. I am so tired and feel full of chemicals. I am also starting to get lots of hot flushes. Like every ten minutes or so. The extremes are horrible. I wake in the night hot and clammy, not exactly sweating, just moist. In the mornings my fingers are stiff, my hands and feet ache. Am I finding out what hormones do, that all this feeling of being off balance, of being foggy, as well as the aching and sweating. Do my hormones normally keep all of this in balance, in control?

One morning I lie in bed watching the rain on the window, heavy streaks, feeling more like November than August. This has been a crap summer I thought, and not just because of the rain, which has been fairly consistent. I want to enjoy the end of summer and autumn at my allotment. It will be special. Summer has been wet and unpredictable, I have been away a lot. Just sort of absent. I haven't felt excited for so long. I can't remember when. But then I thought, well has it been that crap? I've rested, I've had time away on my own and with Ronnie, and Bren. It's felt good at times. But yeah, it has felt crap at others. I need to do something different.

I want to be distracted, to do the things I love, knitting, gardening, but all my thoughts are preoccupied with cancer and it's horrible.

I manage my third monthly injection of Zoladex, knowing that this will have to be the last. I can't live like this anymore. I decide that having my ovaries removed would be preferable, even though the last thing I feel like is more surgery. But I do know that with oestrogen positive breast cancer it's really important to stop production of oestrogen.

I don't want any of this.

❧

In between my bad days I try and do something to regain my old self. I want to start running again. The activity that kept me fit, that meant I could get through the surgery and recover so quickly. Although I am perfectly happy with my one breast and the clothing solutions I have invented, I know that in a running vest my one breasted-ness will be very obvious. I am not sure if I am comfortable about that. I have tried using the swimform, the foam thing I have for swimming, but it is so light it doesn't sit in the right place. So I look for a solution. Thank God for the internet.

I find an unusual prosthesis, called a Been-a-Boob. It is made of soft fabric circular pouch with a special filling which imitates a natural breast. The first one I order is too big and I have to wait for the new supplies to come from Canada. When it does finally come I am thrilled. It is lightweight. It is cool. It is fully washable. And it can be worn in a swimsuit. It is very realistic, as it moves with me. The woman who invented it, Janet Cockburn, was diagnosed with breast cancer age 43, same as me.[9] She had a mastectomy and her recovery involved being active with a dragon boat team. I have never heard of dragon boats, but I see a woman who has risen to the challenge and found a solution. It is brilliant.

I also need to find a sports bra. My old one rubs my scar under my arm. The elastic presses at the exact point of the end of my scar. Both ends of the scar are incredibly tender and so the bra is very uncomfortable, I need something different, softer, wider. Again the internet is my friend here. A solution is found after a couple of size tries, I have found something at last.

I have to wait a few weeks before my new sports bra arrives. It has been ordered from America. It is front fastening with a dozen hooks down the centre, and has deep wide sides, I think it will be a success, that it won't rub my scar. And best of all, it is satin, bright red. I like it. I try it on. I think I look a bit like Wonder Woman.

But I feel so unwell I can't imagine running anywhere just right now.

The monitoring continues. Scientific doctor takes a sample for the second minimal residual disease blood test. He is in clinic on his own today and packs it in the box that has been prepared. When they told me that the sample was sent on ice to Greece, I assumed it was, well, ice. But it's not, it's those blue freezer blocks that we take camping. Funny, to think of my blood going to Greece with a couple of them.

I have a telephone consultation with Patricia Peat of the consultancy Cancer Options, funded by Yes to Life, to talk about my next steps. Patricia was an oncology nurse in the NHS; she left to set up this consultancy with a doctor, because time and time again she saw patients not being given options or choices about their treatment. This consultancy enables people like me to fully discuss their options before making a decision.

So Patricia thinks oophorectomy would be a sensible precaution. I already know from the blood tests we did before I started the Zoladex that my natural oestrogen levels are extremely high. No sign of peri-menopause, the dropping off of hormone levels. There is just too much oestrogen.

It is the beginning of September and we are in Bath again for an appointment with Rosy. I am thinking that I don't know where the summer went as I now feel the beginning of autumn in the air as we walk up to Rosy's clinic.

'I think an oophorectomy would be a good idea,' says Rosy. She is now the third medic to recommend this. Alison did. Patricia Peat did.

It sounds simple, this oophorectomy thing, when just said like that. An oophorectomy. I actually like the word itself. *Ooph-or-ectomy*. It's keyhole surgery, so not *really* major, I tell myself. I feel so wretched, anything must be better than this. But I was sort of hoping that my medical team might have had another idea. Something that didn't involve a general anaesthetic or scalpels.

And I talk to Rosy about fear, I still have so much. I feel unwell a lot and when I feel ill I think it means I will certainly die. I feel unwell because of the drugs. But the mental effect of that is I get down about things. And then I think myself into a negative space. She suggests a retreat. Not like the break I had in south Wales. More like a spiritual retreat, on my own. Doctor's orders. How strange is that? She tells me about a place in the Lake District. She will make a call.

Back in Bath it is my first visit to the new spa. I am so excited. This is an amazing collection of pools, jacuzzis, showers and steam rooms, all using water from the same hot springs that the Roman baths use. The only hot springs in Britain. When we came to Bath in April it was too soon after my mastectomy for my to visit the spa, my scar was too fresh, plus I didn't have my mastectomy swimming costume. Now I can. Ronnie goes off to walk around Bath, water not being his sort of thing. I don't mind at all. I feel I am escaping, getting away on my own for some luxury time.

I hire a robe and a towel, feeling utterly decadent. I take the lift up to the roof. As the doors open onto the rooftop pool I can hear myself breathe in, 'Wow!' I have arrived at a film set, a Hollywood pool.

The water is turquoise and steaming. I walk down the steps. It is like getting into a warm bath, the water at a delightful 36°C and rich in minerals. I float about in the pool as the sun decides to emerge. A couple of hot air balloons, one yellow, one pink, appear. The sun glints on the water making it look even more turquoise. It is quite simply gorgeous. Heavenly.

Down on the level below there are several steam rooms, each with a different aroma, eucalyptus, lavender, frankincense. It is so peaceful. There is a gigantic shower, the shower head is about three feet in diameter. It is like standing under a warm waterfall. While I am in it I burst into tears, the relief of the day, all this water washing away all the bad memories from this year.

A good day.

When we get back from Bath there is a message on the answerphone. From Rosy. She has referred me to Sacred Space in the Lake District. If I ring them they will arrange for my retreat.

I look at the website. It says: 'Sacred Space Foundation is a charity providing peaceful and confidential rest and recuperation facilities. It helps those suffering from the extremes of stress, burnout, emotional exhaustion or spiritual crisis that have severely shaken their sense of meaning and direction in life.'[10] I read the words and I feel it has described me perfectly. I have lost my sense of direction. I just didn't know it was called a spiritual crisis.

I speak to Stephen Wright at Sacred Space. We arrange for me to come the first week in October, in three weeks' time. That's that then. Organised that. I don't really know what I'm in for.

The side effects of the Zoladex seem to come and go. It's like drifting in and out of consciousness. My head is blurred. What day is it? Who am I? What's the point of anything when I feel like this? When do I feel better? I can feel my life simply slipping away, disappearing. Many of those 'spending the day on the chaise longue' sort of days. Not out of choice. I feel so dozy. Forgetfulness is a recognised side effect of this drug. Not even a trip to the beach can tempt me out. Sometimes I realise I have been in the house for two days solid.

I feel like I am the only person in the world who doesn't want to wear a false breast. I ask all my doctors if they have other patients who are like me. Some say yes but then they can't actually think of anybody. Mostly they say no. Or there are women who have lost both breasts, but it's different. They may choose not to wear false breasts, but they have symmetry.

In my asking I am given the name of a friendly breast care nurse at a different hospital than mine, where I haven't found my breast care nurse to be particularly helpful. We talk on the phone. I say I am lonely. She feels sorry for me. I don't want pity. She says that some women don't like the false breast at first. But they 'come round'.

I am enraged by this. I feel like slamming the phone down. I am so angry. I am supposed to be obedient. To fit in with what they want me to do. I am repelled by the false breast. Everywhere I ask the door shuts. I want to be on my own. I am so raw.

I try to recover myself, go to my allotment. I am sitting on the deck outside my shed. I am beyond cheering up. Even my beloved garden here is failing to lift my heart. Why?

I feel so alone.

I speak to scientific doctor about my minimal residual disease blood test result. It is better than last time. I still have malignant cells, but they are going down. He says the fact that the result is going in the right direction shows that my treatment plan is working. I am doing the right things. The combination of my diet, the supplements and the Iscador are working. My immune system can obviously deal with these remaining malignant cells, and is doing so. I do feel good this time. I feel I am making progress.

In all this haze I still feel crowded with appointments, with things to do that relate to my healing. Yoga, counselling, swimming, doctor's telephone appointments, GP for repeat prescription. It's not really a lot, but in my mental confusion it feels that way.

I relish the days that I can do nothing. Like today. There was nothing I had to do, no phone calls, no appointments, nothing. Just me in my pyjamas, and not feeling zonked today. Got dressed at 5.45 pm. Is my life disappearing just as I feared it would? Spending the day in pyjamas. I didn't even possess pyjamas before breast cancer. Why would I? I would never laze around for days on end. Ever. Am I turning into a slob?

During the summer I am continually expressing a desire to do something 'different', something that is not about breast cancer as I live and breathe it all the time. In September it is my birthday. For my present Ronnie asks me if I would like a place on the RHS general certificate in horticulture at night school, one night a week? He knows that I've talked about doing this, but never found the time. I agree, but really I'm not sure if I'm up to it. My concentration. Plus it will be a new situation, I will have to go on my own.

I know that during the first term I will miss several weeks because of hospital appointments and surgery, if I go ahead with the oophorectomy. The course starts the week before my birthday. I go to the first session. I sit near the door. Maybe I think I will leave if I don't like it, if it's too strange for me. Too different to what I'm now used to. Hospital appointments and doctors.

I feel I have lost the art of conversation. I only know how to talk about breast cancer now. It's all I have breathed for the last six months. It's so all encompassing. I feel I will never leave this behind, the haunting dread of recurrence. How can anything else assume any kind of importance?

But it's great actually. We start off with the plant kingdom, about the nomenclature of plants. I am in my element. It is such a delight to do something not about breast cancer. The naming of plants, the families they belong to, the scientific names. I am thrilled.

The day before my birthday Ronnie suggests we go to Blackpool for a trip out. I have not seen the Blackpool illuminations. Bren joins us. We go on the Blackpool Eye, like a smaller version of the London Eye, a big wheel basically that moves very slowly round with passengers in little pods that hang from the edge of the wheel. The pods on this ride are open, not encased in a perspex cabin. Open to the elements. I find it a bit scary, especially the first loop, it's like falling into nothing on the descent. Bren is skipping about in the pod making it bounce all over the place. I am clinging on for dear life with both hands so can't take any photographs. I think I will fall out if I let go. I feel I have been at enough edges this year where I can't see the ground below. This reminds me. It is scary.

The dodgems are great, although I get a bit of a hard time, being picked on as the only female driver. Bren is chasing me like a maniac, trying to bump me. Ronnie watches.

And me and Bren get really taken by the Penny Falls, actually 2p falls, but wow, you know, how much fun can you have with 50 pence? Change it into 2p coins and you're away. Then when you win 36 pence you think it's a gold mine. Just don't move on to the 10p machines.

It is all fantastic. The most fun I have had for ages.

We end the day with fish and chips in a cafe on the main road. It's just perfect. Trams, illuminations and fish and chips. My best friends. What more could I ask for? On the way back to the car I splash out £4 on a blue light sabre and swing it round my head in sheer joy. Joy at last.

CHAPTER EIGHT

Gynae

The day after my birthday I am seeing my new gynae surgeon for the first time, Mr A. He wears a pastel-coloured tie, and a very neatly ironed blue shirt, and he has a domed bald head. He is very clean, nothing about him is slightly crumpled, not a speck of dust on him. Alison says I'll like him. He is certainly affable. His large brown eyes blink very slowly as he looks at me over the top of his glasses.

'So you want an oophorectomy?' he says.

I'm not really sure what to say. I don't really *want* an oophorectomy, anymore than I *wanted* a mastectomy. It is just the next treatment for me. He senses my hesitation.

'You have talked to Miss Waghorn about this, yes?'

'Yes,' I say.

'And?'

'Well I'm a bit worried about it, you know losing my ovaries. The after effects.'

'It is your decision,' he says. 'I don't want you to say that we were horrible doctors and that we have rushed you into the decision.' He smiles at me. I feel completely patronised. I didn't know I would feel like this when I met the surgeon. The person who would actually wield the scalpel. With Alison it felt OK. It sounded OK. Now I don't know. Shit. Am I supposed to say, 'oh yes please, cut me open, dive in there and take out some of my organs that are functioning normally.' Do I want this?

Mr A is quite clearly not here to discuss surgical menopause or whether this is the 'right' thing to do. 'I am just the technician,' he points out. 'Alison is the brains here.'

Mr A suggests he gives me a 'provisional' date for oophorectomy. He has a black diary, like the one they had in the breast clinic for the mastectomy. The one that only the surgeons seem to use. He looks at it, self importantly. 'Ah yes,' he says, 'we would do it then, 13 November.' In six weeks' time. He says I can go away and think about things and ring his secretary when I have decided. No rush.

I have been experiencing some minor vaginal bleeding. I am a bit concerned. It's not normal. And anything 'not normal' now has the potential to be sinister. He seems unconcerned about this. He's a gynaecologist, he hears this symptom all the time, no doubt. It's different, I think, to know about this symptom, rather than to actually experience it.

'I will have a look when you have your oophorectomy,' he says.

'And if I don't have an oophorectomy?' I am trying to cover my options here.

'Well, then you can book an ovarian scan on your way out. We can have a look then.'

He smiles at me. It all sounds so routine. But to me it feels completely invasive, even the scan. I feel like a scrunched up tissue, ready to be thrown away. I can sense he is a busy doctor, he wants to get on to his next patient.

We leave the consulting room. Outside the door Ronnie says to me, 'You didn't tell me?'

'What?' I say. What didn't I tell him? Slight panic, what have I forgotten now?

'That you didn't want an oophorectomy,' he says. 'I thought you'd decided?'

'I didn't know I was going to say that. It just came out.'

Ronnie puts his arm round me and sighs.

We join another queue in the scan department. It is full of pregnant women, sitting there with their hands folded over their bumps. Many of them have proud partners with them, sitting next to them. They look anxious and excited at the same time. Shit, I think, why do they have to put me with them? We should be in different clinics. Them being pregnant reminds me what I will lose, even though I don't want to be pregnant. That's not the point. We book a scan for two weeks' time and leave the hospital.

But the next day I feel differently. I know that oophorectomy is the right thing. I ring Mr A's secretary. She is very pleasant. Yes, she has me booked in. Provisionally, that is, for 13 November. Do I want to go ahead? Yes. OK. I cancel the scan. I feel doomed somehow about this. It feels inevitable.

Days are passing and I feel ill. I was going to say 'wretched'. What does that mean? Both emotionally and physically awful. One day I got up at 9.30, and thought, 'Great, at last I can get up in the morning,' only to be asleep 15 minutes later on my chaise longue, where I seem to be spending most of my life now. Yes, this disease tosses us all in the air and who knows what we break when we fall, crashing to the ground?

When does this end? Do I expect a sort of moment when things feel suddenly better, that I am 'cured', that all thoughts of cancer will simply disappear? That I'll never hear myself say things like, 'well, the scary thing about breast cancer is that it turns up again, maybe somewhere else in your body like your lungs or bones, in ten or even 20 years. You can't ever think you're safe.'

Why?

Why me?

Why am I on this journey?

Why now?

I am spending four days at the Sacred Space Foundation in Cumbria. It is my retreat. The retreat that Rosy Daniel suggested I come on. I agree even though I don't know what to expect. I trust Rosy's suggestion. She knows me. Knows what is right for me.

Ronnie drives me up the motorway to Cumbria. We bring a packed lunch and go and sit on the shore of Ullswater. It is the first day of October, and mild and sunny. I am hesitant. I want time to reflect, but I don't want to be on my own. It's a strange feeling to me, I usually enjoy being on my own, have often in the past chosen to go away alone. And now, I want the safety, the security of what I know. Of Ronnie.

I know that what I am about to do is going to be about my emotional recovery, it's not medical, this idea of retreat. But it is necessary, I sense that even though I am nervous about it. Just like the south Wales experience, I am unsure. Yes to Life, once again, have come up with half the money to pay for this. For me to try and rediscover my life.

We finish lunch and it is time to go. We follow the directions and find the secluded place. It's a collection of stone buildings, like an old farmhouse. It's very quiet. We get out of the car, wondering what will happen next.

There is a neat vegetable garden behind a stone wall; I am just admiring it when we are greeted by Stephen, who appears from nowhere. Stephen, or the Reverend Professor Stephen G Wright, to give him his full title, is tall, with dark long hair which is greying, worn in a pony tail. He's got twinkly eyes and a lovely friendly way. He is like a wizard I think. If he were wearing a velvet cape I would not be surprised, he is a Gandalf-type figure, a good guy. He shows us in and we sit in the small kitchen, which is to be my kitchen, and drink tea with him. He's very friendly and welcoming.

Ronnie leaves and we are on our own. We talk a bit more about me, about what's happened to me, and then Stephen leaves me to settle in. My bedroom is upstairs, out of the kitchen door, into the room they call the 'sanctuary', which is like a barn, and up a wooden staircase. Tucked under the eaves is a small cosy room, my bedroom. It has a double bed with lots of pillows, a glass carafe of water next to the bed. In the window there is a kettle and a rocking chair, and in the corner of the room a smaller, separate room with shower and toilet. Everything is just so. I unpack my suitcase.

Stephen has left a book for me to read about enneagrams, a way of analysing personalities, using nine basic 'types', numbered from one to nine. He has marked the chapter about 'fours', which is what he thinks I am, based on the questionnaire I filled in before I came here. So I cook my tea, a piece of haddock, and read about myself.

An enneagram type four is called the Individualist. I am in good company, other fours include Joni Mitchell, Billie Holiday, Kate Bush, Sylvia Plath and Meryl Streep. We can be sensitive and withdrawn, but also expressive and dramatic; creative and artistic, but temperamental and moody. We love personal angst, apparently, and can often focus on past experiences, and base our identity on our feelings. Well, if that's true then I will have created some wild mixed-up emotional identity of myself with all the feelings I've had over the last eight months. I make some notes about my thoughts, as Stephen has suggested, and close the book.

I go to bed early. Find it hard to sleep. It is so quiet. I am a city person, this quietness is unusual for me.

The next morning. My first full day. The rhythm of the day is breakfast alone, there are hens who have laid eggs and they are left for me on the kitchen table. The yolks are bright yellow, I have two for breakfast. Then I have spiritual direction, time with Stephen in the sanctuary.

The sanctuary is a large room, with stone walls, exposed stone. And it is filled with an assortment of large cushions, all in shades of purple. In the centre of the room is a large natural stone, almost a boulder, like an altar, placed on a rug embroidered in maroon, blue and jade green. Either side of it are vases of flowers, orange marigolds and purple michelmas daisies obviously picked from the garden, some sprigs of hypericum with red berries strewn around it with red autumn leaves. On the stone is a fat orange candle, which is lit while we are in there.

We sit on opposite sides of the room and talk and meditate together. Stephen guides us. He uses the reflections I have from the enneagram book as a starting point to get me talking about myself. It's true, I do have lots of feelings, and I feel them very deeply. But feelings don't define me. Stephen reminds me that there may be a fear that if I don't feel things intensely then my creativity and identity will disappear.

I am trying to make sense of everything and trying to get back to my old self. Everything feels completely different now. Maybe things have changed too much for me to go back. That is why I am here. Is it? I don't know.

Then I have time alone. I spend hours crying sitting in the pine woods at the back of the house. Mostly just crying. Feeling such terrible grief. Grief for what I have lost. Is this what I came for? To cry? It is very intense.

I spend some more time with Stephen in the late afternoon. And then I am completely exhausted and go to bed at nine o'clock to eat jaffa cakes and feel sorry for myself. I am too tired to reflect.

The next day is a better day. Better? Well just not so intense. Being alone on retreat is completely different to being in a group. My experience in south Wales was nothing like this.

Here I have time with Stephen again in the morning. Then I walk in the woods and sit there for ages. So much pain released. I feel so much lighter today. Time with Stephen again in the early evening, and then I am alone.

And that is my routine.

What do I learn here? Well, what did I remember? During some of my time here I sit and listen to Stephen saying wise things. I nod. And it isn't because I simply agreed with what he was saying. It was because I remembered. I had forgotten. That's what happens. We forget. When we run into an emotional or physical crisis we are plunged into complete disconnect. So I am re-learning how to feel. To feel anything other than cancer, or fear of death.

And I learn that feelings aren't facts. I will not become invisible because of what has happened to me. One of my fears is that I will simply disappear. That I have fallen in on myself. I have so much pain about loss, the physical loss, and yet I do learn that my spirit keeps me alive, not my body. I remember this. I knew this. Rosy told me, the first time I saw her, she said 'Your *spirit* will see you through this.' My spirit is burning. Very brightly still.

And so I learn about the leaving behind-ness. My new life. I am starting a new life. I had not looked at cancer in that way before. What a trauma forces us to do. This is my walking on coals moment, a brandishing, a burning.

I think that I must be nearly at the end of this, of this unexpected detour in my life, but Stephen tells me it's early days. Just over seven months doesn't feel like early days to me, unless this is a longer journey than I'd anticipated. But in fact I don't know what to expect.

Stephen describes my situation, 'You have unexpectedly left one safe harbour, your old life, behind and you are sailing to another one, your new life. But right now you are between the two and you can't see either harbour, and it's very stormy. No wonder you are afraid.' He is absolutely right.

I leave the Sacred Space Foundation today. I arrive out the other side in good shape and ready to move on.

Stephen drives me to Penrith, to the train station. I hug him when he leaves. And when I put my bag on the train I see he has slipped in a bunch of flowers, from the garden, like in the sanctuary, purple and orange. It makes me smile.

❧

Back in Liverpool I see Alison. She is on good form. By now she has got used to the idea that I need a lot of time, so we see her at the end of her clinics, the last appointment. She knows we will always have more research to go through with her and she is always happy to give us her time. Ronnie is always saying 'She's the sort of doctor Nye Bevan wanted the NHS to be full of.' She is, and she's my doctor. All is well.

We are still eating well, I am taking my supplements, and injecting myself with Iscador three times a week. Yes to Life continue to support me with financial contributions to see my private doctors and for supplements.

And then I go running. I am ready now to use the new red bra that has come into my life, the sports bra. It is autumn now and I am ready to run. I use my new Been-a-Boob, which does look great. But I decide I don't need it. I give it up and run with my one breast.

I have, at last, thrown away all my bras. It seemed undignified for them, shoved in the back of the wardrobe in a plastic bag. Wrong. I can't see how I will ever need them again. It's too painful to look at them. So with a deep breath I thrust them into the bin. Well, OK, not all of them, I kept the red lace one. Why? I did love how my breasts looked in that bra.

I was in the shower this week and remembering the first 'proper' shower I had after surgery, when I was healed enough and could stand fully under the water. And it made a different sound. The water did not run off two breasts, but over one and then down the flat side, and it was a different sound than before. I don't notice anymore.

And getting into the passenger side of the car and putting the seat belt on, and it's completely flat, the seat belt surrounding my left breast and lying flat on my right chest wall. I don't notice anymore.

And when I stretch out on the settee with a cup of tea, I used to rest the saucer on the shelf of my breasts. But the shelf isn't there anymore. I don't even think about it now.

So I don't notice these things, does it mean it's OK now? I think it just means that we are very adaptable.

Often I'm not feeling so good in the mornings. Ha! I get up at 11ish, how much morning is that? Still wiped out, nauseous, horrible side effects from this sledge hammer drug. I do not have my last injection, as surgery is approaching. I hope for a brief respite of feeling well, but I don't get it. And, even just two weeks off Zoladex and my ovaries started working again and I have sporadic bleeding. When is this over? When do I feel well again? I feel despondent and unsure about the oophorectomy. But I feel backed into a corner, that there is no way out.

I am forgetting things all the time.

In my despondent moments I want to stop all my treatments, but logically I know they will help prevent a recurrence. It's just so all-consuming. Still.

The seasons are passing and I am still in this breast cancer adventure, diagnosed in winter, treated through the spring and summer and now autumn has arrived. Eight months today since diagnosis.

For eight months I have been immersed in breast cancer and my treatments. Hospitals and doctors. Zoladex and rest. I have not worked since diagnosis, and I am self-employed so I don't have an employer to pay me while I am sick. My state benefits, the benefits I've paid for all my working life, are proving to be essential income. But mainly, our life is the way it is, that is financially secure, because Ronnie continues to work, bringing in money. He does all this as well as being my main carer. He shops for food, he cooks, he makes my juice, prepares my breakfast, drives me to the hospital, takes notes at my appointments; in fact, he does everything. And I depend on him for so much while I try and navigate my way through this storm.

But now I do have a sense of the storm passing. The worst over. I still have surgery next month, the oophorectomy, but that seems minor compared to all that I have been through. I have heard people tell me that it will get better, that time will pass, the grief will pass. And it's not that I didn't believe them, that I thought they were saying these things to make me feel better. They said them because they are true. It does get better.

Have been enjoying more time this last week at the allotment, tidying up after a neglectful summer. Sitting in my shed heating up my soup. I think on the whole I'm starting to have more good days. More days with energy and filled with delight. Just delight in being alive. Yes, simply being Sarah.

I plant bulbs today in pots. Hyacinths, tulips and irises. I remind myself that this is a significant thing to do, that I feel positive that I will be here to see them in flower next spring.

Dina Rabinovitch dies. It's the end of October. She's 44, my age. It is very sobering when your contemporaries die of the same thing you've been diagnosed with. She has written about her experience in the Guardian. Describing in detail her next new treatment, ever hopeful that she has found the next wonder drug. She has been living with breast cancer for five years. She has tried so hard. Tried so many different drugs and chemotherapy. Would I? I don't want endless medical treatments that put me in chemical dazes. If I have a shorter life I want it to be rich, like this, of precious time with only the people I care about. There is no time left for artifice, for superficial nice-ness, for anything that does not fill my heart with complete joy.

Fear of death and fear of dying are different. I learnt this at Sacred Space. I am not frightened of dying anymore. But I don't want to die. I just feel I haven't finished yet.

⁂

I am telling people, 'I am going to have an oophorectomy.' I am saying this because I like the sound of the word. An oophorectomy. It sounds like fun.

Pre-op appointment at hospital today before oophorectomy next week. I realise now that I went through my breast surgery earlier this year in a complete state of shock and had not time, or mental ability, to get anxious about it. Too much else to pre-occupy my mind. Like dying.

But now I am growing increasingly apprehensive. I felt well at diagnosis, and yet this tumour was peacefully growing inside me. And now, this breast disease has turned into a gynae thing, no-one's favourite idea of a day at the beach.

I am at a different clinic in a different hospital now. The gynae clinics are all at the Women's hospital. I am familiar with the clinic where I see Alison at the Royal Liverpool hospital, and I am comfortable with that, but now a new clinic. Different set-up. Different parking arrangement. A better hospital? A women's hospital. Better for gynae? I'm not sure. It's just a hospital.

Ronnie is working, so I am here with Bren in another waiting room.

I am weighed. I have my blood pressure taken. I am getting used to this now. The hospital procedures. The repeating of my name and date of birth. More waiting.

A different nurse calls my name. Back to the blood pressure room.

'Oh, I have already had this done,' I say.

'Yes, we know. It was too high.'

'What?'

'We will have to cancel your operation. Your blood pressure is far too high. Is this normal?'

'No, it's always really low. It's just all this,' I say looking round at the new treatment room in another hospital 'it's all new and it's all too much for me.' I realise I'm frightened. I have been taking everything in my stride, but this is just a stride too far.

I think I'm going to cry. But this new nurse is sympathetic and she understands. I'm trying to calm down, not work myself up even more. What's happening to me?

I take a deep breath and she does the blood pressure again. They have these automatic machines that have an inflatable cuff that goes around your upper arm. When they are switched on they automatically inflate and constrict the blood flow to your arm. I have had it done probably 100 times by now, but every time I still hate it, the cuff being so tight. I say, 'I think my arm is about to fall off.'

The nice nurse says my reading is OK this time and we go through to another room for 'some details'.

Giving my medical history now. Which has now grown much longer than it was at the beginning of the year. More surgeries, more drugs. I recite the list. It's not even a year since my medical history consisted of 'tonsillectomy'. It's all done very perfunctorily, I mean, it feels like a big deal to me, having my ovaries removed. I'm not getting a sense from the nurse that she sees healthy normal ovaries getting taken out very often, she asks if I am having gynae problems. I explain that this is a prophylactic measure, because of breast cancer. Truth is, I reflect, that if I had chosen chemotherapy then I suppose I would not be here now. My ovaries would have packed up anyway.

I am all done and leave the hospital.

I drive to my horticulture course this evening, it will be one of my last drives this year as I can't drive post-surgery for six weeks.

In the anaesthetic room. I am staring at the equipment and really hoping that this will be the last time I'm on my way to theatre for a long time, the last time even? There is so much stuff in this room, monitors, tubes, wires, boxes of plastic things. The door ahead of me opens slightly as another person comes through. I am lying down and can just briefly see the ceiling in the room ahead, the operating theatre. The big light on the ceiling, I only know what this looks like from dramas on the TV.

I am exhausted. Tired, so tired, of all this medical stuff. And then I have gone into anaesthetic black-out, and am wheeled into surgery.

Oophorectomy. Removal of ovaries and fallopian tubes. The operation is done by keyhole surgery, and I have a D&C at the same time as the surgery. D&C is the abbreviation for 'dilation and cuterage'. This procedure opens the cervix and then scrapes out the lining of the uterus. The removed tissue is then sent for analysis, just to check. This is because of my vaginal bleeding, even though this is a fairly common side effect of tamoxifen. I've only been taking tamoxifen for five months, it's usually given for five years. How will that work if I keep bleeding?

Back on the ward I feel I have been kicked in the stomach by a horse. I was on the afternoon list and it's early evening now. Ronnie visits with something for me to eat, a poached salmon salad in a plastic box. While he is with me I start bleeding from my vagina. A lot. I hadn't realised this would happen. But the nurses say it is normal after a D&C and give me a horrible thick sanitary towel and mesh knickers to hold it in place.

I don't want to talk to my neighbours, the other three women here on the ward. I'm sure they are very nice, but I plug myself into the iPod and drift away.

I am woken at some point to have my wounds checked. I have been bleeding quite a lot from my wounds. The nurse cleans me with saline solution and puts fresh dressing on and a fresh sheet as well as a clean gown on me. I sleep.

The night is full of shuffling and groaning and 'obs'. That's what they call the observations that they do every few hours. The blood pressure machine puffs and bleeps.

My sleep is disturbed. I hate the sheets and pillows, with the plastic underliners, it is like trying to sleep in a plastic bag. I want to be home. I need a wee now. I manage to get up. The trolley holding my bag of intravenous saline squeaks as I wheel it with me to the toilet.

I have to get up every two hours because as soon as my bladder gets full it's painful. Now I can't sleep so I use my iPod. I watch the programmes Ronnie had hand picked for me. Gardener's World, Monty Don planting tulips. What could be better? I will be glad to get home.

In the morning I have a shower. My wounds are small. Two incisions on my abdomen, where my ovaries were, and two incisions either side of my tummy button, one to put the gas in to expand my abdomen, and one to put the camera in to show the surgeon what they are doing. The cuts are small and neat.

My surgeon, Mr A, comes to see me the next morning at 9.30 am, 16 hours post surgery. I am fully dressed, with lipstick, and am packing my belongings.

He looks surprised. The nurse asks if he wants to see the wounds.

He looks at me, shaking his head, and says, 'Don't let us stop you getting away.'

'No rush,' I say. 'I'm not driving myself and am waiting to be picked up.'

'You could drive though,' he says wryly.

We have a brief conversation about his observations, nothing for concern, and I will see him in six weeks.

As I finish my packing a nurse and another patient ask me about breast reconstruction. Women often do. I don't give my immediate answer of, 'No, of course not.' I sense I need to be sensitive, we are in a sensitive area here. I sense fear.

So I say, 'Well, breast cancer changes your priorities, and my priority now is about staying alive and cancer free, not about having two breasts. I've just had my third surgery in eight months, and that's kind of enough for now.' I think they understand.

Then I say, 'Anyway, it is not possible to reproduce my large droopy breast, really, so my options would include a reduction of my healthy breast. And I don't want a reduction on my healthy breast so I can be given two symmetrical pert half melon breasts.' They do agree when I explain it like this. They never had to fully think it through. I try to be gentle. After all, it happened to me, it could happen to them. I am acutely aware of that when I talk to other women, the fear that it could be them.

When I get home I go straight to the settee. Ronnie makes me peppermint tea but I am asleep before I have even poured a cup. It is so blissfully quiet here compared to hospital. I sleep most of the day, falling into that post-anaesthetic black sleep that's like a stone.

Moving is the worst thing now. I can get reasonably comfortable lying or sitting. But I feel bruised. Already a deep violet stain has developed around my few stitches across my lower abdomen. The incisions are surprisingly small and discreet. I am relieved. That it's done now.

My first visitor at home in the evening, Bren of course, with a beautiful bunch of 'flowers' from the allotment. They are bright yellow mahonia blossom with phormium leaves, plus pine needles from the park. It is lovely and so typical of him to know this would lift my heart.

❧

The week after oophorectomy I am seeing Alison. She whirls into the consulting room, sits on the bed in her unusual doctoring style and opens the file. My blood test results are all OK. I want this monitoring, even though it is fairly relentless. But I feel good when I hear the word 'normal'.

As I am getting undressed I tell Alison that I feel well, that I've not had any symptoms after the surgery. She looks at me, then looks away.

'Well, you know, it can take about six weeks before the effects start.'

'Oh.' I didn't realise. I'll find out soon enough.

I get onto the bed. I am naked from the waist up. Alison examines me, it's done so discreetly but she checks my other breast, the arm pit, my neck and feels around the scar. I am getting checked out for cancer, just like Karol Sikora did in Harley Street. The thorough cancer check.

She looks at my mastectomy scar. It has over-healed, become red and thick and slightly raised, a condition called 'hypertrophic'. I have tried silicone tape for a few months, to try and soften it, but it hasn't worked.

The next step for the scar is steroid injections. These are only used as a last resort to soften the scar. She gets a nurse to come and put some anaesthetic cream on the scar, to numb it slightly, before the injections are done. We wait for 20 minutes for the cream to work, Alison goes off to see another patient.

Alison comes back in pushing a trolley. She looks like a proper doctor. 'Doctor Waghorn,' I say. We are both laughing. She draws the curtains round the bed, in an attempt to block out Ronnie's view. They do this, the medics, they think our relatives will faint when they see needles and blood. He won't. She gets the syringe ready. It's strange, seeing her doing this doctor stuff, because she is my doctor, but mostly I don't see her doing medical stuff, mainly we sit and talk.

'Are you ready?' she says, and approaches me with the needle.

I am looking up, staring hard at the printed patterned curtains above the bed. If I look down I will see the needle of the syringe being repeatedly injected into my mastectomy scar, injecting steroid. It is unpleasant, yes, and quite frankly it hurts. Alison says, 'Keep wiggling your toes.' I don't even know I'm doing that. It is an automatic reaction to the needle, a diversionary tactic. All my other 'procedures' have taken place under a general anaesthetic, I mostly don't see them.

And then it is finished and I am bleeding. One thing about this illness is that I've not had much exposure to pain or blood, and when I do I feel frightened. I realise I am a human I suppose, that I'm fragile.

When I am well enough, a few weeks after the oophorectomy, we go to St Ives in Cornwall. The place we have visited regularly during this adventure. It has become a retreat for us, a place of peace, of rest. It is a much needed break for both of us. We walk on the beaches, go to the Eden Project, and I knit while Ronnie reads.

Ronnie films me walking on Porthmeor beach. I went running on this beach back in March before surgery, and swam there in the summer with Bren. Now it is December and I am still on the journey, returning to the same beach. I am very lucky. I reflect that I often say I feel lucky, but in fact I am very unlucky to get breast cancer at age 43. But I still feel lucky. Lucky to have Ronnie. This is what they meant by 'in sickness and in health'.

I have enjoyed this trip so much, being away. I feel like I am finally nearing the end. I am wrong, I am not at the end, although I don't know it at the time. I am just about to start a surgical menopause.

So the result of the surgery is that I am thrown into menopause, although this doesn't happen immediately. I have four to five weeks post-surgery when I feel quite well, but tired, and, delightfully, I actually sleep through the night. But by late December I'm starting to have hot flushes, wildly hot, followed by shivering cold, especially at night and my sleep is disturbed. Alison was right. And it is horrible.

I continue with tamoxifen after my oophorectomy as I still have very low levels of oestrogen. Tamoxifen is protecting me from the oestrogen. But the vaginal bleeding becomes worse. It is like having a permanent period. Which is really odd as I have no ovaries. So when any slight change occurs I am briefly either terrified if it gets heavier, or elated if it gets lighter. I think it is stopping, but no, it starts up again and I recall that uterus cancer is one of the problematic side effects of tamoxifen. So I am living in a state of heightened concern. If I don't die from breast cancer then will I die of the side effects of the drugs I take to prevent it?

My menopausal symptoms are very distracting, and I am still troubled by poor sleep at times and also aching joints. I am having many bad days.

A typical bad day. I spent a few hours on the allotment yesterday, came home and collapsed for two hours in bed. I have no stamina. Then, very tired today, stayed in bed, depressed and weepy. It's such a slog. Such a long slog. And lonely too, days in bed.

Once a week I am at night school doing my horticulture course. Frustratingly I am not insured to drive after my surgery for six weeks, so can't get there by myself. The journey on public transport would be tedious and long, two buses and a train each way. So Ronnie drives me to night school for 6 pm, having made me a hot meal in a flask to eat at the break, drives back home, and then he comes back to pick me up at 9 pm My personal chauffeur.

Horticulture. I enjoy the subject so much, it is a distraction. I diligently do my homework, escaping into the world of plants, xylem and phloem, mitosis and meiosis.

But I just want some fun.

I am bored with rest. Bored with breast cancer. Bored with the length of this journey. Can't move about. Everything feels difficult. I want to be better and recovered so I can start, well start what? My life? Something, I don't know. At the end of this, when I arrive in the new harbour that Stephen told me about at Sacred Space, will I be safe?

And what will I do there?

Yesterday I tried to knit, but fell asleep. The falling, and it was like falling, it's like floating. I sometimes feel I am floating away, like my sense of connection to the earth has become less. I cling less lightly, but I had expected I would cling more tightly.

The end of the year approaches. Not the sort of year you'd forget. I feel anxious about next year. I don't feel ready for a new start. Far from it, I feel like I'll never recover myself, find myself. That I'll feel this tired forever.

CHAPTER NINE

Happy new year

New year's eve. I sit and wait for an hour for my follow-up gynae appointment at the hospital. I am here to see my surgeon about the histology results from my oophorectomy. I eventually get seen by my surgeon's registrar. I don't think I have met him before. Well maybe I did see him briefly as he did the rounds before surgery, but he doesn't act like he's met me before. He looks at me blankly when I ask for the histology report on my ovaries. He scrabbles in the file and taps at the computer.

'I don't have your histology,' he says.

He then tells me that there is backlog from the lab. I am obviously looking seriously unimpressed at this point.

'But that's what I've come here for, the histology results,' I say.

'There is a problem with IT.'

It's been seven weeks since I had surgery and the results have not made it to my file. Of course, because I am lucky, because Alison is my *real* doctor, she has seen the histology and she has told me there is no sign of malignancy. But I want my gynae team to tell me this, to interpret the report. I want the service I am entitled to.

I don't even know if he realises I had breast cancer, what I'm there for, what I've been through the last 11 months. I try to be nice to him, but I'm not getting through here. No, I think he has absolutely no idea what it feels like to get a cancer diagnosis, to lose a breast, to face treatment decisions that are weighted with life and death statistics, and the emotional impact of all that. To have this chemical and surgical menopause. Just what it feels like, I can tell he has no idea.

He says that if I am still having troublesome menopause symptoms in six months there are drugs they can prescribe, for the hot flushes.

'Six months?' I say. I am gobsmacked.

He looks blank. I don't want to be sick for six months. I am so fed up. I think he can tell. It's not that I particularly feel ill, it's just my sleep is interrupted all the time and I am so tired.

He tells me it's normal to feel tired, it's part of the menopausal symptoms. Tired. I'm tired of all this, as I end the year with my 37th doctor's appointment in 11 months. Tired doesn't describe how completely worn out and exhausted I feel. Mentally and physically. I don't know what I hoped for today. That these gynae doctors would have some magic solution. I think this is just what happens when you take the ovaries out of a young woman. Well young-ish. I'm sort of starting to get it now. I have to resign myself to feeling like this, to wait for it to pass.

He talks about oestrogen and progesterone for my symptoms if they persist. He just doesn't realise. I tell him I had hormone positive breast cancer. And I am not a doctor, but I know that you don't give more hormones to a patient who had hormone positive cancer. The hormones are part of the problem. He looks suitably put down by my comments.

'And the bleeding?' I ask.

'Nothing to worry about, but we can do another D&C if it persists.'

He seems relieved when I finally stop asking questions. He smiles limply at me. I have another appointment at the joint breast clinic in five weeks with my gynae surgeon Mr A and Alison - he says I can discuss things with them. I should have just skipped this appointment and waited to see the proper doctors.

Then he tries to be friendly as we leave.

'Well, happy new year then.'

I am so nearly about to tell him to piss off, but bite my tongue. He has been so ineffectual. I know better than to fall out with any of my medical team. I don't know when I might need them again.

I leave the hospital in a bad mood, the sensation I have is of being completely hollow. I am so worn out by all of this. Happy fucking new year.

So I start a new year feeling pretty pissed off. I thought my days in bed were over, but here I am the second time this week. At night I sleep really badly, alternately hot and cold, in and out of the bed covers, waking up and shivering and then overheated. This goes on most of the night until I finally fall asleep about 7 am, and wake again at 1 pm. Where did my life go? It's like I am suspended. It's horrible. I was so relaxed last month after we'd been to Cornwall. I felt well, happy, rested. Now I'm back on the rollercoaster, but I want to get off.

I'm feeling pretty down. There is a difference between wanting to live and being afraid to die. I do know that, I learned it on my retreat in Cumbria. I'm really not sure sometimes which category I fall into. I have often said, 'But I am alive.' Giving it as a reason for enduring the side effects and the surgery. But I'm feeling it's wearing a bit thin.

There is a sense of apathy I have never experienced before. It's like I am suspended. I hem a pair of trousers and realise I bought them last summer, in Cornwall, six months ago. It's just not me, this not getting things done. But I have no energy.

And then there is the crying. The feeling of being completely bereft. It comes over me from nowhere and I am sobbing until after 3 am. Unconsolable. I am so sleep deprived, confused and I feel wretched. My life is doing nothing much.

I have my next appointment with Alison in early January, a few weeks after the gynae appointment. She's not in clinic. This is the first time I have come to the hospital and she's not there. She is on holiday, skiing. In actual fact I discover she is not just skiing in France, but she is *teaching* skiing. Is there no end to this woman's talents?

So, I see Alison's registrar, her *senior* registrar, Dr S. He is perfectly lovely, charming. He says, 'I have been to your website.' I think I look surprised. And then he says, 'Alison told me to.' I realise that Alison's team, her registrars, are in her control. They will do whatever she tells them to do.

We have a good consultation. He doesn't pretend to treat the menopause. He suggests a blood test for thyroid function as I am so tired. I tell him about my vaginal bleeding, the side effects from tamoxifen. He says that he doesn't do uteruses, he is a breast doctor. We both laugh. I am glad. He looks at my mastectomy scar, says it is settling down well now, getting softer. He leaves the room and he makes me an appointment for the following week when Alison will be back.

January weather is with us. At the allotment everything is sodden. The paths squelch. Mud and puddles. The shed roof is leaking. The polytunnel door has blown off because the frame has rotted. I sense an enormous need for fences to be mended, metaphorically speaking. But I don't have the energy. I tidy up the purple clematis. Lots of new shoots already, fat and green. And the snowdrops are here, early. Beautiful.

Bren and I have a fire. Sit and have tomato soup while we admire it. Fire is such a primitive urge and we feel safe there, the fire glowing orange as dusk slowly falls. It is good to see evidence of spring, the clematis buds.

R3P

Next week and it's time for Alison. Really Alison this time.

She is my lifeline. Or at least I want her to be. I have set her up as that. My lifebelt as I bob about in the sea of cancer, where I didn't want to find myself. In the weeks before my appointments with her I start lists and mindmaps, detailing all the aspects of this disease and what's happening to me. Then the list is produced at consultations. Alison is used to my lists, expects them.

So it's the familiar trudge from the Q-Park car park, up Prescot Street, across the pedestrian crossing, into the smoke-filled external main entrance of the Royal Liverpool hospital, a 'No Smoking' venue. All the smokers just stand outside the door. Corridors, vinyl floors, the familiar sound the floor makes under my feet, that linoleum squeak, and the brown signs pointing everywhere which we no longer read or follow or need because we know the way. We walk through and round and up to the Linda McCartney Breast Unit. The familiar lift to the second floor. The pang of worry as we enter the waiting room, really hoping that today, my day, won't be a standing room only sort of day. The reception where it feels like it could be a dog grooming appointment, not something even vaguely to do with life and death. And then waiting on the padded pink vinyl seats on the wooden chairs. No wonder I want a lifeline out of all of this.

All the weeks lead to this, this window of opportunity with the doctor I like, and trust. And I want to leave this clinic feeling I am moving on. Moving away from all of this.

Alison bounces into the consultation room, after her French holiday.

'Bonjour!' She is a delight.

'Sorry,' she says. 'I was away last week, but I'm here now.'

She has a student doctor with her who sits on the bed and nods enthusiastically at everything Alison says. Alison casually introduces her and proceeds with the consultation. I hope the student will become like Alison, learn from her.

She tells the student, 'You will have heard of patient involvement; well what you're about to witness here is doctor involvement. Sarah tells us what she's decided to do, then lets us have a chance to add in what we think.'

I tell Alison how I'm feeling. It's the menopause. But all my blood tests are OK. That's good. The scar is gradually softening and becoming less noticeable.

I tell her about my vaginal bleeding. How pissed off about it I am. She says it's very common, these side effects. The student doctor is nodding away, looks at me sympathetically. I feel like growling like a mad dog.

'But I am pissed off, can't I have a break?' I ask.

'We don't do breaks.'

Because it's cancer. She doesn't say that, but I know that's what she means. I know this is about life and death. But the life bit, doesn't it have to be worth living, to have some quality to it?

She persuades me to stay on tamoxifen and for us to discuss things with Mr A at the joint breast clinic.

'Any more questions?'

And then she is gone.

I am sure that Alison could treat me, but she defers to Mr A as he is a gynaecologist. I am sure I don't need to see them both together. I am sure Alison could suggest my next steps. But I am in a system. And the next step in this system is the joint breast clinic in early February, a couple of weeks away. Off I go.

I hope one day soon to get my life back, to see an end to my treatment. I dream of a new life, changed in a good way by what I've been through. That more and more time will pass when I rejoice in life and don't think of breast cancer.

But, of course, the haunting fear of recurrence, the shadow that is there remains. It is becoming less.

During all the time I am going through this medical adventure my main support and care comes from my partner Ronnie. In two days' time it is his birthday. What can I possibly give this loving, caring man who has done so much for me during the last year?

I have arranged to have our photograph taken at a studio, with Ellie too, Ronnie's granddaughter. This isn't the usual sort of thing we would do, in fact I've never been to a photographic studio in my life. But I have seen a lovely photo of Ellie taken at this studio. It is bright and simple, the colours are heightened, it is very modern and I like the style. I suppose, if I am honest, I think that if I do die, at least Ronnie will still have this, the photos and the memory of me being well.

I am grateful for Ellie and the delight she brings into our lives. We have a great time and the photos are wonderful. It was a good gift.

I am now approaching 12 months from diagnosis, 21 February, the day I will come to think of as 'D-day'. I had my mastectomy in March 2007, no summer at all thanks to Zoladex, and the oophorectomy in November 2007. It's now January 2008. I am 44 years old. Too young, I think, to have gone through all of this.

Since the new year I have become increasingly anxious and despondent. I thought that approaching one year would feel joyful, that it was somehow 'over', that I was recovered.

But no, here I am eight months on tamoxifen and have had vaginal bleeding for months now. It is seriously pissing me off. The gynae registrar I saw suggested possibly another D&C if the bleeding continues. The joint pains, especially in my fingers, are getting worse by the day. And, of course, I am terrified, every joint pain I get is secondary breast cancer of the bones. Or at least I think it is on my bad days.

Some days I get up and am sailing in 'SS Determination', whilst other days it's a leaky dinghy called 'Despondency' and the waves are very big. Do you ever reach the safe harbour? Will I ever not feel this tired?

I am so pissed off, I stop taking the tamoxifen anyway. I will have a break even if Alison says I don't get one.

I want to get a sense of feeling in control at this one year from diagnosis moment.

First I go for more tests with the scientific doctor. The blood sample, for the Greece test for the malignant cells.

Then I have a new procedure which the scientific doctor has just got equipment for. It is a breast scan which uses heat rather than x–rays. The standard breast scan, a mammogram, uses x-rays to create the image. Opinion is divided about whether this exposure to radiation is actually a bad thing, especially if it's done regularly. I'm not sure what to think, but my scientific doctor says this heat scan is more accurate than a mammogram anyway. There is nothing like fear to convince me. And I am still so afraid.

The heat scan involves sitting in a cool room and having a camera take photographs of both breasts. Then, after 20 minutes the photographs are repeated. Cooling of the breasts, or the site of where one of mine was, should have taken place and the two images are compared. Uneven cooling, or hotspots, can indicate activity that could be tumour related and would need further investigation.

When the images are done I go back to the consulting room to wait with Ronnie. The result is interpreted by the computer and I will be given a number on a scale of one to five. With one being 'nothing for concern' to five meaning 'suspicious, and needing further investigation'.

I am not expecting anything to be remiss. I have not even been worried about this. Ronnie and I are back in the consultation room, waiting for the result. The scientific doctor is smiling as he tells me, quite matter of factly, that my score is a four. Four. Yes, four. Meaning 'suspicious'. I had not even thought ahead to this possibility and I am a bit shocked.

He says, 'Don't worry'.

Obviously I will worry.

He says, 'It is nothing to worry about, but you need to have further investigation.'

'Like?'

'Well, an ultrasound is what I would recommend.'

'OK, so how do I get one of them?'

'Well your medical team on the NHS should be able to provide one.'

I am thinking, how likely is that? So I say, 'Or?'

'Or you can have one here, privately.'

'Which will cost how much?'

'Well, I don't know.'

He gets his assistant to find out. It is several hundred pounds.

I am starting to go off him. I feel like I am in some sort of terror chamber, where once you've had 'the fright of your life', then you will want absolutely anything else, any other test so you can hear a medical professional tell you that there is 'nothing to worry about'. I sigh a big sigh.

'It's OK,' I say. 'Alison will sort this out, I am seeing her next week.'

We leave the clinic. The scientific doctor has given me a copy of the report. The computer-generated report with the colour images of my one breast and chest. I look at it. It says 'left breast'. OK. And it says 'right breast'. I have no right breast. I am a bit pissed off about that. The report and image shows that my left breast has an 'unusual vascular pattern' in the top half of the breast.

Next we go to Bath, and stay at the lovely apartment we have stayed in twice in the last year. And walk up through the now familiar route to Rosy's clinic. This is a much less medical focused appointment. She doesn't dismiss the breast scan. She simply says that I need to get it checked further, so that we can all be happy that there is nothing more to worry about. And then we talk about me. Not about my medical state, but about me. Sarah.

'So, sweetheart, how are you?' she asks.

She is a doctor. She calls me sweetheart? She is amazing.

About my bleeding she says, 'Your womb is crying. You had all those hormones, the oestrogen, and now your ovaries have gone and it's not there. It's not really a surprise.'

This is not really a medical sort of statement. But it makes complete sense to me. She says she is not worried, in that alarm bells aren't going off, but again it's best that it's checked. This is true of everything now. Best that it is checked. Just in case. Everything gets *checked*. It's tedious. Or it feels tedious to me just now. I have had enough of this. This medical-ness, the symptoms. I want it all to stop.

We talk about 'putting it down'. Putting down cancer as the primary focus of my life. Yes, I would like that. A lot. I would like to be sure I don't have another tumour in my left breast, obviously, and I would like to know that the vaginal bleeding isn't anything serious either. But, equally, I would like not to be constantly having tests and seeing doctors.

Rosy is not forceful, but she does make me set a date, a date for 'putting this down', at an appointment I have booked with Alison in April, about ten weeks away. Enough time to have sorted out these last few tests. Then Rosy turns to Ronnie.

'And how are you Ronnie?'

Ronnie says it's like we've run a marathon, where you 'hit the wall' at 18 miles, but now, at last, we're in the last of the 26 miles, and we can almost see the finish line. At last. Rosy makes a lovely little noise of encouragement. 'Mmmm.'

∞∞∞

That evening in Bath I lie in the rooftop pool at the spa trying to immerse myself in the water to keep warm. It is a cold cloudless January evening. Water covers my face with only my nose protruding, as I try to keep as much of myself covered in warm water as possible. The sky is deep velvet blue, the lights of the city surround me. The water steams. Coming here to the spa is becoming part of my routine when we come to Bath to see Rosy. I enjoy the peace and the time alone here.

The time passed so quickly. I can't believe I've just spent two hours immersed in water or steam. It's lovely. Lovely.

It's about to be over. To be put down.

The next morning I am in the bathroom of our rented apartment. The window is open. I can hear the radio from a lorry outside, and from our living room Pat Metheny drifts in. Someone has turned up the volume, everything is amplified. And I look in the mirror and my lipstick seems redder. Everything is vibrant, alive. I am alive and I feel alive.

It's a blue sky day, not as the forecast predicted. I am so grateful to be here: now.

∞∞∞

Back in Liverpool I see Alison and Mr A in a joint breast clinic. This means that I get two consultants together. Good value. It also means that I don't have to have the same conversation with them on separate occasions. Even though it is joint, Alison is definitely in charge.

She bounces in, wearing her usual black trouser suit with a white t-shirt.

I tell Alison I have stopped taking tamoxifen. She looks horrified. She panics a bit.

'You need to be on some medication for the excess oestrogen.'

'I just want my life back,' I say. 'I am so fed up with the constant bleeding, I worry all the time.'

She sighs. She does understand. She regains her equilibrium, her professional doctor stance.

'It's your decision,' she says.

'I know.'

'And if you decide not to take any more drugs then it doesn't mean we won't stop caring for you or treating you.'

I am so grateful she just said that.

The blood test results show that my thyroid function is OK. And my tumour markers are in the normal range. My oestrogen levels are now very low, below 50, in whatever the units are. This is a menopausal level, as you would expect as I have had my ovaries removed. So that's good isn't it? Well, yes, it *is* good, but the bad news is that you still make some oestrogen without your ovaries, plus you don't need very much oestrogen to fuel tumour growth. Hmm.

The usual route for me now would be to change from tamoxifen to another drug, one of the 'aromatase inhibitors', an 'AI' as they are referred to. These drugs suppress the enzyme called aromatase, which is part of the chemical reaction that creates oestrogen by using androgens made in the adrenal glands. This is how post-menopausal women make oestrogen, after their ovaries have stopped producing it. And because some breast cancers, like mine, use oestrogen to grow, then lowering the oestrogen level in post-menopausal women using AI treatment has been proven to be effective in breast cancer prevention. So, now that I am post-menopausal I would be a good candidate for these drugs. The clinical trials for AI drugs show good results for localised oestrogen positive breast cancer, like mine.

Alison tells me that this is what she would recommend.

'I know, I know you think that, but I'm concerned about side effects, especially when I'm still having all the effects from tamoxifen,' I say.

'Well, shall I give you a note for a prescription then, for an aromatase inhibitor, and when you're ready you can start them?'

'OK, when I'm ready.'

She is worried about me. I can tell. There are three different drugs we can try, and we discuss them briefly before deciding which one to try first.

I know I won't take them. At least not yet. I'm not sure this is 'best' at all. I'm only agreeing to the prescription so I don't upset Alison. I can't decide.

We move on to the breast scan result. I show her the report. Tell her it's classed as 'suspicious'. The 'unusual vascular pattern'. At first she says that she wouldn't consider that unusual in a large breast. Then she quickly reads the report. She looks up and looks very worried. More worried than I am.

'OK, you need an MRI on your left breast,' she says.

Wow. I was not expecting this sort of response. An MRI scan is serious. Magnetic resonance imaging. It's one of those tunnels that you lie in for ages and magnets go round your whole body, or something like that, I'm not really sure. I didn't ever investigate body scans or things like that, it was too scary to even contemplate them. Shit. Now I'm a proper cancer patient. Shit. Shit. Shit.

But also, it is the best scan, the most detailed. This means it can give a false positive result, because it shows up in such detail that things that are nothing for concern can be visible. I say I would be happy with an ultrasound, as the scientific doctor recommended. But Alison says that they don't use ultrasound like that in this hospital, so it's an MRI. She wants me to have the best scan, I can tell.

She agrees that I will see her again in eight weeks, in April, by which time I will have the scan results and we can take it from there.

⚘

Six hours after the hospital appointment and I am back at home reflecting on what we talked about. I still feel anxious. I feel tense in my chest, worried about Alison's worries. Worried that I'm not doing the right thing. Worried because it takes so much energy to do this, to be in control of all of this. In control? Am I? In control of cancer? Can we be? Can we ever be sure?

I research on the internet looking for answers to my dilemma, my current treatment decision. This aromatase inhibitor, or AI. Arimidex. Femara. Brand names. More chemicals. More side effects? Some women seem to tolerate them well. Others complain of endless horrible side effects.

The aromatase inhibitors reduce oestrogen levels to almost unmeasurable levels, to minute quantities. But oestrogen is there for a reason, it has a role in about 400 chemical reactions in your body, including skin, hair, temperature and bones, and much more besides. So although it is viewed as a bad thing, in relation to oestrogen positive cancer, there are many beneficial roles that it plays. If oestrogen levels are artificially reduced or depleted, as in surgical menopause as well as drugs to suppress its production, then there may be a number of significant effects felt by the patient. Like aching joints, hot flushes, temperature fluctuations, tiredness, lethargy, and so on.

I am familiar with all these from the Zoladex treatment and now from the oophorectomy, I am still having them in varying degrees. Will I get more? Or will they last longer.? The answer is we just don't know unless I try the drug. Some women don't get serious side effects, but most seem to get some. And they are usually given for up to five years.

I can't face this. It feels like the chemo decision all over again, but I am much further along the road, much more tired, more emotionally depleted. And, frankly, much more prepared to die if I can't fight this anymore. I need to think and to decide what's best for me. I still think my quality of life is more important, that I feel well, even if it means that I have less life.

Why am I spending so much time deciding about what drug to take, when deep down I think I have another tumour in my other breast and that I will almost certainly die. Am I being defeatist? How do you keep up the positive attitude when things are like this?

I am almost beyond thinking.

CHAPTER TEN

Doctored out

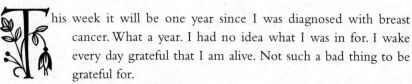his week it will be one year since I was diagnosed with breast cancer. What a year. I had no idea what I was in for. I wake every day grateful that I am alive. Not such a bad thing to be grateful for.

I am off medication while I once again review my treatment options. I feel good, I'm sleeping well mostly.

My anniversary. One year today since diagnosis. Ronnie and I talked about a 'special' day, about going somewhere. But then decided to have an 'ordinary' day by choice. So we go to John Lewis to buy oven gloves, a water filter jug and a saucepan. Such is life in its mundane-ness, but little things that make life better. We have lunch and then light candles in the cathedral.

It's been a very lonely year I reflect. I have had some amazing support, but some people were frightened away by cancer. I want to move on from this, to have my life not be dominated by cancer.

Meanwhile, back in the part of my life that is medical, I am still waiting for the MRI scan to look at the suspicious report I have from the private thermography test. All tests expose me to deep anxiety. The dread of 'not normal' hangs around until the results are through. It has been weeks now since I saw Alison, since she requested the scan.

I am, as it happens, back at the hospital for an appointment with another member of Alison's team, to discuss the possibility of genetic testing. About 5% of breast cancers are caused by a faulty gene. Some research indicates it might be 10%. Whatever, a minority of breast cancers are the result of having this faulty gene, and it usually runs in families. So if there is an incidence of breast cancer in your family, particularly at an early age, then it may be helpful to test for the gene.

What you have to remember, of course, is what you might do with the information if you discover that you possess the gene. Some women who are at very high risk of breast cancer choose to have their breasts and ovaries removed. This seems a very severe course of action. But then the threat of dying of breast cancer at an early age is terrifying. I have lost one breast and both ovaries. I 'only' have one breast to go. But my sister has not had breast cancer. If I carry the gene, then she probably will too. My mother had a breast cancer in her 50s, so not particularly young, statistically speaking. But Alison thinks it is worth me discussing my family history to see whether I want to go ahead with genetic testing. My sister, who lives in France, is also doing the same with her medical team, in Switzerland where she works.

So I have an appointment at the breast unit with a nurse practitioner to discuss this. It is the same person who 'told' me what treatments I was going to have after my mastectomy, and I did not like her very much then. She is sitting there wearing a top which reveals her ample cleavage. Of course I notice. And when I speak of mastectomy she ineffectively shrugs her cardigan around her; I am not sure if she realises how insensitive her attire is.

But she seems like she is trying to be pleasant today. My family history has been drawn into a tree, by her. She holds it up for me to see. There is little cancer. We don't discuss it for long. This nurse practitioner says she thinks a geneticist should have a look, that she will refer me, but doubts that I will be offered the test, as I would not be considered high risk.

I then mention that I am waiting for the MRI scan for my left breast. She says it probably hasn't been requested.

'Oh you know what Alison's like,' she says, 'she's probably forgotten.'

'No,' I say, 'she won't have forgotten, I know she will have done it the same day I saw her. She's like that.'

I am angry, very angry, this woman is talking down my doctor. Head Girl. This is not right.

'But, she saw you at the Women's hospital at the joint breast clinic, by the time she got back here it had probably left her head,' she says.

'No, she will have done what she said she would.'

I mean, let's face it, we're in a cancer clinic here. We're talking about life and death. And yet, this woman is treating it like it's something minor on a shopping list that has been forgotten. I am starting to go off her again.

Anyway, she says she will follow it up for me. She says I am due a mammogram, as it is one year since diagnosis. I tell her I am not sure. I don't say I am against mammograms. I say I am not sure, that I would prefer not to expose myself to radiation if we can find another way. She says she will ring me.

Normal things are starting to happen in my life. I take the first part of my horticulture exam, the RHS certificate. Briefly, just very briefly, I am just a student doing my best. And then I am back to being a cancer patient.

The promised phone call does not come. This unsympathetic woman at the breast unit does not ring me, and another week goes by. Both Ronnie and I get so fed up chasing appointments trying to get the treatment I have a right to. I get so sick of the gatekeepers treating me like a queue jumper. I get angry and I get anxious waiting. Everything makes me anxious. I think I am OK and then I have to deal with something like this and I feel like I am over-reacting. I am so angry.

I am still wondering when I get my life back, when my days aren't dominated by doctors, appointments, tests, scans and worry. But my primary concern now is this scan, so that I can relax about what the suspicious result might mean. I even start investigating private MRI scans. They are massively expensive. Over £500 expensive.

I ask Yes to Life if this is something they could help me with. Robin is, as ever, supportive and concerned and says he will look at some options for me, that he has a contact that might be able to help.

An appointment for a mammogram arrives. A mammogram is *not* an MRI scan, they are different. Alison was very clear that she wanted me to have an MRI, and I was very clear that I did not want a mammogram.

The nurse practitioner who said she would help me is not returning my calls. Even Alison's helpful secretary can't navigate the red tape and work out why I haven't received my MRI appointment, but have a mammogram appointment instead. I feel I am getting nowhere with my team at the hospital. I decide to complain.

First I write to Alison setting out the facts and explaining that one of her team has not been supportive to me. And then I use the PALS service. This is the patient advice liaison service. The woman I speak to knows Alison, says she actually used to work in the breast unit. She phones me back the next day, a Friday, and has arranged for me to see Alison the following Monday. A result.

We are on the third floor of the breast unit this time, not the second floor as usual. This is the floor where I was diagnosed with breast cancer. As we walk through the doors into the reception area I have memories of my diagnosis day. It feels odd.

We see Alison, she comes through the reception area with another patient. She smiles, waves at us, and mouths 'Hello'. She doesn't seem offended or upset. I know I wrote that critical letter about her team not helping me, but it obviously hasn't made any difference to how she is going to treat me.

When she is ready she comes out to get us and takes us into the quiet room at the side of reception. This is the room where they brought me and Ronnie and told us the news on diagnosis day. It is strange to be in here. Alison starts the conversation.

'Sarah, I know, I've been so busy with various things, and re-arranging my surgery and clinics, I've overlooked this and I'm really sorry.'

Well, there's not much I can say to that.

'Now,' she goes on, 'I have tried to speak to the consultant radiologist about your MRI scan, but she is away at a conference today. All I can see from this note is that they have refused the scan because there is no clinical data.'

'No clinical data? The thermography test?'

'Well, what it actually says here, is that there is data given for your right breast. But obviously you have no right breast.'

Yes, she is absolutely right. I didn't like the term 'right breast' on the report. They are right. It is not correct. No wonder they won't take the report seriously.

'But,' says Alison, 'I want you to be reassured, so what I can suggest is that we arrange an ultrasound for you.'

'Yes, that's fine, that's all I ever wanted, that's what the doctor recommended in the first place.'

I am so relieved. I imagine she will go away and then I will get an appointment for an ultrasound. But no, she says she will go and arrange one now, this minute.

'Well, perhaps not this minute, but I think you'll only have to wait a short while, will that be OK?' She smiles her dazzling smile and leaves the room. I am so happy. She is a star.

When she comes back she tells me I will have the ultrasound and then we can see her again and discuss the result.

'Will that be OK?' she asks again.

'Yes. Thank you.' Relief of five weeks waiting for this moment.

I suppose deep down I want to believe that there is nothing for concern. That this is just routine. But being a cancer patient means that nothing is 'just routine'. I am shown into the ultrasound room, the dark room, the place where I was diagnosed a year ago. I don't want a repeat performance.

The ultrasound operative is very pleasant, very professional. She tells me that she would recommend a mammogram for looking at the whole breast, but Alison has requested that she particularly looks at the top area of the breast, where the unusual vascular pattern was seen. Then she gets to work. Back and forth, with the gel and the probe. Looking at the grainy grey screen, which just looks like a TV not tuned in to a station to me. Sometimes she magnifies the image on the screen and peers at it. I am holding my breath, waiting for the moment when she calls in a doctor for a second opinion.

'Nothing there,' she says, 'just a few tiny cysts. There.' And she points at minute grey dots on the screen. 'I can't find anything for concern.'

I am incredibly relieved. Actually, that's an understatement. Relieved doesn't describe what I feel. I could jump for joy. I have worried and worried for weeks now, and it is all OK.

We sit in the quiet room waiting for Alison. When she comes in she is also clearly delighted at the result, smiling broadly.

'So, nothing to worry about then,' she says.

This is in effect my one-year check. I am checked. Alison she says will see me again in three months, in June. She comes out with us to reception and makes the appointment with the reception staff, being careful to avoid her holidays so that I know she will be in clinic next time I come. We go home in good spirits.

But although I am in good spirits now, this is not how I have been for five weeks. I have been unable to think about anything else. I am acutely aware that the distress I have been through has been caused directly by the thermography test I had with scientific doctor. This new test that has not been used in this country very much. I am not sure now whether it was a good thing or even if it is ready for use, certainly not for women who have had a mastectomy, especially if data for a missing part of my body is included in the report. I am also angry that I had to fight so hard for the follow-up, although I have had my reassurance now.

So I write to scientific doctor. I tell him what happened and how distressing it was. I remind him that I am primarily an NHS patient. I need to have access to my treatment and tests using the NHS, not privately, so getting the follow-up I needed, the ultrasound, was difficult because of the way his report was worded. And because of this I am not prepared to pay for the test.

He says he will waive the fee for the thermography test, on compassionate grounds, not because he agrees with me.

☙

At the allotment the tulips I planted last year are about to come into their perfection. Gorgeous purple tulips and that fresh green colour of tulip leaves. I plant out the sweet peas and Brendan clears the space for the two pear trees that I am about to plant. The pear trees are a symbol of my lost breast, I am going to plant them in memory of pear-shaped breasts.

Everywhere is green, fresh new growth. I sow lots of seeds in pots and trays in the polytunnel. Every time I do it I feel I am about to witness a miracle. So exciting. I feel deep joy.

I am sleeping well now that I am back at home. I am preparing to end my convalescence, to do whatever is 'next' for me. I am relaxed.

Then I get a bad cold. Miserable. I want to be better. I have spent so long being ill, feeling tired, being patient, and just when I think my convalescence is over, here I am, sick. I am at the end of my tether with sickness and bored of it too. I'm bored of every day feeling the same, of a lack of structure to my life.

My throat is sore and my chest burns. I go to the doctor. I want a medic to say, 'It's just a cold.' She does. So it is not secondary breast cancer in my lungs. Calm restored.

And then I am better from my cold. Feeling happier. I can enjoy my wellness. I can finally feel I am approaching the end of this.

The spring has fully arrived. We've had the first proper sunshine of the year. So I am shocked to find myself in an emotional place, I am depressed. Women are wearing less clothes and it's so obvious to me that every one of them has two breasts, except me. And I feel so left out with my one breast. Everywhere I look it seems there are cleavages, and it makes me sad to think of my right breast sliced up into sections and then analysed in a laboratory.

Everything is suddenly on the surface and I feel I have come down to earth with a massive jolt. What has happened to me? Is there anything good in this? I haven't worked for 15 months. What is this anxiety I feel? Finally sleeping ten hours a night. I am so sleep deprived from a year of emotion.

I receive a letter from the genetics department, following my referral from the family history clinic. They are offering me an appointment with a specialist genetic doctor to discuss genetic testing. My sister's doctors in Geneva say there is not sufficient evident of family history to justify the genetic testing process. I am doctored out. I have had enough. I thank them for the offer, and turn down the appointment.

After all, this genetic possibility, it is such a small risk, maybe at most 10%. What about the other 90%? Are we looking in the wrong places?

❧

It is May now. A month ago I said I was preparing for re-entry. But I've missed the 'putting it down' date I set with Rosy, and now I don't want to re-enter. I don't want to create a version of my life where nothing has changed. Because it has, it is not the same. I have not had enough time for healing. Yes, physically I am much better, but emotionally still need rest and peace. I am so lethargic. I am fed up of being brave. I don't want this scar, this fear, this pain, this emotion. Nothing feels right. I think it is one-breast blues.

I feel like a stranger in lingerie departments. I still need to buy underwear, thongs and vests, but not bras, so I am in the department. I feel like an alarm will go off, that I will be discovered, that I shouldn't be there. It's weird.

I didn't choose cancer, but I did choose to recover, to pick up activities that are beneficial to my health, like swimming. I ask the breast care nurses, remember the one who is supposed to be my friend in all of this, if they can fund my swimming prosthesis. I had not thought to ask before. How they delight in saying 'no'. I am angry that they think wearing a prosthesis every day is 'normal' and 'important' but not for swimming. I will be doing something about this.

I have lived now for over a year with one breast. I look around and see that everyone else, in my eyes, has two. I am distraught. I can't leave the house. It matters. I had not expected to feel like this. I thought I was happy, glad to be alive. I am, but I am not completely happy about the one breast. I hate hiding in the swimming baths showers, I think people will find this frightening. I feel shame, fear. Fear of how other people will react, and I do not like the feeling.

❧

I dismissed reconstructive surgery during my diagnosis and for the following year. I don't even like the word - reconstruction. Sounds like a heavy, messy, concrete and bricks term. It's about as far removed from the image of a female breast that I can imagine. And anyway, why on earth would I want to put myself through all that surgery? But the desperation I feel now, the sense of paralysis I have, is almost overwhelming.

One day Ronnie is out, working, and I spend the day in tears. I have this familiar paralysing feeling which means I can't go out, because I will see other women with two breasts, and I just can't face it. So if I can't leave the house, how can I re-enter life? Or work, or do anything. I can't even leave the house. I feel desolate. Even though I have proudly tried to be one-breasted, I have to admit to myself that my vision of myself is a two-breasted person.

I go to the internet, to the forum I have found which is only for women who have had breast cancer. I am looking for an answer, a solution. And what I find is that many women recover their sense of self through breast reconstruction. By having more surgery to create a new breast mound. Is this my answer to one-breast blues? Is it? Well, perhaps I need to explore this some more.

I've only seen one photograph, just after diagnosis, the breast care nurse showed me a clinical photograph the day she visited me at home after my diagnosis. Clinical photographs are always taken without the head or face visible, to keep the identity of the patient anonymous. And they are usually front or side on, like a criminal photo. A breast shape on the woman's chest, with no nipple. It was not encouraging. I was still in shock from my diagnosis, from the fact that I was about to have a mastectomy. I was not ready to even contemplate the thought of this.

But I am entitled to reconstructive surgery on the NHS. Yes, it is my right to plastic surgery that will give the appearance of two breasts. It is not considered a 'cosmetic' operation. It is still part of the treatment for breast cancer, for emotional recovery. And I want emotional recovery.

So I start to do my own research about how to reconstruct a breast. A new breast is made one of two ways; by using either an implant, or my own tissue.

The implant options are either a silicone or saline pouch that is inserted under the skin on the chest. The skin has to be stretched first to accommodate it, and the result is fairly firm and pert. Also, implants don't last forever, so they are changed usually about every ten years. I hated the silicone prosthesis, how on earth could I possibly think having one put inside me would be any better. I cannot even consider this option. I am so sure I don't want an implant, a foreign object under my skin, so that leaves the tissue options.

This involves using tissue from either the stomach, shoulder or buttock. It can be done using muscle as well as fat to make a new breast. The muscle provides the blood supply to keep the new breast mound alive. I am not keen on the idea of taking muscle, even a small amount, so the final option is surgery that takes fat and skin only. This is done using the stomach or the buttock as the donor site, depending on where you have spare fat. It is called a 'flap', the piece of skin and fat that is taken. This option involves microsurgery to connect the flap to the chest, and an artery is joined to ensure a blood supply to the flap so that it doesn't die.

The method of using fat and skin from the abdomen is called DIEP surgery, named after the deep inferior epigastric perforator, the blood vessel in the abdomen which perforates the fat. The results are good, very natural, surgeons can create a realistic soft breast mound using this method. But it is big surgery. Ten hours or more in surgery, and several months of recovery.

DIEP is a complex procedure and a relatively new procedure, introduced in the UK just over ten years ago, but now done regularly. I scour the breast cancer forum, looking for recommendations, for success stories, happy women who have had this surgery. And I find women who are happy, who like the results of their surgery, who are happy to recommend their surgeons.

And there are a number of them who have had their surgery done in Norwich by Miss Elaine Sassoon. She has also published a book of her work, The Boudica Within, and I order a copy on Amazon.

Her book arrives. The pictures are amazing. So realistic. I just did not know this was possible. I am enthused and inspired by her book. All these photographs of real women, some younger than me, some a lot older than me, yes they all look like they have two breasts. They have nipples. They look happy, smiling. Their scars are visible if you look, some are fresher and more noticeable, others less so. But they all look so happy. I am excited, it feels exciting. The possibility that this could be me. Two breasts.

This year we have started a new routine. On Mondays we look after Ellie, Ronnie's granddaughter. She is nearly two now. A delight. A complete distraction for me as she demands attention. All day. A chance to use all of our creative skills to provide entertainment. We have a big roll of paper and we get a piece laid out on the floor in the yard. And paint. Life is not as bad as it felt lately.

And I also get back to film-making. Finally making some use of all the filming and interviewing Ronnie has done since I found the lump. Part of my instinctive desire to record this, to capture it while it's happening, was to ask Ronnie to film it, so we have, regularly interviewing me about how I'm feeling, what I'm up to. In the gloom of last week my hard drive arrived from Ronnie with all the film from the last year, captured and catalogued ready for me to work on. To my own surprise, and delight, I have found that my film-making instincts are still there, just like riding a bike. I have spent much of the weekend beginning the 'Being Sarah' film.

Watching everything for the first time has been emotional but also helped me feel that I am moving on, moving away from this, that there is life after breast cancer.

It's June now. The gynae clinic today. I haven't had a hospital appointment since March, nearly three months since I last saw Alison. Had I forgotten?

That anxious, boring, waiting feeling. I can't read, can't knit. The clinic is running hours late. I am so bored.

Finally, I see yet another registrar who is seriously suggesting I have a progesterone coil fitted for the vaginal bleeding and I am nearly losing my temper. My cancer was progesterone positive, it's the last thing I need. Sensing my anger, and knowledge too, she backs out of the room and half an hour later I see the consultant, who doesn't mention progesterone or coils. Mr A, the surgeon who performed my oophorectomy, is looking at my notes. I ask him what he thinks about the bleeding.

'You want me to tell you something is wrong?' he says.

Well, yes, if that's what he thinks, or maybe no, if that is also what he thinks.

'I would just like your opinion as a gynaecologist,' I say.

'Maybe I am going to suggest that we take your uterus out.'

He says this lightly, almost a joke, I'm not sure I understand. I think he's just trying to tell me that he doesn't really know yet, not unless he does some more investigations.

'I think we need to have a look with the camera and probably another D&C,' he says.

'With a general anaesthetic?' I don't want another anaesthetic.

'Well, we can do it without. How would you feel about that?'

I agree because it can be done sooner this way. The first date he offers me is the same day as my final horticulture exam, the end of all my night school and studying. I have passed the first part with commendation, I want to do the same with part two.

'Would I be well enough to do the exam in the afternoon if I have the D&C in the morning?' I ask hopefully. Mr A says not, smiling, so another date is agreed. He also says to book a trans-vaginal scan of my uterus, which we do on the way out.

We leave the hospital but I don't feel right. All day I feel sick at the thought of this 'procedure' to investigate my vaginal bleeding. I am trying so hard to let go, to put this down, to move on. How can I when tests loom on the horizon? It's horrible. I am dredging my reserves trying to find courage and to be positive.

The next day I ring the hospital. I tell them I can't have the D&C without a general anaesthetic, and ask for a new date. I feel like a wimp, but the woman I speak to is really sympathetic.

'Oh, I don't blame you love, I wouldn't have one of them without being unconscious.'

It's strange, it's not really the procedure itself or the pain I am worried about, I just don't want the indignity of having a gynae procedure and being awake. After all I've been through, it just feels like too much. I can have it done with a general anaesthetic, but Mr A's list is full, so they put me on a different surgeon's list. I don't really mind at all as I won't know who's doing it.

Later the same week I see Alison. She is a breath of fresh air compared to my gynae experience earlier in the week. She says that vaginal bleeding can be caused by polyps and are a common side effect of tamoxifen, but it should be checked. She doesn't seem concerned. I tell her I am still thinking about the aromatase inhibitor. I have even collected the prescription.

'They are under the kitchen sink,' I say.

She gives me a look, as if to say, they won't do any good there. She doesn't need to say anything.

'After my gynae surgery,' I say, 'I will try them.'

She seems reassured by this.

And then I show her Elaine Sassoon's book. She looks at the pictures, she is impressed. She says Norwich is a long way to go for surgery. I know that. But I am so inspired by what I have seen in this book that I want to meet the person who did the surgery.

It is a strange feeling, this feeling of wanting to explore reconstruction, because I was so sure that I didn't want it before. But Alison says she is not surprised that I am now thinking about reconstruction. She says a lot of women change their minds, usually about two years after diagnosis.

Alison reminds me that there are other surgeons, that I don't have to go to Norwich. But I am stubborn, and I have decided.

❧

The next day I am walking along Greenbank Drive to my allotment. It is a beautiful early summer day. Green and blue. Sunlight falls through the new leaves and creates gorgeous dappled patterns of shadows and light. I feel bursting with life. Glad to be alive. More than glad. Delight. Joy. Did I need a reminder? It is like a sensation that comes to me, a realisation that I am turning a corner, that I am going into a different stage of this. A feeling that

I will be able to look back at this one day and see that it was an interruption. This thrills me.

We are about to go camping. It is summer. I need a break. We both do.

CHAPTER 11

Another missing summer

We are camping in St Ives again. It has become our current favourite place, during this breast cancer journey. This time we are with Bren again in his small tent next to us. We are very relaxed, and slip into the routine of camping. It all blurs into one memory of tent, beach, ice cream, sand, sea, reading and sketching. I'm not thinking about breast cancer. If I sit still for too long I will pleasantly drop into a light sleep and wake feeling refreshed. Life is good.

We are blessed with the weather. It is sunny and dry. We visit Sennen and do a beautiful scenic walk. Cliff tops and sea. Simply gorgeous. Bren says, 'You couldn't really ask for more than this could you?' A recognition of how simple happiness and memories can be. We laugh in the sunshine and blue day. It is good to be away.

On the way home we visit Wells cathedral. It is gorgeous. I get talking to a guide. She compliments my jewellery: I am wearing a blue lace agate pendant, the large lilac oval-shaped stone is set in an asymmetric silver setting; it's a very unusual piece and often attracts comment. Then she says, 'Mind you, you can get away with a large piece of jewellery because you've got plenty, you know, up there.' And she points to my breast. I am inordinately delighted. She hasn't noticed I only have one breast. I let her into my secret. She is surprised but asks if I am in remission and says I am so young.

I reflect on the incident. I said to her, 'I had breast cancer.' I am starting to talk about it in the past tense.

Back in Liverpool. People see me outside the house, I am dressed well, groomed, wearing lipstick. They think I look well, so they think I am fine. I am, but it's still a roller coaster. It's still wildly scary and sometimes too much. Where did my life go? My second year of 'living with breast cancer'. It takes over. Life disappears into emotional chaos which you have no control over. Disappears into medical intervention and hospitals. My life is dominated by it still.

People don't see my bad days, only Ronnie. I am turned inside out by this. I am tired a lot, I ache a lot. I am spending so long on the chaise longue, ages actually, the table next to me gathering the paraphernalia of a sick person, tissues, pills, used syringes and their sterile wrappers from my Iscador injections.

I have an appointment at the Women's hospital for the trans-vaginal scan. I have worried myself about this, wondered what it would mean, what sort of probe would be inserted into me. Again I am in a waiting room with lots of pregnant happy women. Then it is my turn. I am so relieved, it is two women who are doing the scan. I tell them I am anxious, they say it is less invasive then a cervical smear. It is. They use a rounded probe at the opening of my vagina and from there they can measure the thickness of the lining of my endometrium in my uterus. They can, apparently, also see my ovaries, although Mr A has reminded me to tell them I don't have any so they don't start looking for them. He laughs lightly when he says this. I didn't think it was funny actually.

It is good news anyway. My endometrium lining is only two millimetres thick. That is normal. The side effects of tamoxifen can cause the lining to thicken, and it can then shed, which can cause the symptoms of vaginal bleeding. I have been off tamoxifen for four months now, so things are settling down at last. Good. A relief.

But the alternative to tamoxifen is Femara, the aromatase inhibitor. I have told Alison that I will try this. So I have started the daily tablet, just after we came back from our camping holiday. But now, already, just a few weeks in and already I am sleeping a lot. I don't know if this is because of the Femara, but it's a fairly common reaction to hormone treatments.

Then I am in hospital, again, for the hysteroscopy and D&C under general anaesthetic. It is only a day treatment, I will not be staying overnight. Ronnie delivers me to the hospital and I ask him to leave so I can simply lie in bed and wait for my turn on the list. The iPod has just enough charge in it for me to listen to a Rosy Daniel meditation. So I have a 'lovely wave of deep breathing' with her and then gaze around the ward. I have a sudden sense of misery, of a remembering of just how many hours, days, of my life have gone like this. Simply washed away waiting for medical treatment. I look at the pastel green walls and want to see strong colours, not washed out, pale, insipid hospital spaces.

When the time comes for theatre I am greeted by a young doctor. I am not with my 'usual' gynae surgeon, Mr A, so I haven't seen a doctor yet. I have a lot of questions. The new doctor doesn't know the answers to my questions and disappears. I see her joking with the nurse, complaining that I have given her 'a round of 20 questions'. She looks embarrassed when she sees me staring at her. I am probably giving her one of my looks.

In pre-theatre, and I am amazed actually at just how many people are involved in even minor surgery like this. There are three or four nurses around the bed, checking everything. I am still asking questions. The main nurse jokingly says, 'Get the sellotape, we've got a gobby one here.' She means to tape my mouth shut.

I laugh. I say, 'The doctors say I ask too many questions but I'm not going to stop now.'

What is it with opinionated patients? They don't like us. She starts flicking through my file, sees that I have had surgery here before.

'Oh, you've been here before,' she says.

'Are you wondering why I'm back, why I haven't died of breast cancer yet?'

They all look a bit shocked. I feel acerbic, glad to get my own back on her. I will be glad to move on from this bit to the real thing. The surgery. Soon enough the porters come and wheel me through.

The scrub nurse in the anaesthetic room is friendly and we quickly establish gardening as a shared interest and chat about my allotment. The anaesthetist self-importantly comes in, interrupts us and takes over, checking my tubes. I close my eyes, I have had enough of all this. The anaesthetist says, 'Open your eyes please so we can see when you are losing consciousness.' I would like to tell her what I feel just at this moment, but the liquid sensation through my veins is making me feel very heavy and I am starting to slip away.

Last thing I see is the scrub nurse's eyes smiling at me and the black of the oxygen mask. Half an hour later I wake and burst into tears. I thought I was in a garden but I'm in recovery. I am shivering with cold, as usual, as the blood returns to my vital organs, but not my limbs. A young female doctor wearing surgeon kit comes to see me.

'Just a polyp,' she says. 'We have removed it. Nothing to worry about. Everything looks fine.'

Back on the ward I am soon feeling myself again. I have discovered I have an ability to recover quickly from general anaesthetic. This is my fourth in 16 months, so I know now. I am hungry, eat the breakfast I have brought with me and drink my fresh juice. I am anxious to go home. The staff nurse comes to see me and I am discharged.

I ring Ronnie, get dressed, put my lipstick on and wait for him to collect me. I feel impatient, can't do my knitting, I want to come home. I have had enough of hospitals. My last procedure, I hope. I have hoped this before, but I still hope it is the last.

❧

A week later we are driving to Norwich. It is my appointment to see Elaine Sassoon. Yes it is a big step to go this far. Liverpool to Norwich – 250 miles through nine counties. But now that I have seen a possible future I want to explore it. I want to meet the person that inspired me with her book. And I am excited.

At this point I have done some research about breast reconstruction. I understand that it is a process. It's not just one surgery, a single fix to put things back how they were. And I know too that it will not be a breast with sensation, at least the same sensation as a real breast. Or a nipple that is responsive and changes shape and colour. No. That is lost forever, cut off and taken to a lab. The reconstruction is only a sort of 'version' of a breast.

And also it is not possible to copy my existing breast. Alison had told me, very nicely by the way, that no surgeon would be able to match my existing breast, the droop. So several months after the big surgery to create the new breast has settled, I would need a reduction and lift on my left breast to achieve symmetry. And then it might need some surgical revision, depending on how it settles. And then there would be minor surgery for a nipple, if I want it. And then the tattoos, done over several sessions. And, of course, the scars from every surgery.

And, through all of this, every surgical procedure carries the risk of complications.

Do I really want to go through all that?

Do I really want to drive to Norwich all those times?

No, of course I don't want to do any of that, really. But I want, so much, to find something better. Better than I feel now. I have laid in bed too many nights crying myself to sleep, hating how I feel. I want the end result. I think I am even prepared to risk a poor result, or failure even, thinking that this might actually make me happy.

I am not the happy, brave Sarah my doctors see. The one with the lipstick and the lovely clothes. I am unhappy.

Elaine talks me through the options. She tells me that although DIEP is her specialism she also thinks that good results can be achieved using the latimuss dorsi flap, the muscle from the shoulder, called an LD. In my case she would recommend an implant, in addition, to create volume.

She also points out that Norwich is a long way to come for surgery, although she will do my surgery if I want her to. She recommends other surgeons, in Whiston and in Glasgow. She says that if I see another surgeon I will be making a choice. She suggests I think more about it.

She is right. Just like Alison. Norwich is a long way. This is such a big decision.

We spend the afternoon in Norwich cathedral, in the cloister. Ronnie is reading quietly. I am thinking. I am now shifting the focus from saving my life, to rebuilding my life. There was a sense of drive and urgency over my previous four surgeries, they were important, life-saving. The risks and complications of those surgeries don't seem so important, all the things that can go wrong. But this, this choice I have now; this is different.

The next day we drive home, it is raining. We stop at Cambridge and have lunch. We go to the good bookshop, Heffers. I am looking for books about earthworms, but don't find any, and settle for bumble bees instead.

When we get home I ring my GP and ask her to refer me to Ken Graham, the surgeon that Elaine Sassoon told me about at Whiston.

We have decided that I will not try to re-enter this summer, but to give myself more time to recover. I need to remember I need to be kind to myself, I still need to give myself some space, to breathe fully and deeply again. To rest.

But my latest hormone treatment, Femara, is kicking in big style. The aching has crept up on me, I clamber out of bed in the mornings almost bent double, and stagger slowly to the bathroom. And the flushes, it's worse than that really. It's a hot fog, I turn red and feel sick. Happens several times during the day. At night I am freezing cold. I feel I am sinking into a chemical fog, like the Zoladex. I don't want that again.

I wake today and my hands are numb, then tingling. Should I be worried? I have trouble getting the lid off the shampoo, I drop my hairbrush. I turn the shower up, hot nearly scalding, but it warms my bones and I try and regain the use of my hands with the heat. This is not great. Ronnie says it is distressing to see me suffering so much.

⁊ᶑ⅌

In the UK we have what is called a 'state run' medical care system, the National Health Service, or the NHS. The NHS is a big organisation, and it is easy to find its failings, to criticise. But it has one triumph. It exists.

Healthcare, free at the point of need, from the cradle to the grave. OK, it is not technically free, we all pay for this through our national insurance contributions and taxation. And also some NHS services, like prescriptions and dentist treatment among others, are not quite free any more for all of us, but for the most part affordable. Many criticisms of the NHS say that it is too slow, that waiting lists are too long and patients don't get access to medical treatment quickly enough. But what I have discovered about front line care, about cancer care in particular, is that it is amazingly responsive. It is quick, almost too quick actually. There are targets for dealing with breast cancer patients, to make sure that treatments are delivered quickly, to try and make this a disease that we manage, but not one that we die from. At least about 80% of us anyway.

But many of the systems I encounter in the NHS often are not patient focused. They involve me being passed from one doctor or department to another, no doubt a victim of some sort of funding or budget issues.

In particular I have become frustrated to the point of complaint about the treatment rooms service, a new service where 'routine' medical tasks are done at a central location, and there are several of these clinics. They have been set up so that district nurses are not wasting time visiting patients at home who could in fact travel to a clinic for treatment. Like, for example, having stitches removed. I understand that, but my frustration in actually trying to use the service has caused me to write to my GP. I was unable to actually get an appointment at the treatment rooms, so I ended up going back to the ward where I had my oophorectomy to have my stitches removed. The GP's surgery understand my frustration, they also don't support the system, and they ask if they can send a copy of my letter to the Primary Care Trust, the PCT. This is the trust responsible for commissioning NHS services on behalf of local people. I am more than happy for them to hear my views.

But I have almost forgotten about this, it happened months ago, last year, before Christmas. But now I have been invited to a meeting with two directors of the Primary Care Trust. I agree.

'We hardly ever meet patients,' says the friendly female director, as she shows me into the meeting room. We are then joined by her male colleague. The subject of the meeting is primarily about my initial complaint about the treatment rooms, which we discuss at length. They are understanding and pleased that I have come to explain the problems. Then I ask if I can raise a number of other issues, seeing as how I am here anyway?

You see, this is not about me. This has all happened to me, it's too late to change it. My overall aim here is to make sure that the services available are improved to make the journey through breast cancer as smooth as possible for the next woman who has to do it, and that real choice and individual treatment plans are offered.

They are very responsive to the constructive criticism I make about a number of aspects of my treatment for cancer. These are in the areas of dignity and choice for patients; a 'joined-up' treatment package with GP and various hospitals all sharing a patient's history; and better response times for tests and results, so that cancer patients aren't waiting anxiously to find out results. And, finally, some very specific issues around support for mastectomy patients. One of these points is about providing the prosthesis to wear for swimming, the sport one – different than an everyday one which I was offered – the one they wouldn't pay for. And to reinforce this particular point

I get my Been-a-Boob out of my bag and slap it on the table. 'Thirty quid,' I say. 'That wasn't too much to ask for, was it?'

I have now been on Femara for four weeks. Twenty-eight days. One packet. It's time to start the new packet. But I can't. I know what it is doing to me. It is horrible. These drugs, what do they do to you? I am crying at the slightest thing. I go to bed sobbing, I am bereft, beyond sympathy or soothing. It's horrible. And the aching. Aching all over. Can't get comfortable in any position.

And then there's my confidence. My life has disappeared. I am only OK in situations where I feel safe. Outside of that I am more uncertain. Why does getting out of the house sometimes feel like an achievement?

What has happened? It's coming to the end of the summer now. I have missed another one. Mostly because of the drugs. No more Femara, it feels like poison. I can't take it. So, once again, I stop my medication.

I am still so emotional, crying about everything, I don't know why I am feeling this. I thought I was moving on, getting to the 'putting it down' moment. I ring Rosy's clinic and arrange a 15-minute telephone appointment with her. I need some empathy, some understanding. She has a free slot that afternoon.

She thinks that my hormones are still upset by the Femara, that would explain the crying. She says it will settle.

And then she says, 'You are on the lower slopes.'

It doesn't always feel like that, but she is, of course, right.

However, it may well be the lower slopes, but I still get up late and am back in bed an hour later. Depressed, weepy and aching. How long does this last?

I have just seen my NHS homeopathic doctor for Iscador. He tells me that in his experience surgical menopause is more severe than natural menopause, and lasts longer. I did not want to hear this. Great, I just found this out in my bleakest, darkest time, nine months post-oophorectomy and about seven months into menopause. I was expecting it to end sometime soon.

I had not expected this. Being in bed on a raining afternoon, feeling crap. I feel I should be grateful to be alive as I approach 18 months from diagnosis. I am grateful. I get the result of my horticulture exam. I have passed part two, again with commendation, like part one. It is a good feeling, a moment, a little light in a dark miserable time.

In August I see Alison. She is her usual chatty self. No other doctors come close to her, can match her patient-doctor relationship style. She is so approachable. She is very understanding at my frustration with the Femara. Too much hormonal fluctuation. She agrees that I should have a treatment break and review things in December when my hormones 'should have settled down'.

We have a long conversation about reconstruction. I tell her I have asked my GP to refer me to Ken Graham.

'You have to really want it,' she says. 'It's really big surgery and a long recovery.'

Do I look unsure?

'Do you have patients who are not happy after reconstruction?' I ask.

'Well, women don't always feel whole again. They don't get back what they thought they would. Sometimes anyway.'

She goes on, 'But you seem quite happy with yourself.'

I know she means that I seem comfortable in my body, that I have found a clothing style which works for me, and that I look good. I present a good look to the world. I have worked very hard to do this. It matters to me. But I don't want it to be superficial. I mean, yes I look good when I go out of the house, but when I take my clothes off, I have one breast. It is not how I want to look.

CHAPTER 12

Activity

have just been out running today. First time in nearly nine months, since before my oophorectomy. It feels great. I am able to move. I don't ache today. I feel alive. The sky is so blue, the grass so green and the sun is shining. I feel ridiculously happy to be out of breath. It's now late summer. I have a pretty good week, and am being more active.

It is four weeks since I stopped taking the Femara. Are my hormones returning to a more balanced state now as the drug leaves me? I really hope so.

But then the next day I can't get comfortable. I ache. A lot. What is this? I am immobile. This early menopause, this oestrogen depletion. I didn't know it would hurt so much. I feel like I have been trampled on by a horse. I can't plan anything because I don't know when the bad days will come.

The thing is, when this happens I get depressed really quickly and cry. I feel like giving up, that nothing has worked, that there is no point to anything. I feel like boiled shite. And I have been sleeping erratically, falling in and out of the weirdest dreams.

I am grieving for everything I have lost. My previous life, my sexuality, my breast, my ovaries. It feels like everything is taken away. Anything meaningful.

It's not possible to know if I have done the right thing with my treatment. I could still die. Why am I even thinking about that?

But I have, I feel, turned a corner. I have recognised that I need to, want to, regain my sense of self using exercise. I have always enjoyed movement, liked running and swimming. Liked being active. Although I have kept up gentle swimming and yoga throughout the last 18 months I have not done vigorous exercise, I haven't been able to.

And then a friend of a friend tells me about dragon boating. It does sound familiar. That's because my Been-a-Boob, my bean-bag-like false breast that I use for swimming, was invented by a Canadian woman who is in a dragon boating team, a team of women who have all had breast cancer. But I didn't know then what dragon boating was. I am about to find out. There is a club in Liverpool and there is a group of women who train there; I am invited to join them. They are breast cancer 'survivors', that is what they choose to call themselves; although it is not a word I use about myself.

So, it's Sunday morning, Ronnie drives me to the water sports centre and it's very hard for me to get out of the car, to go to something new and unknown. It's a real challenge. But everyone I meet is so friendly. I don't realise immediately that there is a dragon boating club, and then there is the group of breast cancer women who train with the club. I had thought that it was just the breast cancer women. But it's OK. We all train together.

I am given a safety briefing, shown how to put a buoyancy aid on, and handed a paddle. I would have called it an oar, but it's called a paddle. It has a T-shaped handle, like a spade, and a flat blade. And it is very light. I feel nervous.

When it is time to get in the boat, I gingerly make my way onto the pontoon. I can spot the breast cancer women, mostly they are wearing pink. I introduce myself. They are friendly, laughing. I say that it is strange to be doing this, that I don't feel I have done anything except go to hospital and doctors' appointments for so long this feels odd.

A dragon boat is a long narrow boat. When full it holds 20 people, who paddle, plus one person who steers, the helm. The boat has wooden benches fixed in it and two people sit on each bench, one either side of the boat, with a paddle. The boat moves, effortlessly it seems, as the paddlers all synchronise their movements. I am in the back of the boat, and the women tell me to copy the person in front.

I like the sound of the paddles going in the water, the splashing and the reflections. I love being on the water. We are in a dock, actually four docks which are connected and we go under the bridges, using all the space. I get a new view of Liverpool from here. New views of familiar places like the Albert Dock and the Anglican cathedral. It's very special. I'm having fun. I like it.

Ronnie picks me up and I have a sense of achievement that I've not felt for a long time.

I go back again, one evening in the week. I still like it. It is great actually, to be out on the water in the evening. I like the water, I like to be near water.

And I go back again the next Sunday. But I feel like I am not here this time. Everything is happening around me and I don't feel part of it. I felt I didn't want to be there because of breast cancer. I wanted to be there because I am me. I don't see anyone else with one breast getting in the shower.

Once again I feel isolated. I feel desperately lonely.

I wanted a change of scenery, something to break my routine. So I'm in Dunoon, on an Odyssey holiday, or I will be in the morning. Adventure holidays for people who have or have had cancer. They are free, organised by the charity Odyssey. It was a last-minute opportunity. Of course, when the day came to leave home I didn't want to go. Another challenge. But I have arrived, here in Dunoon, ready for the start tomorrow morning.

I go out for something to eat. I go in a shop and ask why there are so many people here. I can tell by the way the shopkeeper looks at me that I must be the only person who doesn't know. The reason being it is the final evening of Cowal Highland Gathering, and Dunoon is full.

I am sitting in an Italian restaurant on the main street. The procession of pipe and drum bands begins. Hundreds of pipes. After my meal I go out into the street. It is deafening and actually very moving. Lots of young people in the bands. Each band leads with a big drum, some of them have members who throw a stick in the air, sort of like tossing the caber, I feel ignorant and uncultured not knowing what this is called. It is fascinating to watch. And each band is full of about 20 people playing bagpipes. Brilliant. I was hoping to find somewhere quiet to go for a drink. No chance. I stay in town, enjoying the festive feel.

I walk back from town along the shore. The light is translucent blue, the waves gently lapping. Across the water I can see unfamiliar shapes rising up, hills, grey silhouettes. It is beautiful. I am definitely somewhere different.

The next morning it is raining. I am to be at the ferry terminal to meet my Odyssey team. That is all I know. I have been sent a list with some essential items, warm clothes, trainers, that sort of thing. Other than that I don't know anything else about what I will be doing, where I will be staying or who I will be with. Am I frightened? No, not really, because this is what cancer is like, you never really know what the next day will be like, so how can you prepare for it? And, by the way, lipstick was not on the list of what to bring, but I have brought mine.

My hotel is on the front, and I walk along the esplanade to the ferry terminal. It is raining more now so I put my waterproof jacket on. And then I find shelter in a bus stop. I can't see anyone who looks like me, or a group of people, all I know is that there are 11 participants. Then I see a group of people striding purposefully across the car park. I think, I can hide here in this bus shelter, I can change my mind and go home. But I don't, I am ready for an adventure.

We go to the nearby hotel and are taken downstairs to a small room and there are hot drinks and biscuits. When everyone has arrived we have our introductions. Hugo and his team of four friendly people will be looking after us. There are 11 of us, mostly women. I feel safe. And then we all get in the mini buses and it's off to our first destination.

We arrive at the middle of nowhere. I have genuinely no idea where we are. It is strange. We turn into the drive of an enormous house. This is turning into an awfully fun adventure, we are all giggling like school children. We eat our packed lunch in the enormous sitting room, on huge sofas and remind each other not to make a mess. It's all very exciting. And then we discover this is where we are staying and we are shown to the bedrooms. It's like a country house hotel.

We unpack and get settled in, before our first activity. It has stopped raining now and we all make our way to the beech woods at the back of the house. In the trees there are a collection of ropes and planks, high up in the branches. We are told that we don't have to join in any activities that we don't feel comfortable with. But everyone has a go, we take turns holding the ropes that are the safety guides. It's quite thrilling. I actually have two goes. I feel like a tightrope walker. I have a real sense of achievement.

That evening we have a delicious meal at the dining table. It is a long table with candles and crystal glasses. We all feel spoiled, treated. It's heavenly.

The next five days continue to unfold, a series of outdoor activities. The group is split in two so I spend most of time with a group of six, all women. We go canoeing across the Kyles of Bute, yes I know where we are now, I have looked on a map. I am reminded of dragon boating, this is great.

We stop on the Isle of Bute at a stoney beach, collect driftwood and make a fire, boil water and make tea. Eat our packed lunch. The sun comes out. Our canoes are tied together and have a makeshift orange sail. They look great sitting on the edge of the water. There is nowhere else I would rather be right now.

Then, the next day, the rock climbing. I knew I wouldn't like this. We have a route up a nearly vertical rock face about 20 feet high. I don't like the look of it, it looks hard. I am reluctant and take the last turn. I do not want to miss anything, don't want to seem like I'm not trying to join in, to make the most of this opportunity. I have a harness and a helmet and I am hooked up to the safety rope. I set off, going up. But then I get stuck and it feels horrible. I can't move, I am paralysed. I look down, behind me, miles away it seems, is the water we canoed across yesterday. And I freeze. I don't want to cry, but I just start sobbing. I just can't stop crying. I am clinging on to that rock for dear life. Hugo asks me if I want to go down, but I don't, I don't want to give up, to have not reached the top. I force myself to do it, just a few more agonising footholds to go. Going back down is easy, like abseiling. I am massively relieved to reach the bottom.

It has unsettled me, I feel emotional. We go back to the house and I have a sauna. I am exhausted from this morning.

And then we drive to a new place. It is a boat, a big boat with sails. Dark red sails. Big wooden masts. This is our new home for the next two nights. It's so unusual, but I don't like it. I can't do anything except lie on my bunk and cry. So many tears. Where have they come from? This is exciting, fun, a real treat. I should be thrilled but I am bereft. This reminds me of what I have lost, confidence, sense of fun, adventure? I want to move on, away. I want to sleep.

We sail down to Arduaine Gardens. It is lovely. We cruise along and it feels great, brilliant actually. Is this why people have yachts?

I help make dinner for ten people, the Odyssey participants plus the staff and the boat crew. My skills are useful. My resourceful-ness is drawn on. I like that. We end the day laughing. Life is good again.

And then the five days are over. It was a good thing for me, this outdoor adventure. I realise I am much more capable than I thought I was. It has helped me regain my sense of confidence, a realisation of my own ability.

❧❦❧

I am back from my Odyssey adventure and I am so tired today. Everything aches. Everything is an effort. Many days are still like this.

My appointment to see Ken Graham, the plastic surgeon at Whiston hospital, has arrived. Another chance to discuss reconstructive surgery. But at a different hospital, another one. Ronnie drives me there, we park in the multi-storey which is over the road from the hospital. There is a courtesy bus, a mini bus, which shuttles between the car park and the hospital buildings. There is a new hospital being built, next to the old one, a modern, visionary building; but for now the hospital is a sprawling collection of old and not so old buildings linked by long corridors. Finding your way around is confusing.

We find the clinic. First of all we see a registrar, a friendly woman called Isabella. I ask her if I will see Mr Graham today, I want to make sure I meet this man. She says I will, and then she takes my breast cancer history. She works some of her time in Liverpool, tells me she works with Alison Waghorn. I can see that she is out of the same mould of doctor, which is good. She says I am very clear when I talk about my diagnosis and my treatment decisions. She has a tape measure and she measures my stomach fat, and carefully looks at my breast and chest.

I show her The Boudica Within book, the pictures that I feel are the sort of result I would like.

'Am I being unrealistic to expect this?' I ask.

She says not, but that no result can be guaranteed. She goes on to say Mr Graham is a brilliant surgeon. She says she will just get him.

We have to wait, as he is with another patient, so I get my knitting out. I am knitting a pair of fingerless gloves for Bren, he has admired mine that I wear for gardening.

A gentle knock at the door and Isabella returns with the man who must be Ken Graham. He's tall and wiry, short curly hair and glasses. He is wearing a shirt with the sleeves rolled up and his tie is tucked into the front of his shirt. It looks like he is hands-on, doing his job properly, not sitting behind the desk. He nods and shakes my hand, and Ronnie's. I like him immediately.

He's very dignified. He asks me what I am knitting, before we discuss the surgery. I like him even more.

He is so polite, so unassuming, I find myself slipping into feeling safe here. He asks if he can examine me and apologises that we are in an old bit of the hospital and that there is no curtain round the bed for me to change behind. I am already wearing a gown anyway as I have been examined by Isabella. He goes to the corner of the room, smiling, and turns away while I take the gown off. I am really surprised at how dignified he is, and how careful he is to make me feel comfortable. When I am standing next to the bed with my gown off, he turns round, comes over to me, and kneels down in front of me, so that his head is roughly at my breast level. I am astounded. He is a surgeon and he just knelt on the floor in front of me.

He looks at me and very gently touches my mastectomy scar and the skin around it.

'Yes,' he says, 'your skin is nice and soft, that is good.'

And then he asks if I can push my trousers down slightly to he can look at my stomach. He pauses, and then looks again.

'Well, now let's see, we can take this,' touching my stomach, 'and put it here,' pointing to my mastectomy scar, 'and create a new breast.'

'You make it sound so simple,' I say.

He smiles and looks down.

I know it is far from simple. I know it is hours and hours in theatre carefully connecting one bit of tissue from one part of my body to another. And inches and inches of scarring where the tissue is taken from and where it is sewn up. I know it is very complicated. And not just one operation. I would need a reduction on the other breast, to match the new breast mound. It is far, far from simple.

'OK,' he says, 'put your gown back on now.'

I do, then sit down and we talk. He says he could do the surgery for me next year, maybe in January or February, it depends on the waiting list. That would be in about four or five months.

I feel I could consider this surgery with him. I feel I have options opening up to me. The possibility of the appearance of two breasts. But I am worried, unsure, maybe I won't like the new breast, maybe it won't feel right. I ask him what other women feel, do they say that it doesn't feel like a breast?

'Well,' he says, and then pauses to think, 'they say things like "*It changed my life*" actually.' And he smiles. His lovely smile revealing the gap in his front teeth.

And then he says, 'But it is *your* decision.'

I can't decide. I can't say yes because I'm not sure. I am visibly dithering. I tell him I am not sure yet.

'Well,' he says, 'why don't you come back and see my colleague, Tina, she is a breast reconstruction nurse specialist. She can talk to you all about it. Then come and see me again when you've had more time to think about it. How's that?'

'Yes,' I say, 'that's just about right.'

We leave the hospital. And I think about them both, Ken Graham and Isabella. They were so empathetic. So careful to tell me it was my right and my choice. It just made me feel all over again that this is a disaster. A disaster in a healthy person's life. This shouldn't happen. But it does.

I am so torn about more surgery. I just don't know if I can do it. But I don't like living with one breast.

I came back from Odyssey feeling strong, capable; that I could look after myself. Now I feel like I am in treacle. My head is heavy, my body is heavy. I can't think properly.

When I think I am regaining my equilibrium I lose my balance somehow and the pendulum swings the other way. I want my life back.

❧

We are camping on Islay, in the southern Hebrides. It has taken nearly two days to travel this far. It feels like thousands of miles away from home. So remote. So wild.

Bren is with us too, as we have given him a birthday present of a bushcraft course here in Islay, and he will be spending a day and night in the 'wild'. He's excited.

We walk one day around Machir Bay. The wild Atlantic waves rolling in across miles of sand. And there is only us on the beach. Bren and I pick up these big seaweed plants, they have long stems, about five feet, and frondy, palmate leaves. We chase each other with them on the beach, trying to flick each other with them.

The day Bren goes off 'into the wild', we are left alone. I want to visit Jura, the next island to Islay. We drive back to the ferry terminal, and the drive-on ferry across to Jura. The Isle of Jura is easily visible because of the three dome-shaped mountains knows as the Paps of Jura. The island is long and narrow - about 28 miles long and seven miles wide - with a road only along the east coast. The west coast is practically impassable, made up of raised beaches and sheer cliffs. It is one of the largest Hebridean islands, but one of the least populated. And it feels like it. As soon as we drive onto the island it feels remote, wild, more remote than Islay.

We drive through the deserted island. At one point we spot a deer, a large stag with antlers. We stop the car and he stops too, looking straight at us, only about ten feet away. There are lots of deer on Jura, but we hadn't expected this. We stop at Craighouse, have our packed lunches and then find a quiet beach further up the coast where we sit peacefully and enjoy the silence and beauty of this amazing place.

That evening we are alone, wondering if Bren has found a dry place to sleep.

I am relaxed here. I enjoy being away, I enjoy camping. A lot of time I am wearing plenty of clothes to keep warm. One night when I get into my sleeping bag I am only wearing my thermals. I was happy, I have forgotten I only have one breast, and I am shocked when I notice.

Bren returns to civilisation – well to us anyway – the next morning, having slept in a shelter he made in a wood. His guide left him in the afternoon, so he had the evening alone, and then had to find his way out of the wood in the morning.

On our last day we go back to the beach at Machir Bay and have a picnic. We collect driftwood and Bren makes a fire, using his new bushcraft skills. He does this by making the fire in a hollow in the sand, so it can be covered up after we have left. Leaving no trace of yourself is a key thing that he has learnt about - living in harmony with nature. He has brought his cooking pans and boils water to make tea.

Afterwards we drive up the Guinart estuary and forage for mussels. At first we don't find any, then soon discover a good place, and lift up the seaweed to find them. It's muddy, but we enjoy it. Even Ronnie, who is a vegetarian and won't be eating them. We take them back to the tent. They are delicious.

I am relaxed. Happy. This has been a great trip.

Returning from remote Islay and there are now too many people. Everyone else has two breasts and I am the only person this has happened to. It rushes back in. I am overwhelmed by emotion.

It is my birthday. I feel I should be glad. Glad that I am 45, that I am still alive. And yet it seems absurd that I should approach a birthday in my middle years and not expect to have been here to 'celebrate' it. I have a heavy heart.

Back in Liverpool I go dragon boating. I know now that there is a world wide movement where breast cancer 'survivors' take part in dragon boat teams. That it is a good thing, a sense of showing that there is life after breast cancer. On the internet I read that, 'All over the world women who are survivors in every sense of the word are demonstrating their 'can do' attitude as they take part in dragon boat racing.'[11]

But I don't feel like a 'survivor', I don't feel I want to be in a 'special' club, I don't feel that I am in any way special because of the disease I happened to have had.

And I am still finding new situations extremely challenging. So, for me, even going to dragon boating is a big step. To actually go into a new group of people and make conversation is difficult. I thought I would want to be with women who have had breast cancer. But I feel I am defined by the fact I have had cancer. I do not want that.

On this Sunday the women are having their photograph taken and they include me in their boat. They have their own boat called 'Hope', it is black and pink. I am very new here, have only been a few times and I haven't been able to fully express or even understand what I am feeling about the special nature of the club just for the breast cancer women. I am given a pink t-shirt to wear, they are all wearing them. I am reluctant to wear it, but I feel I should join in, after all these women have been through a similar experience to me. We share something. I change into the t-shirt. It is too small, and my one breasted-ness is very obvious. I don't wear clothes that are this tight anymore. I am glad to put the bulky red buoyancy aid on, so it covers me.

They tell me that when we get in the boat I will be asked to take off the buoyancy aid, so that for the photograph we are all wearing pink.

'I can't,' I say. I can feel minor panic. 'Look.' And I unzip my buoyancy aid and show my shape, my one breast and my flat side. It is so painful. I am in the wrong place. I am not ready. I should not have done this. I can't do it. I say I will not go in the boat. But, they are friendly, they do not want me to feel left out and they suggest a solution, I can wear one of their buoyancy aids, which is black, and fits in with the colour scheme of the club, pink and black. This buoyancy aid belongs to someone else, a smaller woman, but I can just about fit into it. We paddle up and down a few times under the bridge so the photographer can take his pictures. When they are done I can change back into the bulky buoyancy aid and forget about it. I find the whole experience completely demoralising.

I reflect on this incident. I so much do not want to be defined by breast cancer, by pink t-shirts. I feel so uncomfortable about it. It's not that I don't support them, or that I don't understand that there are women there who enjoy being in the exclusive club. But it's not for me. So I give the pink t-shirt back, and leave the breast cancer 'survivors' club. I then join the 'ordinary' club where I'm not expected to wear pink, where the fact that I have had breast cancer is not why I am there. I buy a club cagoule, black with a yellow ribbon sewn down the length of the arms, and a yellow dragon emblazoned on the left chest. I wear it proudly, proud to have achieved some normality for myself, to have stepped away from breast cancer.

In the changing room I get in the shower with my one breast. I cannot hide the fact that I have had breast cancer, it is too obvious. I am glad I found this club, it is an activity I enjoy, and it challenges me, but I do not want to join in, not in that way.

I so do not want to be branded by breast cancer and wear pink t-shirts.

It is October now. Autumn is here. A lovely afternoon at the allotment. It is sunny. That golden low light that shines through the leaves making them look like stained glass. I sit on my deck and enjoy leek and potato soup, it is delicious. I have a feeling that I have to pause to recognise. It is peace, I am at peace, and I haven't felt this for so long.

I am having a good week. I am active, been running, swimming, going to the gym and now paddling as well. I feel I am moving through at last. Being active is the beginning.

part **three**
Being me again

July 2008 - Norwich cathedral.
'I want, so much, to find something better.'

CHAPTER 13

Anger

I looked in the mirror tonight and I saw muscle. I am losing my excess fat from being inactive for so long. My fit strong body is re-emerging. And I so want it to have symmetry, two breasts.

But I have mixed feelings about breast reconstruction. I am thinking, wondering, am I in the eye of a hurricane? If I start this all off again with more surgery, the reconstruction, am I going back into the storm? Am I ready? Will it be a storm? Or will it be heavy weather? My mastectomy scar is fading now, not gone but fading. Do I want to re-open the wound? Emotionally and physically. How do I decide?

The downside of the surgery is that it is a long time in theatre, about ten hours or more, plus there are lots of big scars. A hip to hip scar on the abdomen, and scars where the flap, the abdominal fat and skin, is attached around the chest to create the new breast. Because the abdomen is cut and stretched the tummy button is repositioned in the correct place. Then at a later date, say six months later, more surgery to lift and slightly reduce my healthy breast because they can't make a new breast the same size and droop as the old one. Plus minor surgery and tattooing for the nipple, if I want it. But what I get is a warm, realistic looking breast.

I do not want to rush into this.

I am on the train going to Yorkshire to give the sample for my third minimal residual disease blood test. It is nine months since the last one. I go on my own, my first medical appointment in over 18 months that I have done on my own. It is straightforward, at least in the sense of it 'just' being a blood test. But of course the next stage after a test is 'results', and even coming back on the train my mind is full of 'what if?', playing out all the possible scenarios that a poor result would mean.

I hope for a good result. I don't expect otherwise, except, well, except what? You just can't rest, stop being vigilant. It is the 'not good' results scenario that I worry about. I had stepped out of this, the test mode that I lived in for the first year post-diagnosis. It is less, but it still feels the same. Scary. Things will become a bit tense in about seven days' time when I am expecting the result.

On the way back home I listen to my cathedral music on my iPod, Barber, Elgar. It is calming, soothing. Leeds, Manchester, Warrington, Liverpool. Autumn is now everywhere. The trees are all turning and it is chilly. I am wearing gloves. The season has changed. I missed a lot of this summer because of the medication and side effects. That makes two summers. I hope next year is different.

I overhear snatches of other people's conversations in between tracks on the iPod. Work and office talk mostly. It all sounds so unimportant compared to life. Compared to my experience of life this last year and a half.

❧

I have a memory. On diagnosis day I sat in the waiting room for a chest x-ray. My last stop in the hospital, after six hours in several different clinics, the first of many long visits. That kindly woman who came over to comfort me when I was crying and I told her I was going to have a mastectomy. She sat down next to me and, unasked by me, told me, 'My friend, who is young like you, had a mastectomy, but she had reconstructive surgery and now you can't tell.' I know she meant well. But that phrase often comes back to me. *You can't tell.* What can't you tell? What does it mean?

Does it mean you can't tell I have one breast? Or does it mean that you can't know the terror and fear I have felt? Or that you can't see the nights I woke in desperation fearing that I would die soon? Or that you can't see the hours of hospital, tests and surgery that I have been through? Because, actually, *I can tell.* All the time. And especially every time I take my clothes off. A reminder of just exactly what has happened to me, part of my body cut off. Not always feeling brave, like the Amazon I secretly hoped I would feel like.

I think a lot about this, this expression. *You can't tell.* What does it mean? Does it mean that when people say it they are covering up the fact that they are afraid, that if it happened to them it would be OK? Is it good that if it happened to them then the best thing about it would be that other people *can't tell*? Is it somehow dealing with *their* fear, not *my* feelings? That it is, in fact, about them not being afraid?

Well, be afraid. Be very afraid actually. Because of the terrifying increasing statistics of the incidence of breast cancer, but also about when this happens there are a myriad of feelings you go through. Shock. Fear. Terror. Anger. Rage. Just to name a few. Doctors didn't mention these feelings, although of course they are trying to help me and they do this in a medical arena. The rage is sneaking up behind me, I am not prepared for it. Rosy Daniel, a doctor, although she is a doctor of the emotions as well, had said to me that it was OK to feel rage, to howl with anger about the unfairness of what had happened to me. But I never did. I was too busy in and out of consultations, researching my options. I never felt I had time for anger, only for loss. Perhaps now I will feel the rage, but not just about me, about how we see breast cancer in our society.

October is breast cancer awareness month. Yes I support awareness, of course I do. We are all familiar with that phrase, 'Early detection saves lives', much used to encourage us all to take some responsibility for our own health. That somehow it is up to *us*, that we can stop this spread of breast cancer. I'm starting to think that it's not up to us, actually.

And in October breast cancer becomes fully pink. Maybe you see all this pink stuff, all these things you can buy and think it is a *good* thing. That the money that is raised goes to research, that somehow we're just a break away from some major research that's actually going to end this escalating statistic, the incidence of breast cancer, now increasing rapidly in younger women, women like me and even younger. It has a big mass appeal, almost sexy really in marketing terms, this pink charity stuff, it's good business sense. Does it make me really believe that the businesses that 'support' breast cancer awareness month actually care about me? Am I being cynical to think it might just be good business sense?

After all if you think about, say, a supermarket, how many of their customers are the right sex to be personally concerned about this? I mean women. Well, probably most of them. Actually, that's just a fact. Do these women think that somehow the supermarket is researching into prevention of breast cancer? To help them?

Oh, and actually did I mention that National Breast Cancer Awareness Month was founded by a pharmaceutical company?[12]

When I think about this, start to think deeper about it, I am cynical about just how much effect this actually has on my chances of staying alive. And I just don't like all the pink. I can't take to it.

I hear the pink brigade defend their stance by saying they are giving hope for newly diagnosed women. Hope? I don't want hope. I want determination, courage, spark and, most of all, I want *facts*. Tell me about this disease. Tell me the causes. Help me stop a recurrence. Show me the results so I can decide what treatment I want. Don't give me a pink t-shirt, a pink product, a pink anything, I do not want anything pink. I feel that this whole pink thing will push aside any serious debate about options or a real look at the causes of breast cancer. And I feel it forces me to be an obedient patient, accepting of this 'nice' pink association of breast cancer. No. I won't do that. Not that I won't, but I can't.

I feel alone with my opinions. I am shocked by them. I did not expect this anger. And then I discover that I am not the only person that feels negative about pink. Libby Brooks writes a scorching article in the Guardian called, 'Let's not pinkwash proper discussion about this disease.'[13]

I am thrilled, delighted by this, as she voices exactly what I felt about the whole pink thing. Although she has not had breast cancer herself she writes about her mother's experience, and pink, she says, was not how her mother felt about being diagnosed with breast cancer. And nor do I.

But, even better, Libby Brooks' article introduces me to another angry woman: the American writer Barbara Ehrenreich. She has had breast cancer, and in 2001 she wrote a seriously anti-pink essay for Harpers magazine, called Cancerland.[14] She writes:

'In the mainstream breast cancer culture, one finds very little anger, no mention of possible environmental causes, few complaints about the fact that, in all but the more advanced, metastasised cases, it is the treatments, not the disease, that cause illness and pain.'

And she goes on to say:

'Let me die of anything but suffocation by the pink sticky sentiment embodied in that [ribbon-branded] teddy bear.'

Oh yeah, me too sister. Thank you.

Breast cancer very much dominates my life and I am wondering when that might stop. I am now in my second year since breast cancer turned up, and I still don't have a sense of 'putting it down'. And now I have been asked to speak at a conference in Liverpool about breast cancer. Is that putting it down? Or not?

The conference is being organised by Blackburne House, a women's training organisation. I have worked for them before, on films and conferences, and they asked me to be involved with this event for breast cancer awareness month.

Anyway, now I feel so angry, it's sort of just as well I have this conference coming up so I can get myself worked up about my emotions, that I have an audience for them. All about the pink stuff, and all my feelings now about *why* breast cancer is so common, and, that the statistics are going up. And that it's all just not OK.

I enjoy preparing my conference talk. I scribble pages of notes about statistics, about treatments and mostly, about control and choice.

On the day I am not nervous at all. I am the last speaker, the others include my breast surgeon, Alison Waghorn; Robin Daly, the founder of Yes to Life; and Patricia Peat from Cancer Options.

There are many subjects that encompass breast cancer. We hear about surgical options and treatment choices; about current thinking that the causes of breast cancer may be mainly linked to the food chain and the environment; about being a patient and managing the oncology clinics, getting control of treatment; and about the work of Yes to Life, supporting people like me through cancer.

I am very clear about what I want to say; I am also very opinionated. I briefly describe my story, very briefly outline my diagnosis and my treatment. I have pictures to illustrate my speech. The photographs Ronnie has taken are coming in very useful again.

And I talk about support, the support I found, both inside the NHS, and the support I paid for outside the NHS. I talk about taking control, researching my options, being clear about the facts of my own medical case. I tell them that, actually, cancer is *not* a gift, even though you hear people say it is, that it makes them value life more. And please, don't ever say to me, *'you can't tell',* because I can.

I say that current scientific thinking is that the cause of cancer is a combination of factors. That it's down to environmental factors, like chemicals and toxins that we can't see.[15] Also that there is a genetic factor too, although this is a small percentage of cancer, about 10% probably at most.[16] And, it's probably also about individual factors, that is the things that we do, like smoking and poor diet. And it is these 'individual factors' that the media like to use as 'blame' for why cancer is so prevalent, while handily passing over the environmental factors that for the most part involve big businesses making even more money while we continue to get cancer. OK, so this makes it sound all a bit like a conspiracy theory, but I'm just trying to make the point that we're not looking for the *cause* of cancer.

We are getting better and better at treating it, throwing drugs at it, and frankly *accepting* it. And that drug companies make a lot of money out of cancer. That is a fact. We are in danger here of accepting that cancer is 'normal', that it happens, but that we then treat it. I would much rather we started putting a lot more energy and money into prevention, into it not happening in the first place.[17]

I finish my talk with some statistics. There are loads of statistics I could use. But I have just one. If breast cancer incidence increases at the same rate it has increased in the last 40 years, it means that when Ellie, Ronnie's granddaughter, now age two, is my age, just 44, then breast cancer could affect one in four women.[18] Is that the future we want for our children and grandchildren? I am nearly crying. I really don't want that future for women.

But afterwards I am despondent. What's the point in having opinions about breast cancer? About being able to talk powerfully about them? What's the point? What does it change?

❧

I still don't know when the bad days, the 'not me' days, will come. My concentration is hopeless, I am all over the place. This time last year I was about to have my oophorectomy. I thought it was 'starting to be behind me'. Huh. I still have moments when I feel that. But then I get physical lows that lead to emotional lows and it all adds up to a 'not me' day.

The result of the blood test looms. I feel emotional and anxious. What if? What if? Over and over in my head. Ronnie rings the clinic for me, I feel that I should have had the result by now. Yes, the result is at the clinic, but it has not been sent to me because the scientific doctor has a new policy now, that the test is paid for before the result is sent out. I am a bit pissed off about this, not about paying, but having the test result delayed. I don't know if it is a new policy or it's because I didn't pay for the thermography test.

The result is good though. The lowest ever. This is a really good indicator that the disease is in remission. Good.

We go to Bath to see Rosy. And to see Westonbirt in autumn. The acers. Westonbirt is an arboretum, about 20 miles north of Bath. We visited Westonbirt for the first time when we came to see Rosy, and now it's part of the ritual, of our trips to Bath. We have been in all seasons now except autumn, and they have an outstanding collection of maples which are famous. And rightly so. They are absolutely magnificent. The colours are burning, glowing, shining. Reds, oranges, yellows. Gorgeous.

We are staying in a different apartment this time, in the north of Bath, and we enjoy exploring a different part of the city. I have my now ritual visit to the spa, and then it is time to see Rosy.

I see her on my own, at Ronnie's suggestion. Ronnie has come to all my doctors' appointments with me, faithfully sitting next to me, taking notes. But he senses my growing independence, that I can start to do things on my own. Plus, medically, I don't have anything specific to worry about.

We talk about how I am doing, how I have become more active, enjoyed the conference. My test results are all good. And yet. Yet. There is something wrong. Or at least I don't have a sense of being recovered. I am torn about the reconstruction, but I am unhappy and reluctant to stay as I am.

She says, 'You don't look like a wounded person to me, that is not the impression you give.'

'Well,' I say, 'that may be so, but on my bad days I feel mutilated.'

Mutilated. So, I have said it. I have admitted it out loud. I suppose I have made my decision in that case.

Rosy tells me about a friend of hers who has had breast reconstruction. She went to Brazil for the surgery. Hmm. I think Norwich is a long way away, and it is. Would I seriously go to Brazil? Oh, and by the way, the NHS does not operate in Brazil.

Rosy's expression, a 'wounded person', stays with me. Am I? My doctors don't think so. No, Rosy and Alison see confidence. They see my superficial veneer that I have grown to deal with breast cancer. To conceal hurt? This shitty shitty disease takes so much away. Does reconstruction give it back? Or attempt to?

In November I go back to Whiston to talk to the breast reconstruction nurse, Tina. She works with Ken Graham, the plastic surgeon. I have been having strange dreams of Ken Graham which also involve an enormous axe. Yes - I suppose you could say I am feeling reluctant.

Tina is enormously pregnant, due to finish work in a few weeks. She has lovely big blue, almost violet, eyes, and lilac eyelids, and I can't decide whether it is make-up or just her skin colour. She obviously has a lot of time for me, this is her specialism, to talk to women about reconstruction, to help them decide if they want to go ahead. I think I have decided, I mean I do like Ken Graham, and I do want the appearance of two breasts. But. It's such a big step.

So, Tina talks through the surgery experience. I have more details about arteries and perforators, and micro-surgery. It all sounds massively complicated. She has to tell me though, that there is a possibility, a small possibility, that the flap could fail. It happens with all surgeons. I know that. An unlucky complication with the artery, the delicate micro-surgery, a blood clot, nothing that reflects the skill of the surgeon, there's that slight chance it could fail. It happens in about 5% of DIEP operations. But if it happens to you then it's 100%, which is a sobering way of looking at it.

And Tina explains that this is a process, a journey, this reconstruction. It's not just one lot of surgery. It's the first surgery, but then it's revisional surgery if needed, plus the mastopexy, the lift on the other side to match the new breast. And a nipple, eventually, if I want one. This would mean that once the scars fade and things have settled down, assuming I have no complications, then I could be looking at being 'finished' around the end of 2009, nearly three years after diagnosis.

Tina has some things to show me. She has a white cardboard box, and inside she has a selection of silicone nipples. They are fantastically realistic. She says they are made from taking a cast from your nipple and then colour matched to make a new nipple.

'Oh,' I say, 'I want one.' I am so excited.

I'm not sure if I want to laugh or cry. It just reminded me what I'd lost. And how much I didn't want to lose my nipple. I remember now, when faced with the mastectomy how I asked if they would keep it, even though I knew the answer would be no. But I was serious.

We leave the hospital. Today has made me remember. That one day this bomb goes off and blows your life apart. Then one day, a long time afterwards, you will wake up and look at the debris. And start picking up the pieces. I feel that sometimes. Picking through the pieces, like analysing my blood, poring over it. Looking for cancer. Fragments.

But overall I feel excited. This shitty disease has taken so much away. I have a sense of getting some of it back. At last.

❧ ❦

I am staying active. I have felt good, mostly anyway, for nearly two weeks now. Apart from some tiredness.

I am still going to dragon boating. Now that I am no longer in the breast cancer club I feel I have to make more effort to talk to other people. We all meet in the café, which is what they call the room with a vending machine and some tables and chairs. Invariably the breast cancer women group together. And I don't approach this group now.

I make friends with Mike. He's blind so when we do our run, as part of our warm-up, he needs to link arms with someone to run together. I offer to run with him. He asks me if I am one of the breast cancer women.

'Yes, I have had breast cancer,' I say, 'but I want to be in the ordinary club.'

He immediately understands. Does he want to be in a team of blind people? No, he doesn't want special attention. And nor do I.

Sometimes Bren comes dragon boating with me. He is tall and strong, the sport suits him. I feel protected by him, I feel safe with him around.

One cold Sunday morning in December I am scraping ice off the car windscreen. Today I go paddling in the dragon boats. In the afternoon I have my first go in a small single craft, called an '01', for one person. It has a float on one side for stability. Doesn't feel very stable to me, but I am determined to rise to the challenge.

I get the hang of it, I am doing OK. And then I capsize. It's not really the sort of temperature to be doing this. Falling in. It's so cold, the shock of the cold water as I am suddenly immersed. But I cling to my upturned boat, and then follow the directions to safety. As I am swimming in the dock I am thinking, 'This is not the sort of thing a sick person would do, I must be well, I can do this.' I reach the pontoon and am hauled out by two club members, lifting me out of the water using my buoyancy aid. Nothing hurt. Just my dignity as I have an audience now. I slosh along to the changing rooms and get in the shower fully clothed and gradually remove everything, peeling off my soggy clothes. Afterwards I feel like I have had a sauna, glowing. It is a pleasant feeling. I feel well. Well. All is well.

Later in December we go to the cathedral for evensong. It's not on. They are rehearsing for Handel's Messiah this evening, the concert is in the top end of the cathedral, away from the choir and organ. We go to our usual place where we light candles for me, Ronnie says for my confidence. We sit in 'our' place, the place we sat when we decided to get married, this time of year 12 years ago. The sound of the orchestra and singers floats down the corridor and I can hear children laughing. The blue lights on the Christmas tree, the smell of the cathedral. And I briefly feel peace and I feel I still have a life. I do.

Since I spoke at the conference and so thought about my real feelings about the wider issues around breast cancer I have been feeling angry. Angry that this happened. Angry, at 43, to lose a breast. Angry to have this hole kicked in my life. Hole still not finished, not mended. Angry at the silence, the collusion, the unwillingness of others to talk about this. To do something to make it stop happening.

This silence. It will not do.

I suppose I feel I want to voice my pain, for the pain not to be wasted, as Audre Lorde said. To try and understand the loss I feel. Have felt. Still feel. To reclaim some power back from the experience. It's all very well having these drugs, these treatments, this surgery for breast cancer. But it's still crap to go through it all. That doesn't change. I don't like the acceptance that it is OK. Because it isn't. OK I am alive. Well. Healthy. But it's nearly two years since diagnosis and my life has disappeared. Does anyone want this?

But, on the other hand, I am unwilling to accept some sort of baton. That I am the person to break this silence. I need to protect myself. To heal. I need peace. I need the sort of peace and space that we find in the cathedral. I am too vulnerable. I cannot expose myself. I haven't finished my convalescence yet. I want more time for me.

The next day we are at Whiston again to see Ken Graham. It is two weeks before Christmas. I have decided. Even with all the possible complications, the possibility of failure even, I have decided. I am going to have the reconstructive surgery, the DIEP, and I want him to perform it.

'Excellent!' he says.

I am surprised. *Excellent?* Excellent that I am clear, that I feel sure I want this. This opportunity to have my shape back.

It feels so right. I feel excited.

I have found the right medical team to look after me, for the next stage, the reconstruction. Ken Graham sits at his desk, nodding his head, and looks at my file, writes briefly on the page. Then he turns to me, after I have expressed my intimate desire to this man I have only met once before, my desire to have a cleavage again. And he says, 'I will do my best.' And smiles, showing the gap in his front teeth. I believe him.

We go for lunch afterwards. A celebration. The lunch we were going to have on diagnosis day, that February day, nearly two years ago, hoping we would leave the breast unit without a cancer diagnosis. Feeling positive. Well, we have it today.

The sun is low and bright and shines directly onto Ronnie's face, his lovely brown eyes. My beloved partner who has been next to me at every point on this journey, and he is still here. He says it is great that my spirit is so strong. I feel that too. My physical being, my body, is a bit battered round the edges, but my spirit is on fire, burning brightly. I felt fully myself today in the consultation. I am burning with life.

The decision is made. I come home and I am unsure of what to do. My focus is done. I can get something back for me. At last. A good day.

CHAPTER 14

Loss

f breast cancer were just a single one of the ordeals I have faced then that would seem enough. If breast cancer were 'just' a mastectomy that would be a tough experience. Or if it were just an oophorectomy that would be extremely difficult. If it were just four general anaesthetics, or a couple of D&Cs. Or all those doctors' appointments and blood tests and waiting for results. If it were any one of these it would be enough. If it were just physical, a simple medical condition, but it's not, it's charged with emotion. With the possibility of dying. And it's still not over. The reconstruction is another round in the boxing ring. Several in fact.

But breast cancer and the treatment to prevent recurrence is so complex. So many things, so many decisions. And you face all this with the background knowledge that it might kill you. Death hovers at all stages of the journey.

I have heard people express an opinion about reconstruction. 'You don't *have* to,' they have said. No I don't *have* to. But I want to. So, in a sense, I do have to, because I want to. I had not expected this, I had wondered, at the beginning of all this, why women did this. Reconstruction. I remember so clearly that day, diagnosis day, when that kindly nurse said, 'There are lots of options now.' I think this is what she was referring to. The options of reconstruction. The different ways to recreate a breast. At the time I didn't know what she meant. I mean I didn't understand. I mean I was in shock. I mean I had no idea what I was in for. Absolutely. No. Idea. God.

In the bath I look down at my scars. Not just the scars from the last two years, but all my scars. Our bodies are maps of the places we've been, and I am mapping them now.

Long thin white scar on my right shin. Barbed wire cut from a fence on a family holiday, probably 35 years ago now. Me wearing my new needlecord trousers and waistcoat that my mother had made me. A yellow and brown honeycomb pattern. I ripped the trousers beyond repair. 'Don't worry,' said my mother, 'we can make them into hot pants.' Yes, it must have been the 70s then.

My right thigh. A flat wide C-shaped scar. About the size of a tea cup. Another family holiday incident. Again 35 years or more ago. The sheep dog that attacked me. Afterwards my parents said, 'He was only playing.' I was taken to the nearest hospital in north Wales, probably Bangor, where I was stitched up and even now can remember the feeling. On the ceiling of the room where they did the stitching they had pictures of animals. Zoo animals. Then when we got back to the cottage I couldn't use the chamber pot because I had a big bandage on my thigh. Remember sitting in the garden while my brother and sister played cricket.

Moving up to my abdomen now. I have to move my tummy fat a bit to find these two scars, one either side of my abdomen. These neat expert scars that show where my ovaries were. They are barely noticeable now, even though they are fresh, in scar terms, just over a year old. They are definitely done by a crack team of experts, smooth and neat, the scalpel incisions confident. One like a small cross, one like a larger T-shape. They may or may not end up being on my new breast mound. And then my tummy button. Cut vertically to both sides, one side longer, the scars almost invisible. This was also part of the oophorectomy, to allow the gas to be pumped in to me, to expand my abdomen to fit the camera and the scalpel in. But they are neat, very neat.

On my left upper arm another dog incident scar. The same sheep dog incident as the leg scar. Rough and red. About two inches long. It never faded. People assume it is my inoculation scar. But that is a faded small circle on my shoulder, only visible if you know where it is.

And, not visible to me, only to the world, the scars on my face. The small dint in the bridge of my nose. I laugh when I think about it. Me and my bike, age 17. Inseparable. I got a new gadget, a mileometer which I fixed to the front wheel. The first trip out and I couldn't stop looking at it, instead of the road ahead, and then rode straight into the back of a parked car and flew over the handle bars. I was only at the top of the road and walked home, bloody and ashamed. How could I be so stupid? My father guessed straight away what had happened, but didn't berate me for it. I had a scabby face for weeks. The rest was only bruises.

And on my left cheek a patch of white smooth skin. An acne scar which has been operated on using dermabrasion to smooth it. Not a fully successful treatment, but better than it was.

And finally, the biggest trophy. The mastectomy scar. Eleven inches. Horizontal. Starts from my mid-chest, next to my left breast. Points at my heart and stretches away under my armpit. This end on my chest, the end I see most, is the end that hasn't healed the best. The scar here is flat now, but wide, wider then the rest. It was this end that over-healed the worst, becoming red and thick and hard, reminding me of an earthworm. The steroid injections softened and flattened it. But still it is often red or reddish purple, especially if I am hot. And a small lump of scar tissue, a 'snick' as Ronnie calls it. Alison says it is a bit where she put a suture in, the plastic stitching thread didn't all dissolve and a bit came out weeks after surgery. A lumpy reminder remains. The rest of the scar forms a neat white line. I hope my new scars are all that successful. Above the main scar is a shorter scar in my armpit, about three inches long, the sentinel node biopsy scar, again, a thin line now.

So, when I have my reconstruction, this multitude of surgery, I will have a new collection of scars. Of reminders. Are they? I mean do they remind me? Yes, certainly they can take me places, like the childhood incidents, where the whole scene is vivid in front of me, like a film in technicolour.

But scars fade.

I remember when I was an art student, exploring experimental dance, finding a performance artist called Pina Bausch and her company from Wuppertal in Germany. Her work is intensely personal, often using the dancers' own experiences to create her work. Humour and sadness often intertwine. I would watch grainy video tapes of her performances, mesmerised by the strangeness. One piece sticks in my mind. The dancers are all wearing evening gowns and they walk in a line through the audience, coming back to the stage and one by one they talk about their scars. Scars like mine, stories of childhood injuries and accidents. And bigger scars. But they are there, on the surface. They never go. But they fade.

I thought the scars would mean that I wasn't perfect anymore. I remember thinking that after the dog incident.

And, out of the bath now, I stand in front of the mirror. In the soft morning light which is falling on my left side, my good side, as it were, the scars on my right chest and armpit are barely noticeable, really, they look natural, part of me now. If I stand sideways, with my right side facing the mirror, I can position myself so that my left breast is not visible. I stand there and look at myself. Flat. Just a torso and bottom. Boyish looking almost, with my short hair. But it's not even boyish, it's sexless. I am reminded why the breast so defines sexuality and femininity. The lack of it is so obvious, so bald. Yes, I appear bald without it. So, this is why I want it back?

Maybe I am trying to analyse this too much. It is not so complex. It is very simple. I want to look like a woman again.

I know, I have heard Alison say this, that some women don't feel whole again. I think of her saying that. That I am fine the way I am, that I seem quite happy. And she knows, she's seen me with two breasts and now one. In fact, I often forget, she cut off my right breast; she's held it, felt it, put it in a receptacle for it to be sent to a laboratory, labelled as my right breast. And now she examines the scar, carefully, looking for changes. She knows my breast and my chest well, her expert fingers confidently tracing over the skin. I trust her. When she says I look fine, is she trying to tell me I might not be happy with my reconstruction?

Over and over again I have told myself that it is only a breast. *Only*. What do I mean? I mean, well let's be really frank about this, I mean I don't actually need this appendage. It hangs on the front of my body, I am talking about my remaining breast now, and it has no purpose. Or does it? Is the purpose that it defines my female-ness?

But in saying, 'It's only a breast,' what I meant was that it has no function. Function, as in an eye or a hand. It doesn't help me function and get by in the world. What is the breast's function? To feed babies. I am past that, even though I chose not to have any babies, and therefore didn't get to feed them.

And so my mantra to myself has been and still is, 'Being alive is better.' By *better* I mean better than dying. So having one breast is not what I would have chosen. That, by the way, is an understatement. Having one breast, for me, sometimes, has felt like a mutilation. Necessary. I understand that. But a mutilation nevertheless.

Being alive is better. Even that mantra has worn a bit thin. Not that I have wished myself dead. No. I have never done that. But the loss I feel, is so painful, so extreme. And it's not just the breast, although that's where it started. The loss continues, loss of dignity becoming a cancer patient, loss of control of what happened to my life, loss of status in the world as I am not working, loss of confidence. Loss of people around me who I thought were my friends. Loss of ovaries. Loss of energy. Loss of trust in myself.

I could go on. You get the picture. Loss.

Last year people said to me, 'It's early days.' What did they mean? I didn't know then, I think I do now. That a life will evolve that lives with the fear, or acceptance, of cancer. And it is OK. It is different now. The storm passing. This too will pass. Yes, all of this will pass. Things are perfect just as they are. We don't need to be constantly questing, searching, pushing. Now is perfectly perfect. All is well.

I have to find the courage to accept that.

I have found out I am determined. Resourceful. I have depths I didn't know about before. I know about them now. Life feels different now, now that I have this possibility of two breasts. The surgery won't happen for several months, probably April next year. But that's fine, I am OK with that. I accept it.

I feel a bit different now. I mean different from Sarah 'before'. Less worried about things I can't change, like being late. A sense of perspective about time and a realisation that some things just profoundly don't matter. And if it's not life and death, then it probably doesn't matter as much as I thought it did.

Throughout the autumn and winter Ronnie and I started walking together, finding new undiscovered places to walk, to look for wildlife. From West Kirby we walk at low tide to Hilbre island in the Dee estuary. On the sandbanks a colony of seals. Over Christmas the weather stays sunny and we enjoy being outside. On Christmas day we walk at Formby Point, through the pine woods and the sand dunes onto the beach. Have a packed lunch sitting in the marram grass on a sand dune.

Just before new year and I have an urge to clean the house. I am cleaning the grill pan with a Brillo pad. Washing nets, hoovering cobwebs on the cornice in the living room.

Normal. Is. Restored.

I am sleeping well. At last. Visited by strange dreams. A strange jumble of me getting lost on motorways, grassy tracks, and cliff tops. Me falling, all my supplements in containers that burst open and the tablets are everywhere, slipping through cracks in the floorboards. I can't control anything. When I look down into the cracks I see glimpses of them, not tablets any more, nestling amongst the detritus of dust and years of time passing. They have become lollipops with patterned wrappers, shiny objects, baubles, jewels; the things that are lost forever.

I went shopping today in town. It is Ronnie's birthday soon, and I have gone to buy his present. But this was different. I was on my own. Yes, I haven't been on my own for nearly two years. I rely on Ronnie, to take me, to park, to make sure I don't get too tired.

My heart is beating very fast as I negotiate the multi-storey car park. These things I used to do without thinking are now a trial. Sarah, pull yourself together. Mild panic. And yet it is not a difficult thing that I am doing, I am just out of practice.

In John Lewis I find myself rooted to the spot. I have come up the escalator to go to haberdashery. But I am staring at the lingerie department. I can see turquoise lace, pink lace, lovely bras. I feel so left out. Tears fill my eyes. I must try and avoid this department.

A sense, I think, of how much this two breasted-ness matters to me. Why I am prepared for this surgery. I want to go back there. For it to feel like home again. Feminine.

I am in this gap between now, being well, and surgery starting again, reconstruction. I mostly don't feel afraid. I have made my choice.

I left the swimming pool this evening and I stopped outside. It is February. The sky is a deep translucent blue. Not dark, but not light, somewhere in between the two. But, I can hear birds singing. Yes, I can. On the drive home I open the car windows so I can hear them more. Does this mean spring is on its way? I notice so much.

I thought before, and by 'before' I always mean before breast cancer, I thought that I was living my life mindfully, giving each moment the respect it deserved. Was I? I don't know. Since the death of my father in 1999 I had been aware of life in a much stronger sense. That's ten years ago. But was I really aware or just thinking I was?

I am two years on, two years in, whatever it is, nearly two years since diagnosis. At diagnosis I was barely able to think this far ahead. But I am here. Some days I am despondent. Two years in it doesn't magically just stop.

The down days. It's part of it. The down bit of the rollercoaster. It is the day before the day I call 'D-day'. Diagnosis day. Tomorrow will be two years exactly since I was diagnosed with breast cancer: 21 February. Will I ever forget the date?

We have our two years 'celebration'. Not really a celebration, but a recognition of the day, not wanting it to pass without some sort of ritual being observed. We made a packed lunch. Walked through Greenbank Park, into Sefton Park, sat on a bench and ate our lunch. Then on to Princes Park and down the boulevard to the Anglican cathedral. Went up the tower, looked out across at Liverpool from 330 feet. We are the last visitors and the guide takes us down through the bell chamber. The bells are enormous.

And then downstairs in the beloved Everyman Bistro for tea. A lovely day, and we didn't talk about cancer.

'That was a lovely day,' said Ronnie. Let there be more lovely days.

Sometimes I'm not sure about how I will ever let go, feel safe. The 'Is it cancer?' worries could come at any time. It doesn't ever 'end'. Not really, but then life doesn't ever end either. Even with death there is no end, because life continues. Those that live on keep the dead alive with their memory. I found that consoling didn't I when my father died? But I think we just make up these things to make us feel better. Because deep down the human condition is frightened of death and we don't want to think about it too much. We do funerals and the rituals of death, without very public displays of grief. The grief is done privately for the most part.

I suppose I can't help relating the thoughts of death and grief, with what I have now experienced. The loss of my breast, the fear of dying, and now.

Now I am facing some sort of revival, a bringing back from the dead. My breast can be remade, in a fashion.

Getting to the two-year mark feels like a big step in terms of my medical treatment. The big major things are done, mastectomy, oophorectomy. Hormone treatment tried and rejected. Iscador part of my routine. Bone supplements for bone density, because of early menopause. Things feel settled. But I still want the reassurance that I am doing the right things. I have lived in doctor-land for so long, it is strange not to have the appointments. I decide to review my current situation with Dr Chris Etheridge, from Cancer Options. In many ways you could say I don't need this, I have made my big choices, but I still want reassurance.

We have a telephone conversation and very thoroughly discuss all the aspects of what I have done, the supplements I am taking, still using Iscador, my worries about the next big surgery.

I feel I am doing all I can to stay cancer free.

When I met Patricia Peat, also from Cancer Options, at the conference last October I asked her, 'What happens now?'

She said, 'Time now to live some life.'

CHAPTER 15

Retreat

s we drive north I have the sense, the same sense I always have, of really getting away. Things slip into irrelevance. It is the feeling of passing, of moving on, through. It is a perspective you can't have when you are pushed right up against it. That you think you will never leave the world of breast cancer.

We are going to the Isle of Mull for a week's holiday. This was chosen for a retreat holiday, somewhere quiet. It is March so we're not expecting to have a lot of good weather, but we are prepared with waterproofs and thermals, and also indoor activities, reading and knitting. We stay one night at Oban, the next day we are on the ferry and arrive late at Calgary, where we are renting a converted loft. It is quite delightful, a perfect little bolt hole. Perfect.

We are a few minutes' walk from the most beautiful sandy beach. As it turns out the weather is unbelievable. It is sunny every day and we go on long walks. We can walk all day and not see anyone else. We walk on sandy beaches, on squelchy heather moors, boulder strewn paths, through pine woods edged with larch, along sheep tracks. We are outside everyday. I collect shells, but don't get much knitting done.

Stephen Wright from Sacred Space has suggested Mull. I told him I wanted to retreat and asked for his advice. He sent me a long email extolling the virtues of Mull, recalling for me some of his own fond memories of trips here. It was a mouth-watering description and it is the perfect place for us right now. As ever, he is spot on.

One day we have a trip over to Iona. We walk across the machir to the sandy beach. The sea is turquoise, the sand white. It is magical. We have our packed lunch sat on the grass, looking out to sea. The next place across the sea would be America. It feels incredibly special. It is called The Bay at the Back of the Ocean.

After lunch I take off my boots and socks, and go for a paddle in the sea. It is cold, but bearable. I am happy. I look for a stone on the beach to take home. I want to take a reminder of this day, I am praying, if that is what my wishing is called, for a good result for my reconstruction. I find a small egg shaped grey stone, perfectly smooth and put it in my bag. This will be my special stone.

We briefly visit the abbey on Iona, the main reason many people visit the island, but I feel we have been given the spirituality that we came here for, our time on the beach. I am sad to leave. But it has been such a lovely day. We drive back to Calgary up the west coast of Mull, it is unbelievably beautiful. Every turn in the road reveals an even better view. The sun is setting and we are driving through golden treacle and honey-coloured sea views.

The trip is a success. This has been so good for us physically and mentally. Refreshing, relaxing and challenging. We will come back here.

I have another trip lined up. So soon after Mull. But this was booked last year, by Ronnie; it was my birthday present back in September. It is a five-day bee keeping course in Gloucestershire. We didn't know back then what we would be doing in April, in seven months' time. I, of course, was anxious when Ronnie gave me the present, wondered if I'd be able to do this, do something on my own. And that self-limiting anxiety of not being able to plan things that far ahead, just in case. In case of what? I don't know, that the cancer will have come back, reclaimed my life? Now I have the new feeling, the nervousness of new challenges that I didn't have before cancer. But I want to learn about bees. Maybe I will keep them, I'm not sure, but I'd like to know more.

I find a small one-bedroomed stable conversion to rent, just south of Gloucester. It is perfectly fine for me alone. I arrive on Sunday and the next day I am off to college, being a student. It is Hartpury College, an agricultural college.

I love it. It is fascinating. Each day we have theory in the morning and practical in the afternoon, so I get to wear a bee suit, to handle the bees, look at hives, learn how to identify the different types of bees, and the stages of the larvae turning into bees.

So I love all this learning, but I also love the time alone. In the evening I drive back to my little house and cook my evening meal. And I am happy. One day after college I go to Gloucester cathedral. Another day I go swimming and have a sauna. On my last day, the Saturday, before I drive home I go to the Rococo gardens near Painswick. They are splendid, if a little formal for my liking, but signs of spring are everywhere, tulips. And I visit the pretty little village of Painswick, buy presents for the people I care about. Italian bread and cake for Ronnie, a skipping rope for Ellie, and a hand-made wooden bookmark for Bren. Then I drive home, on the motorway. It is the first time I have driven this far for two years. On the way down here I chose not to go on the motorway, but it took hours. So that is another hurdle crossed, another thing that I have now done. Another sense of achievement.

Back in Liverpool I am hoping that my April surgery date will arrive. But it doesn't. They are apologetic at the hospital, say they are still trying to find a date for me but it will probably now be May. I am frustrated about not getting a date, but there is nothing I can do. The hospital say that Mr Graham has had some emergencies and immediate reconstructions, so my slot has not come up yet. I feel like I can't do anything, knowing that this surgery is imminent, that I will be going into convalescence.

On the one hand I feel disappointed, on the other I try to be positive and say to myself, well more time to get fitter, to be prepared. And I know that in the whole scheme of things this is not a bad place to be. The reconstruction is necessary for me *because* of cancer, but not *about* cancer. So I do feel I am moving on from that. I know I am lucky. But lucky is relative.

I see Alison Waghorn for my routine six-month check. Tell her I have done things on my own, been away to my bee course. All my blood tests are normal. She says I look really well. She says I have looked at everything in detail, understood things and done what I had to. Have dealt with the emotional side, and not everyone does, she says. I have faced 'it', and can now move on. I am choosing to and ready to have my life again. The word cancer is rarely spoken in consultations.

But I still feel quite lost. Vulnerable.

I have an interview with the Ministry of Fear. No, it's not actually the Ministry of Fear, it just feels like it. It's a medical assessment to see whether I can continue to claim state benefits. I am summoned to a sterile basement office. At reception I am asked for my proof of identity. They do not say 'hello'. We wait in a stark, blank room. Royal blue chairs in rows. No plants, no leaflets, no magazines. Nothing. It's like a prison waiting-room. All of this does not add to my sense of being a person. I have fallen into a hole. I am just a number.

When I see the medical assessor, she seems reasonable enough. I explain that I am waiting for major surgery and that this whole interview seems unnecessary. She does not say she thinks I am lying about the surgery, but I have no proof. But she does agree that my focus at the moment should be to prepare for the surgery, although of course that it is not up to her to approve my continuing benefits, that is for the 'decision makers'. That's what she calls them. It is vaguely threatening.

The whole event makes me feel that I am in a process where they assume you are cheating. That you are not eligible for the benefits you are claiming. Not that you paid your national insurance and tax all your working life for a scenario just like this, I mean serious illness.

I leave feeling very intimidated and down at the bottom of the hole. It's like Alice in Wonderland. Small and lost.

The first of May. It is the phone call I have been waiting for now for months. It's Alison, the breast reconstruction nurse, from Whiston hospital.

She says, 'We have a date for you.'

It is in just over two weeks' time. 18 May.

My immediate instinct is not to tell anyone. This is for me and me alone. At last. Of course, now that I have the date I feel unbelievably anxious, frightened even.

But I want to be me again.

CHAPTER 16

Preparing

am in hospital-land again. We had thought that we might manage to go camping before my surgery. Now that I have a date, and it is so soon, we can see that it won't be possible. Pre-op appointment, CT scan, things start to fill the diary. My notebook fills up with lists. But I so want to carve out some space for us to do something. We decide on a day out, Ronnie says it's my choice, we can go anywhere I want. Lake District, north Wales, it's up to me.

I choose Anglesey.

But first, the day before our day out, it is my pre-op. One of those six-hour visits to a hospital, reminiscent of diagnosis day because it lasts so long, because there are so many doctors to see, tests to have.

In all the surgery I have had so far, no-one did a blood test to determine my blood group in case I need a blood transfusion. Because the risk of transfusion, of massive blood loss, was not a big risk in any of my other surgeries, that really starts to put things in perspective. But it is all good, it is for a good reason, it is for something I want. But doing this, this hospital visit has just made me remember that this is a really big deal, this surgery I have chosen to have.

The next day, our day out in Anglesey. The weather is atrocious, windy, rainy and miserable. I wonder if we should cancel the trip, but we don't have the luxury of time, only a week now before I go into hospital, and I won't be walking much after that for a while. As we drive to Anglesey the weather continues to get worse. Damn. I just want a nice day. We cross the bridge across the Menai Straits, three times in fact as we take a wrong turn, end up back across the bridge and then back again, but then we are on the road to

Newborough and I say hopefully, 'It's brightening up.' Well, it isn't raining as heavily now and I think I can see a crack of blue in the clouds, ahead of us, where we are heading.

We arrive at Newborough nature reserve and park. There are sand dunes in front of us, so we can't see exactly where we have arrived. We walk through them and then, wow, look. We are on an amazing long sandy beach with views across the water to the mountains of Snowdonia. Wow. And the sun just came out.

We go back to a picnic bench and eat our lunch, all the while the weather continues to get better, sunny, drying the ground. We set off on our walk, to Llandwynn Island. It's magical.

On the island, crunching along the white tracks, made of crushed cockle shells, deep blue bluebells everywhere. Mossy grass studded with blue flowers like stars, and pink sea thrift in tufts. The rocks on this island are 600 million years old. How amazing is that? We arrive at the beach at the far end of the island. Sit on the sand and watch the waves. I want to drink it up, to bring it all with me, the energy of new horizons.

Walking back across miles of sand with the mountains behind. Beautiful.

It was like a camping day. But, unlike a camping day when we go back to the tent, we drive home. It is a good day. I feel the future approaching.

A week before my surgery. A Monday, so an Ellie day, as we have come to call the days we look after Ellie. Spring is in full spring, so we go for a picnic in Calderstones Park. It is so perfect, this day could have been dreamed up just for me. The sun shines, Ronnie and Ellie pick daisies, I make a daisy chain. I have moments when I think, 'This time next week, I will be in theatre.' It is bizarre, actually, thinking that it will be so different, so soon. And that Ellie knows nothing about this. That this time next week she will play with grandad, and I will be lying on an operating table.

Another hospital. St Helen's. A new hospital. Looks like an airport, an architect drawing of a vision of a new NHS. Nye Bevan would be proud.

Clean and bright, and with art on the walls. Yes, art. A patient information leaflet tells me that it helps patients feel at ease. Friendly staff at reception greet you and point you in the right direction. X-ray, CT and MRI scans are all in one department. I am 40 minutes late because of a traffic jam on the motorway and when I rang them from the car they said don't worry. And now I have arrived they are unconcerned that I am late, welcoming, reassuring. It is a good feeling.

I knit. I must be relaxed, often I bring my knitting but am too anxious to knit. The art must be working. I am here to have a CT scan of my abdomen to locate my perforators. These are the arteries that perforate the fat on my abdomen giving it a blood supply. They want to find the best perforator to connect to the artery in my chest, so that the fat continues to have a good blood supply and will stay alive. I've not had a CT scan before and am expecting something like an x-ray.

I am called through. A friendly nurse who chats easily to me. Yes, the hospital has only been open since last October, eight months. It's so clean. Friendly nurse gives me a plastic shopping basket for my clothes and two gowns.

'Sorry about the gowns,' she says.

'I've already told the PCT,' I say. It was on my list.

They are not really big enough, the gowns, so it's two gowns, one with the opening at the front, the other on top with the opening at the back. It works quite well. I can leave my knickers on, but no jewellery.

I am now in another smaller waiting area by the changing cubicles. There is a row of chairs. I put my plastic basket on one. I don't sit down. I'm feeling anxious now, this has echoes of diagnosis day. The gowns, cubicle, basket. I pace up and down the small space, it is off the main corridor leading to the scanning rooms. Even though it is new and clean it is still sterile. It is still a hospital. The floor is that hospital non-colour, even in its newness. Grey-beige-white. Walls are a pale yellow, paler than primroses.

I wonder, very briefly, why I have chosen to immerse myself in this. To go back to these spaces. It reminds me of diagnosis day when I was pissed off that I would spend so much time doing exactly this. Waiting in hospitals.

Another woman, similar to my age, joins me. She has changed and comes out of the cubicle, gives me a '*Do I look unstylish?*' look after she emerges wearing the two gowns and her sandals.

'Nice shoes,' I say. They are those gladiator style sandals that are currently fashionable. She smiles weakly. She has obviously not done this before, this living in hospitals. She looks apprehensive. I feel like an expert.

The friendly nurse comes to get me and takes me through. We open the door to the scan room and I think I have just slipped into another story here. The first thing I see is a big machine - I mean, this machine is enormous. I've had an x-ray in Liverpool on a small, ancient machine. But this machine is brand spanking new. Digital displays all over the top of it, displays of big green numbers. It is a big circular thing with a hole in the middle, and a human-sized flat bit. And I am going to go in it, am I?

'OK, what's happening?' I say. Trying not to sound nervous. It's strange because the people who do these sorts of things do it everyday, and it's not strange or alien to them. And sometimes they don't seem to remember how frightening it is to the patients.

There are two nurses, or operatives, or technicians. I'm not sure what they are called. The woman does most of the directions and the talking to me, and the younger man does things with plastic tubes and medical objects. I am on the bed bit now. The woman says I will have an injection, it will feel warm, and I may feel like I am weeing myself, but it's OK I won't be. OK? Sure? Er, yes.

She then puts a 'locator' on my tummy button, she expertly puts her hand under the gowns and tapes it in place. A needle in my arm for the injection. I'm looking away, but then glance down and I have an enormous orange plastic thing sticking out of the vein on my left inner arm. It wasn't quite what I had expected. Then they connect me to a long clear tube, which is joined to a bottle of clear fluid. It looks like half a pint. What exactly is going to happen here? They both leave the room, the door slams behind my head and I'm alone. Then I hear the voice through a speaker. Breathe in, hold. Breathe normally. Whirr, click. The machine cranks into action. I keep my eyes shut. I'm desperately trying diversionary tactics. Think of the beach on Anglesey. Think of Ellie picking daisies... anything. Then I remember my friend's old trick of counting in sevens backwards from 2,000. I can't even think of the first one. So I just start counting slowly in my head. One. Two.

Breathe in, hold. Breathe normally. The disjointed voice is telling me. Three. Four.

'The injection is going in now.'

Five. Six.

God. It's horrible. Burning sensation immediately in my cheeks, on my chest and then in my groin. I am keeping my eyes tight shut. I want this to be over. Breathe in, hold. Whirr. Then it is over.

The young man comes back in and disconnects me from the tube.

'What is that?' I ask.

'Contrast dye.'

'Dye? But it has no colour.'

'It's iodine. It shows up white on the scan.'

I can taste it in my mouth. It's horrible.

The woman now joins the man just as he is about to remove the thing in my arm. I glance at it. There's blood oozing out from the clear covering taped to my arm. She says to him, 'Leave it in,' and goes back through the door. I can't see, only hear the slam.

'Why am I bleeding so much?'

'Because the contrast fluid is forced through your vein at five millilitres a second, and we use a big needle,' he says, completely matter of factly.

He's bending down now, to wipe my blood off the floor. Wow, five millilitres a second, that's fast. I'd really like to leave now. He's behind me now washing his hands in the sink.

I thought this would be like an ultrasound, or a quick 'click' like a photo and it would be done. I did not expect needles and blood. And why am I still lying here?

The woman comes back and tells me the doctor is looking at the scan. Doctor? I didn't even know there was a doctor involved in this. She disappears. I look up to my right and see a clock above the door. It is ten past eleven. I have been here at least half an hour, including waiting by the cubicle. Ronnie will be wondering what is happening to me. I watch the red second-hand moving. I don't want to look anywhere else, it's too clinical, too much like serious medical intervention. I don't want to see it.

I hear the noise as the door behind me opens. 'We need to do it again,' says the woman. She comes over to me and says, 'Is that OK?' in a way that quite clearly means I don't have any choice. She leans over me and says, 'Did you get the glow?'

'Yes, so why are we doing it again?'

Apparently the contrast went through my system so quickly they didn't get the image. This time they will be quicker.

'At least you know what it's like now,' she says cheerfully.

Oh. Yeah. Right. That's alright then. Know how horrible it is.

Same procedure. This time I watch as the injection is done. The bottle of fluid is forced into my vein. The green numbers above me on the machine start moving faster and faster. I close my eyes, follow the breathing instructions. And then it's over.

They remove the needle and clean me up. The woman says, 'Looks like we've tried to hack your arm off, but it's only blood.'

I get changed. I feel odd. I feel sick for the rest of the day.

We have come to Formby to go walking. The day before I go to hospital for my reconstruction, time for my last outing for a while. Today, driving here, I feel emotional, frightened even. I realise the fact of trying emotionally for two years to say, 'No, it's OK with one breast,' has been really hard work. In fact, now that I am about to have two again, or a version of two, I almost feel I can allow myself to feel how 'not right' I find it.

We find the path to the dunes which opens out onto the beach. Acres of sand. It is deserted. The sky is deep grey and full of rain, the wind whipping up the soft sand in the dunes. I am laughing, excited. The tide is coming in, and we walk along the shoreline. Sun, rain and wind. Ronnie says enough weather today to last me all week in a hospital. We have our lunch sitting in the sand dunes and walk slowly back to the car. I am reluctant to leave.

Driving home and we are just in time to go to the cathedral, and light candles for me.

Today I go into hospital. I have been making lists and half packing since I got the phone call with my date. Most of my stuff is in a box in the studio, ready. I get up early, and go dragon boating. It's windy and rainy. We have a full boat. I feel alive. Driving home I am actually starting to feel nervous. I am shaking slightly. I do not feel safe to be driving.

Ronnie takes me to the allotment and we have our lunch there. There is so much weeding to do, but I feel paralysed. I know that this will be my last opportunity to be very active, to rush round the plot tidying it up. I don't though. Bren joins us and I help him work out the dimensions for the frame for the new deck he's going to make while I'm in hospital. I ring the ward and arrange to go in at seven o'clock that evening. When it is time to go home, Bren hugs me at the gate and says he has a few flutters in his chest feeling nervous for me. 'Imagine how I feel then,' I say.

Ronnie has made pasta bake for our tea. He says, 'If you were going to run a marathon you'd have pasta the night before wouldn't you? And you are doing a sort of marathon.' He is right. Marathon surgery.

And then it is time to go to Whiston hospital. We arrive at the ward. We are shown to a bed, my bed. It is in a ward of six beds. Ronnie helps me unpack my things, puts them all into the locker next to the bed. I sit on the bed. Ronnie sits on the chair next to me. The woman in the bed opposite smiles at us. And then we are just sitting around. Waiting. Made me remember, this is what hospital is like. Just waiting and waiting. Everything seeming to be done for the convenience of the staff, not the patients.

Then I am 'admitted'. The friendly nurse goes through all my notes and checks all my details. She reminds me that I will not be in this ward after theatre, I will be in my own room, and I will not be getting out of bed for probably two or three days, and that I will have morphine to control my pain; they will make sure I don't have any pain. Do I have any questions? No. I am beyond speech I think. She puts my name band around my wrist. I am done. Ready. Am I? Ready, that is? Well, I have waited five months for this moment. To be here. Now I am. Ronnie leaves me. It is only eight o'clock in the evening. Too soon to go to bed. I don't want to talk to the other people in the ward. I put on my iPod. I think I would rather be doing what I usually do on a Sunday, be in a wine bar with Bren after a day at the allotment.

The curtains are closed around the bed. I take the sleeping pill that is offered, I never have before in hospital, have never felt like this. It's like being nervous, but also vaguely terrified at the same time. Time to sleep. Or try to anyway. I drift in and out of sleep. It's too hot. I feel I am sleeping on plastic bags, the pillows have plastic covers under the cotton ones.

I don't feel excited now when I think of the next few days. I remind myself I want this. I do. It's the end result, not this bit, that I want. I have to tell myself it will be worth it. It is the end of breast cancer. I hope. Forever.

CHAPTER 17

Regaining

My surgery is today. I haven't slept well. The sleeping pill didn't work, 6 am and I am wide awake. I can see the leaves on the trees outside the window blowing, a fresh spring breeze. Just not in here, the stifling hospital atmosphere. I go and have a bath, with lavender oil, it's early, about seven. Put my surgery gown on. Come back to bed and wait for 'it' to start. It doesn't take long before there is a waft of the curtain, and my morning begins properly.

I meet my team. First it's Mr Koshy. I have not met him before. He has very dark brown almond eyes and he is wearing a suit and tie. He tells me he works with Mr Graham. He outlines the surgery I am about to have. I tell him I understand.

'You will be fine,' he says, several times. Perhaps he can tell I feel anxious.

It is his job to consent me. To get me to sign the form that gives my consent to the surgery. He continues to provide me with some more details. He has a form, and is going to fill in the details.

He draws a little diagram on the top of the page. A female body, one breast, a groin. He explains that they will cut a flap of fat from the abdomen, he draws an elliptical shape, and disconnect the artery blood supply in the groin, he draws a line across an artery. And then, he says, the flap will be re-attached to the chest, the artery being joined to one behind the rib, and part of the rib will be cut away to allow access.

Wow, they cut the rib. I didn't know that, actually. Just another detail about this massively complex surgery.

Next he outlines the benefits of the surgery, writing them down on the form. It's funny, I think, I don't remember any other consent forms for surgery having 'benefits'. Benefits of mastectomy. Benefits of oophorectomy. Mr Koshy has carried on talking. So, the benefits.

'Reconstruction of the right breast,' he says.

'Yes,' I nod.

'And improvement of the appearance of the abdomen.'

Er, well, that wasn't actually why I'm having this surgery, but I don't say that. Instead I say, 'Those are physical benefits, there's a whole emotional benefit to this too.'

'Yes, of course,' he says. But he doesn't write that down. He moves on. It is his duty to tell me all these things that can go wrong, to make sure I understand the risks involved. The possibility of failure. I do. I sign the form.

The curtain opens and a young doctor - well younger than me anyway - introduces himself as Rowan. He says he will also be one of my surgeons today. He goes off to get the results of my CT scan.

Mr Koshy then very politely asks if he can examine me. I stand up and he comes to my side of the bed. He asks me if I am wearing knickers, yes I am, some revolting paper ones that have been presented to me as part of my surgery outfit. He then removes my gown from the top half of my body and tucks it into the knickers so I am sort of just half dressed. I mean, after all, I have only just met this man. And then, in that way only surgeons seem to do, he produces a pen from nowhere and starts drawing on my body with his thick red pen.

He puts his hand under my left breast, as though it were supported by a bra, and then he draws the curve of the top and the underside of my breast, and then he draws the same curves on the right side, my flat side, mirroring them. And then he draws a broken red line between my breasts down to my tummy button, like the white lines in the middle of the road, only these are red. And finally he puts two marks on my hips, one either side of the tummy button so they can re-position it in the right place.

He leaves. Almost immediately my anaesthetist comes to see me. Paul. He's also friendly. I like the way he used his first name as well. Good, I have a friendly team. These men who will be spending the day with me, it's just I won't remember anything. He leaves and then it is the final pre-theatre examination.

Now it is time for Ken Graham to do his supervision. He is wearing his usual shirt and tie. Sleeves rolled up, tie tucked in. He is his usual calm self.

'How are you feeling?' he asks.

'Nervous,' I say, my mouth is dry. Am I also shaking?

'That's OK.'

'Are you nervous?' I ask him. Why did I say that?

'No,' he says, 'I'm not nervous but it is good that you are because it means you realise what you are about to do. Now, would it be OK if I examined you please?' He always asks so politely, he never lets my dignity feel bruised in any way.

Mr Koshy and Rowan are also there now, they have slipped in, and stand just inside the curtain. They are now both changed into surgeon outfits. They stand and watch Mr Graham skilfully assessing the drawing that Mr Koshy has done. He is carefully studying me, gently touching me. There is no doubt here that he is in charge; Rowan and Mr Koshy will be helping him.

While he is looking at me, looking very closely at my chest and my breast I say, 'Mr Graham, I am 45, I've had the menopause, and this is what my breast is like now.' I mean droopy. He nods. 'I don't want to have something different, something like a 20-year-old. Am I clear?' He nods, he understands.

Then he asks me to lie on the bed. He produces a small hand-held machine with a probe attached to it. It appears from nowhere. Surgeons always do this, produce things like a magician. I think one of the others handed it to him. That must be how it is, they give him the equipment he needs to do the next bit of the procedure. Now he is going to listen to the perforators, using this machine, he explains. He expertly moves the probe around my abdomen using some gel, holding the machine in his other hand, his ear turned towards it. As the noise on the machine changes he pauses and then presses down with the probe. When he lifts the probe up, Mr Koshy appears with a pen and draws a purple dot at that location. Rowan is then reading out the CT scan results to him, which say where the next perforator is, in relation to my 'umbilicus', my tummy button. So that's what that locator thing was for wasn't it?

This is so technical, so medically advanced, even as I am lying there I am thinking that I am witnessing a medical miracle. That the possibility that they can do this surgery is just so amazing. I am lucky, three surgeons are assessing me, working out their plan for today. I like the way they all seem so confident, are so serious about this. I feel safe.

And then they are gone. A porter comes with a bed on wheels. It's time for theatre.

During my visits to various operating theatres in the last few years I have always been surprised at the jovial atmosphere in pre-theatre. The staff become difficult to distinguish because they all have those surgery outfits. In other hospitals I have seen mostly green, sometimes a faded orange. In Whiston they are blue. All blue. Blue cotton trousers, blue cotton shapeless top, and blue hats with all hair covered. And I am also always surprised at just how many people there are. Now there seems like there are at least a dozen in this small room of monitors and equipment. All for me, to get me ready. Someone is sticking monitors on me and linking me up to some sort of machine. My consent form is waved in front of my face.

'Is that your signature?' says a man in surgery kit.

'Yes.'

And now someone is talking about blood loss.

'So, do we think it will be more than 500 millilitres,' he's saying, but not really a question.

'Too much information,' I answer. He wasn't asking me anyway. Then I realise it is Paul, my anaesthetist, I just didn't recognise him in the blue outfit and hat. His colleagues are patting the back of my left hand trying to find a vein so they can put the anaesthetic in.

'Abject terror has set in,' I say. 'All my veins have disappeared.' I don't know why this happens, I just know it does, from my other surgeries.

'Yes, OK, well let's just put a small one in, we can put a bigger one in later,' they say, not really to me, but to each other. I barely notice the prick. And then Ken Graham is in the room as well. In a blue outfit now. The hat suits him, I think. The other people in the blue outfits are chatting and laughing. I smile at Ken. He nods.

'I will do my best,' he says. He has said this before.

'I believe you.'

And then, the feeling, the slipping away.

'Here we go,' I say out loud. I only meant to think it. It feels like a lot has happened to me already today, but it's only about 9.30 in the morning.

I am looking at the clock, trying to get my eyes to focus on it. The time? What time is it? Quarter past seven. Is it the evening then? I'm not sure.

'Don't leave me,' I say to the nurse who is next to my bed. 'Don't leave me.' I don't know why I am saying this. Oh, here I am again. I am in recovery. I know what this feels like, coming round, drifting away again, not knowing where I am. In and out of some kind of weird dazed state I see Ken Graham, he lifts my dressing and shows me the surgery, I can only see blood, I think he says, 'It has gone well.' I say my throat hurts, and I see Paul who says, 'That's not surprising because you've had a tube down it for the last ten hours.' I'm falling into myself, trying not to. They are not there now, only two nurses talking across me in a language I can't recognise.

'Can I see,' I ask the nurse. 'Can I see my breast?'

I am covered with a thick wadding, like very thick cotton wool, and a theatre gown. They lift it up and I look down. It is a breast shape, although there is a tape dressing across the top which is already covered in blood. It is the same shape as my other breast, and it looks right. It feels right. I just burst into tears. The nurses give me tissues.

'But I am happy,' I say.

I am wheeled back to the ward very carefully, with pillows around the end of the bed, it is like being wrapped in cotton wool. I am put into a small room on my own. The equipment is set up around me on stands. There is a nurse and a doctor standing next to my bed. The doctor is explaining that I have my own supply of morphine that I can use when I need it. He says it is not good to be in pain, it will slow the healing, so I should use the pain relief when I need to. The nurse is saying to me, 'You are very alert Sarah.' I want to say to her that she looks like my GP, ask her if she is her sister. But I don't seem to have the use of my mouth.

Ronnie visits me briefly. And then I am alone. Alone, but checked on, regularly. Ken Graham makes an appearance at some point. Stands at the end of my bed, looking at me. He seems so caring, so concerned that I will be alright. It's late now, he's been in the hospital for many hours, caring about his patients. A good man.

There is a wire, one of the many wires and tubes attached to me, this one is coming out of my new breast and is plugged into a machine, like a bigger version of the one they used to find the perforators before theatre; it's called a doppler. The wire inside my new breast has a microphone on it and the blood flow through the valve is monitored. The machine pulses and gushes, it is the noise of my blood flow. It is a good noise. It is like listening to a new baby peacefully sleeping and breathing. I feel comforted by it.

It is a very, very long night. They did warn me. But I had not expected this. It is worse then they told me. Every time I think I am about to drop into sleep, I wake up with a jolt, terrified that I will somehow fall and pull my tubes, pull off these wires and things that I feel must be somehow keeping me alive. Are they?

The green light on the morphine button glows. I am not in pain, no, discomfort maybe, but I would not describe this as pain. The Flowtron boots which are on my calves are noisy, they squeeze my legs alternately, to help prevent a blood clot. The oxygen I am breathing through the mask is noisy too, to me it sounds like the noise of a radio not tuned in to a station. Like white noise. It is the sound of the humidifier, the water in the supply gushes and gurgles. Sleep is impossible. I discover the morphine is the best way to drift off. But then I slip into a morphine haze and press the emergency button to call the nurse, frightened, because I think the noise of the 'new baby' has changed. It's four in the morning. That horrible, scary, time of night when everything feels worse. She checks everything, all is well.

⁊ ℐ ❦

The next morning the door opens. The house doctor and his team are doing their rounds. Someone puts the big light on. The group of people squeeze into my room at the end of the bed. How many people are there? At least six I think.

'How are you feeling?' asks the doctor. He has introduced himself but I have immediately forgotten his name.

I have had no sleep, the morphine had kicked in and I feel wretched. I pull off my oxygen mask so I can speak.

'Well, I didn't do this because I thought it would be a laugh.'

I am looking at the team, one of the women smirks at me. I smirk back, and then disappear back into the oxygen mask.

The doctor comes over and asks to look at my flap, the flap of skin and fat that is now my new breast. Makes an observation, his colleague writes a note in my file. And then he turns to leave. Over his shoulder he says, 'Try and get some rest,' moving quickly towards the door, which is difficult because there are at least three people blocking the exit. I shut my eyes.

When I open them again they are all gone. The door is shut, I am alone. Staring straight up at the fluorescent light they put on when they came in.

It is painful on my eyes. I reach for my buzzer to get someone to come and turn it off. The buzzer is not there where it should be, by my right hand. I am seized with panic. The doctor moved it when he lifted my dressing to look at my wounds, and now it is not there. I can move about an inch and I am feeling frantic now trying not to pull any tubes as I try and use my left arm to reach over my body to my right side. I do not want to move my right arm, I think I will pull my stitches out. God, I will be here forever, staring at the light, the white noise of the oxygen machine drowning me, it will be torture. Just for a moment this feels like prison, not hospital. Horrible. And then I find the wire and pull the monitor towards me. Thank God. I press the red button and Sharon, the young woman who does the breakfasts, appears, asking if I want a cup of tea.

There are wires everywhere, and things on stands all around the bed. On one side of the bed I have a supply of oxygen and am wearing the mask all the time. There is the doppler machine connected by a wire to the microphone in my flap, my new breast. The Flowtron boots are like inflatable pads which wrap around my calves and they alternately inflate and squeeze, inflate and squeeze, the machine goes *ssssch*, pause, *ssssch*, pause. On the other side of the bed, next to the blood pressure monitor, which is on wheels, is another stand, again on wheels, and on this are two drips, sacs of colourless fluid, antibiotic and saline drips feeding into my left arm. And also on this stand, the pain control, the morphine. It is in a special machine attached to a wire with a button which has a green light on it. When I press the button I get a dose of morphine. The light goes out and won't light up again ready for use until I can have another dose, so I can't overuse it. Three drains come from my wounds, two in the abdomen, one in the breast. And somewhere there is a catheter.

Later that morning the woman who smirked at me comes back to see me. Turns out she's a physiotherapist, she's called Annette, and she's going to get me to start moving. What? I am lying in bed attached to all this stuff, and I am going to move? Very small movements, my legs, or feet and ankles anyway, and my arms and shoulders. I proceed very gingerly. She says I am doing well and she will be back tomorrow and maybe I will get out of bed. What? I don't think so.

Annette also explains that because I've had a long anaesthetic then my lungs will take some time to recover fully, so I may find that I am coughing up phlegm. And, she warns me, I must spit it out, not swallow it. I tell her that I have not experienced this so far. I will, she says.

Two nurses come and wash me. I have a special bed which raises at the back at the touch of a button, and also raises under my legs too. So I can change the position of the bed to suit myself. And also so that my abdomen is comfortable. It is impossible for me to straighten my legs because of the cut in my abdomen.

Lunch arrives. Somewhere in this morning I was asked what I wanted from the menu. I can't eat anyway. I can't move anyway, and the tray of food is plonked on the table next to my bed. No, I could not even pick up a fork. I click the green button. Morphine. Release.

In the afternoon, after two o'clock it is visiting time. Ronnie appears at the end of my bed. I feel there is a glass wall between us. It is the morphine. I feel weak, weepy. Mostly I just want to sleep, but the noise, it's horrible. I can't sleep. Ronnie has an idea, ear plugs, and says he will get some for me. He leaves and I am not expecting him until that evening, but he is back in ten minutes and has bought a pair of ear plugs in the hospital shop. He looks triumphant. I try and sleep, but the ward outside my door is noisy.

Later on Alison, the breast reconstruction nurse, comes to see me. I am crying a lot. She says it's OK, just cry.

At tea time I do manage to eat. I get the plate onto my knees and slowly put some mouthfuls in. It's cod in parsley sauce. Soft white mashed potatoes and peas. Soft white mush is all I want.

Visiting again after tea and Ronnie is back. He feeds me the tinned fruit that came with my tea. I am upset. Ronnie doesn't want to leave me. He has bought some other ear plugs as well, so I have a choice. After he leaves I put them in, and bliss, I can feel myself falling asleep. I am only aware of the observations as the nurses come and take my temperature, my pulse and oxygen saturation. I think these are only happening every four hours now.

In the morning, the house doctor comes again. Always a different one. It's eight o'clock, and I have been mostly asleep now for 12 hours. I feel much better. This doctor is American, he reminds me of someone off a TV show. He has a super confident manner about him. He says they will take one of the drains out. I have three, two in my abdomen and one in my breast. He says I will be more comfortable then. As he leaves I expect him to say something like, 'way to go'. Like in an American film. But he doesn't. I think maybe I am hallucinating and press the morphine again.

I use my ear plugs all morning, drifting back into sleep. The physio woman comes briefly, Ken Graham comes, says to take all the drains out, I wait for the nurse, eventually she comes and the drains are gone, and the physio comes back, Annette, with a nurse this time. She was right about the phlegm, I am spitting out thick green gunk, it looks disgusting. They have given me a little plastic pot with a lid, which says 'SPUTUM' in small black capital letters. Annette says I am doing well.

She then proceeds to get me out of bed, as she said she would. Very gently, very slowly, I roll onto my side and using the amazing folding bed, get my feet down low and then onto the floor. Very gingerly I stand up. I can't actually stand up, well not straight anyway, I feel I will snap across my abdomen. Pause. I have some morphine to help me with the next step. Annette guides me to the chair next to the bed, it's one of those old person chairs, like you see in homes, with a white quilted pad on the seat that looks like an incontinence pad. Everything is so difficult as I have so many tubes and wires and equipment that has to be carefully moved when I take a step.

It is an achievement. This getting up, this sitting in a chair. It must be Wednesday now, my surgery was on Monday. I feel terrible. Do I still want the morphine, they ask me. I am nervous to do without it. They say they will give me oral painkillers instead. I have my last 'hit' of 'go-go' juice, as they call it, and then agree. It will be one less thing to have attached to me. They bring me a little plastic cup with a tasteless clear liquid. They call it Oromorph. It's morphine. And then I am alone.

And then I start crying, sobbing in the chair, filling up one of those grey cardboard dishes with crumpled tissues, messing up my tidy table. I don't care. A nurse comes to change my sheets, I think she feels sorry for me and gets me a bowl of water so I can wash myself. I wipe my flannel over my face and down my arms, it's all I can do. Every movement is so difficult. Lunch arrives. What is it? Some more white mush but I think it is cauliflower cheese.

Hours seem to pass and I am still sobbing. I don't know how long I am here. And then a nurse comes in.

'I don't feel well,' I say. I am too hot, I ache, I can't stop crying.

'Time to go back to bed,' says the kindly nurse.

Hours pass with obs and nothing. I am so tired. Ronnie visits, cuts up banana into the hospital bowl of tinned fruit and feeds it to me. While he is there Ken Graham comes again, says I will feel a hundred times better tomorrow. I don't believe him, actually.

That night my intravenous drip starts to leak, the vein has been in constant use for three days and the cannula now needs to be moved to a new vein. There is mixture of blood and intravenous fluid on the sheets, I don't know what it is, antibiotic maybe. A doctor is sent for and puts a new drip in. Then I have to get out of bed because the sheets are damp. I ask if I can use the commode, I so want a poo, but nothing happens. They offer to remove my catheter. Yes. That is much more comfortable. 'But it does mean you'll have to get out of bed to go to the toilet,' they warn me. Yes, I am starting to get mobile again. I put my ear plugs in and sleep. Proper sleep. I barely move when the nurses come in and the obs are done.

In the morning I wake, realising I have slept well. Time for the commode. I desperately want a poo and they have given me a laxative. The nurses leave me alone. It is a busy time on the ward this time of morning. They have a staff change-over and they get ready for the doctors' rounds. Breakfast is done, medications are given. People keep knocking on my door, so how on earth can I have a poo? I am sitting on the commode wearing a large piece of cotton wadding clutched over my stomach and breasts, with a hospital gown on top of it, not really covering me at all. And it is so hot in here. I am sweating with the exertion of trying to poo, I am very constipated. In fact it is the most constipated I have ever been and it is extremely uncomfortable. It is the combination of morphine and anaesthetic apparently.

I can hear the nurse talking to the doctor outside my door, yes all is well, my drains are out, and then something I can't hear, and then, 'The only problem is she hasn't had a bowel movement.'

God. I'm trying, I nearly shout out.

'I think she's on the commode now,' the nurse says. I look over my shoulder and see a movement behind the small narrow window in the door, the glass is covered with a privacy film, but there is a small clear bit at roughly eye level. The nurse has gone on tiptoes and looked in at me on the commode.

'Yes she is.'

I feel like a caged beast. This is so frustrating, I will never be able to use the commode if I am watched. So I decide I must go on a toilet. I call the nurse and she puts the lid on the commode, how handy, it doubles as a wheelchair. She gets my wash bag, towel and picks out some pyjamas, asking me which ones I want, and suggests I have a wash as well. Then she wheels me down the corridor, past the ward desk, and into my own private disabled bathroom, and locks me in. Thank you. Finally. Privacy. Even though there is noise in the corridor, the noise of morning, the bustle of the ward. I am safe from it. I throw my gown on the floor and relax. I cry out in relief when I have my poo, which is enormous by the way.

Clinging on to the grab rails I move to the sink. I wash my face and under my arms. I fill the sink and wonder if I would be too ambitious to wash my hair. I can't use my right arm, the arm on the surgery side, so I do my best with my left hand, even though the port in the vein catches on the wadding, which I have still clutched to me, to keep me warm. I struggle, very slowly, into my purple camisole and purple pyjama bottoms. I have also got the purple and pink stripey silk loose jacket; it's evening wear really, but I thought it would look glamorous. I put it on and I feel more myself. I sit on the toilet while I dry my hair with the towel and brush it. I am exhausted.

I pull the orange cord, something I have never done in a hospital bathroom. I have to admit that I need help to get back to bed and I find it difficult. The same nurse who brought me here opens the door. 'A new woman!' she says, seeing me sitting there, a vision in purple silk. Well, I suppose so, it's all relative after all. And I walk back to my room. Very slowly, gripping the rail along the wall and then, I feel I am giving in, I take the nurse's arm.

❧

Annette comes and we do more exercises. I say 'exercises' but I mean I lift my arm above my head, that sort of thing. Annette mentions going home. What? She nods.

I don't think I am anywhere near ready to go home. Am I? But then one of my surgeons, Rowan, comes to see me and says, 'How do you feel about going home tomorrow?' Er. OK then. That seems quick.

I sit on the edge of the bed. I don't want to get back in, that's what sick people do, stay in bed. I'm not sick. I'm going home. I get some coins from my locker and very slowly make my way out again past the ward desk to the payphone. I ring Ronnie and tell him I'm coming home tomorrow. He's delighted. I'm still not sure I'm ready.

❧

Back in my room I have another visitor. It is a young woman, Gina, from the prosthetics department. She says her colleague came earlier in the week but I was not well enough to see her. She has a box with her which she opens. It is full of silicone nipples in plastic bags. She says the nipple cast procedure is quite messy so it would be difficult to do it in bed. Or I would have to go to the lab which is downstairs.

'So,' she says, 'I thought, we could find one here which is suitable and I'll make a copy.'

'No,' I say, 'you don't understand. I don't want someone else's nipple. I want mine.' I had so wanted this when I saw the silicone nipples, now I feel at the final hurdle it's slipping out of my grasp. Gina can see I am serious.

'But are you OK to come downstairs?' She looks worryingly at my ganje, the dressing is under my purple camisole, and it looks as though I am bandaged up.

I don't know. But I am so determined. I don't care if I have to walk down the stairs one at a time clinging onto the banister. I will do this.

'Let's see then,' I say.

Slowly we go down two flights of stairs. Yes I am clinging onto the banister. I feel triumphant when we finally get to the lab and there is a chair for me to sit on. Gina gets various things out of the fridge and then, using some green stuff in a tube, covers my nipple. When this has set she removes it, a nipple cast. Then she mixes up silicone and adds various powders, patiently matching up the colour of my nipple. Several colours actually. Then she puts it all in the fridge, with my name on it, and takes me back to the ward.

I sleep again, exhausted by an active morning. I sleep through lunch, which I eat later. I have moved on from the white mush and am having tuna salad. Outside, through the open window I can hear a blackbird singing. I have missed the outside. Ronnie visits me with ice cream in a flask which we share with a chocolate flake. It tastes exotic compared to what I have been eating. Then I spend the afternoon with Monty Don, visiting the gardens of the world on DVD, using the portable DVD player Ronnie has carefully unpacked from my locker for me.

That evening when Ronnie visits me for the last time, Ken Graham and Rowan come to see me. Ken stands at the end of the bed, his shirt sleeves rolled up, his tie tucked into his shirt. He always wears it like this, he bends down a lot to look at patients and this keeps it out of the way. He is very confident about my operation, says that the healing is going well. I know there is still a very tiny possibility that the flap could fail now, but Ken reassures me. I compliment him on his bedside manner. He is genuinely touched.

'I knew you would be OK,' he says. 'I knew when I saw you in the recovery room, you were smiling. I said to the nurses, "I want some of what you have given to her because she's still smiling after *that* operation." '

But, I say to him, there is a hole kicked in my life that's so big I can't see the edge, and I still can't. I am referring to breast cancer. What can this dignified unassuming man say to me? He nods. He looks at me with something deep, I'm not sure what. But it's not pity, it's something else. It's care. He wants everything to be alright for me. He really does.

While I am at this hospital I meet so many people who care. Who want to make this better. That I will have this hole mended, filled in, that my life will be mine again. Yes, I would like that. A lot.

I feel there is finally a chance that it could happen. All these people doing their jobs. It feels like a miracle to me.

I do feel reassured by Ken Graham, he is so confident that this surgery has been a success, but that night before I get into bed I plug in the doppler to the machine and switch it on. The comforting reassuring noise of the gushing pumping of blood in the perforator. It has a rhythm of its own. *Ppussh. Ppussh.* Forceful. Determined. Alive. I wanted to reassure myself, wanted to hear it. Proof that it has worked. That this will all be worth it. It will. My last night here.

The next day, the day I leave, I feel well. I have a shower this morning and look at myself in the mirror. A lot of fresh wounds. Really a lot. And my new breast, well it looked good when I was lying down and I couldn't see it all, now I see that it's smaller and higher than my other breast. A brief tang of disappointment. But I know that it will drop and change. It is very early days.

Alison, my breast reconstruction nurse, comes to see me.

'Is this a good result?' I ask her. 'Really?'

'Yes,' she says, 'it is.'

My doubt is kicking in.

'Really?' I ask.

I am not dressed yet, and have brought a couple of soft bras with me. Should I put one on I ask her. Yes, she says Mr Graham likes you to wear a bra. She suggests one and helps me put the bra on.

'Look in the mirror,' she says.

I do. I have two breasts, they are practically the same size. The bra, even though it is soft, has lifted my 'old' breast. They look nearly even.

Later Alison told me that when she saw my face, she knew I was happy. Yes, it's a breast then.

Ronnie comes to collect me after lunch and packs up my belongings. I put my make-up on. A porter comes with a wheelchair to take me to the main door, Ronnie goes ahead of me to get the car and brings it there to meet me. I am looking well with my make-up on. I feel I need to tell the porter that I have just had a ten-hour operation, that's why I need the wheelchair. As we go along the corridors it is a strange feeling. A breeze. The feel of the outside. Fresh air.

Ronnie has the car as near as he can get it to the main entrance and is coming through the main doors of the hospital. I go home to start my new life with two breasts. It is a good feeling.

CHAPTER 18

Happiness

pring is turning into summer. We are having the most lovely sunny weather. Ronnie buys me a reclining sun lounger which he gets out each morning and sets up in the back yard with a blanket and my cushions off the chaise longue. My outdoor version of it. I am unable to do very much at all. But also, I don't want to. I just want to rest and heal.

Emergency shopping. Two days after getting back home and we do a mercy dash to M&S, well it was hardly a 'dash' actually. Ronnie drops me off at the door and then went to park the car and came to find me amongst the underwear. Because the dash was to buy big knickers. I had thought that my life would be absent from them forever, as I had previously been a thong wearer. But the abdominal scar being so 'fresh' needs some gentle support and softness, and my lacy numbers just aren't doing that. So I have to buy some knickers that I would not normally consider. Plain, black, cotton, big knickers.

I live in my pyjamas, or lounge-wear as I prefer to call the collection of soft trousers and floaty tops I have selected for day wear. I have tried to get dressed, but nothing is comfortable, especially around the waist, with the big wound. So, we have another shopping trip and I buy a long jersey dress, thin straps, black with a big exotic green and orange flower pattern. The woman on the till asks me where I am going, it is obviously a holiday dress. I don't tell her I'm planning on mostly staying in the back yard for now.

After surgery the wounds were covered with a thin adhesive tape, which formed a scabby covering. In the shower I have gradually been trying to clean up my wounds, gradually losing bits of sticky stuff, tape, scab, gunk, and it's all starting to reveal itself as pink soft new skin. I peeled some tape from my cleavage and saw a red line pointing away from the new breast. It took me a while to realise that it is the end of my mastectomy scar, I had forgotten already that I had one.

It is only two weeks since surgery and I could not imagine I'd feel so well. So able and excited about the future. For me, this surgery has been absolutely necessary for me to leave breast cancer behind. In just two weeks I have started to forget. I look in the mirror now. It is much better, even with the new wounds and tape. Much better.

But really I did not know what to expect, how I would feel. Getting very, very tired. Napping a lot. I learn how to properly rest.

Back at dressings clinic and I have the surgery tape completely removed by a very proficient nurse, as well as the doppler, the microphone. So I no longer look like the bionic woman with the wire hanging out of my new breast. It looks smaller than my other breast, but it is the same curve. They have done a good job, my three surgeons. And I am given my nipples, yes they make me two, one is a spare. They come with a little pot of white glue. They are very realistic, I am excited. Something good. At last.

❧

I am at the allotment today with Bren. He is finishing the new deck, putting in all the final screws. I am being 'the Queen of Sheba' - at least that's what he calls me as I sit on my sun lounger that Ronnie has carried here for me. It is five weeks now since surgery, and I am still sore, it is difficult to move at any speed or over any distance. And bending is uncomfortable. My abdominal cut is nearly healed up, and is starting to form a good neat scar.

But being here, seeing all the weeds that have appeared during my absence, I find that a bit frustrating. I'm not able to do anything, to pull up a single weed. But equally I am also astonished that, even though I can see a lot of weeds, there are some real star performers that are putting on a good fight with the weeds. Geranium 'Anne Folkard', a deep pink free-flowering geranium that is keeping its flower heads well above the competition, and smothering them very effectively. Other geraniums too, 'Johnson's Blue' of course, so very prolific, but also 'Splish Splash' making a minor entrance, lilac flowers streaked with white. And various tall grasses, the stripey miscanthus and green and white phalaris, doing a good job of looking stately. Spires of yellow sisyrinchium, which I always thought of as a bit dull, are looking great now, peeking up through the lush growth. The pulcherrium has produced the most flower spikes this year, nearly five feet tall waving up gracefully, the various pink bells on long arching stems. Angel's fishing rods, their common name, seems appropriately apt.

And everywhere there is nigella, one of my favourites, blue star flowers everywhere and the delicate frondy foliage. The nasturtiums have not yet got fully going, but some are starting to meander out of the borders and onto the paths. And the sweet peas are doing OK, not their best year, but nevertheless I picked enough today to bring a small mixed bunch home, purple, red, white, maroon.

We who garden are lucky, there is always next year. Next year will be better, next year I will plant different plants, sow more seeds. Next year I will spend more time tending my garden. The possibility of next year, another chance to make my garden how I want it.

❧

I buy a dress form on the internet, an adjustable dummy of a female body from the hips to neck with shoulders but no arms. They are used for dressmaking, to make clothes and also to make alterations on clothes, something that's difficult to do on yourself. It's something I've always fancied but never got round to buying. Using a soft bra I pad the breast shapes to match my own, different sizes, using the foam out of the foam softie false breast. I make myself linen and silk long dresses, clothes that are easy to wear over my stomach scar, and that are feminine.

Even though my new breast is slightly firmer and higher than my existing breast I am still thrilled every time I look in the mirror. The silicone nipple Gina cast from my other nipple is amazing.

I realise now that I have found the mastectomy and the loss of my body image sharply painful. Now that I have something back I can admit that. And, also with hindsight, I can see that I enjoyed, in a way, the waiting, from knowing I had decided to getting my date was nearly six months. And in those six months I chose not to work, let Ronnie support us both, we went on holiday to Mull and Iona, I did the bee keeping course, and took time to get fit again after all my medical interventions, to do things I enjoyed. It was time to withdraw, retreat and reflect. It left me in good shape for the surgery.

I also realise that I am lucky. I am lucky that recon was an option for me, if I chose to have it, that my prognosis was such that I was able to do this. I am pragmatic enough to know that breast cancer may not be out of my life forever, although I hope it is. But it is enough for now, to feel so good, at last.

Some days I am impatient now, I want a bath, not a shower, I want to go swimming, to get really physically active again, to go dragon boating. That will come. There is time for all of that.

I continue with my Iscador injections, but I no longer have fat on my stomach for this. So I now use the top of my thigh, alternating left and right. It's become normal for me, just part of my routine, the glass vials and the syringes.

Lying here earlier waking from a nap. My left arm across my chest, my breast moving up and down as I breathe. For a moment I have to think which breast it is I lost, because it feels so natural for them to be both there. Part of me, fully already, only six weeks post-surgery.

⁂

Ronnie has taken photographs of me all throughout the breast cancer journey, and continued to after this latest surgery. Now that my new breast is becoming more and more like my own, as it settles, I want a record of this, this lovely new shape I am becoming.

But what to wear? For the previous photos we've done I haven't worn anything, it's just been me. But now, I feel, what, something like, well I'm not sure. Different? More like me.

I look in my underwear drawer. On the top of course are the big knickers, the knickers that I have been wearing these last few weeks out of necessity. Underneath them, my lace knickers I wore before surgery, and lace thongs too. All too uncomfortable to wear for now. And then there are camisole vests, lots of lovely colours, pink, red, turquoise, purple, some are silk, some have lace details, some are soft viscose. I have tried, really really tried these last two years to have a sense of femininity about my underwear, the underwear that is not bras. But today, they just look like vests.

And in the corner of the drawer, a pink silk bag contains my collection of other underwear, the sort of underwear that should be called lingerie. Inside I find suspenders, stockings, lots of lace. And my red lace bra is there. Gosh.

The only bra I didn't throw out. It's still here. I put it on and look in the mirror. There are almost no words to describe how I feel. Emotional, yes, I hadn't even thought this possible. Me in a red bra, with a cleavage. It is too much. I take it off and put it back, and there is another bra there. A black one. This has been one of my favourite favourite bras for years. It's my Marlies Dekkers bra.

I am instantly returned to the day I bought this bra. We were away in Hebden Bridge in Yorkshire, a small town, very attractive. One of the smaller streets has a collection of independent shops, including a lovely lingerie shop. As we passed I could not help but notice the bra on display in the window, a black bra with lattice cups, unashamedly sexy. It spoke to me. I had to have a bra like that. We went in. I emerged with a different bra, but by the same designer, and a thong. The shop owner was delighted to sell me the items from this new Dutch designer. The next day I went back and bought a black suspender belt as well, in the lattice style. This is lingerie that will make you feel beautiful and seductive, but at the same time powerful and independent.

The thong has left my life, after many years of active service, but the suspender belt and bra are still here. The bra is black, the cups are soft sheer mesh, cut low, with a strap detail along the top of the cups, so that part of the breast skin is revealed. The cups are separated by two black straps and the shoulder straps cross at the back so they go diagonally over your shoulder. It is underwired. Not recommended by the hospital, the underwires, but I think it will be OK if I just try it on for a minute. I slip into it easily, it feels like an old friend. It fits beautifully, the soft fabric accommodating the slightly different breast sizes. My cleavage looks amazing. I am absolutely delighted. I have found what I want to wear for my photograph. I look proud. And I am. To have arrived here.

I book to go on a bra making course in the autumn, so I can learn to make my own soft but sexy bras. Yes, that is how positive I feel.

❧

June melts into July and I am still resting. We are having good weather, sunny, and hot. I spend hours resting in our small, but perfect back yard. A blackbird decides to use the TV aerial on the house behind us as his summer perch. He sings varied delightful staccato tunes. It is a treat.

One evening in July we sit outside in the yard drinking wine. We eat our tea out there and stay there even as it gets dark. The French windows in the back of the house are fully open so the computer plays music for us from the studio.

Ronnie brings a lamp out and puts it in the corner of the yard, and I put out tea lights in clear glass holders which twinkle. Ronnie ceremoniously turns on the fountain. OK, not quite a fountain in a classical garden sense, but it's a pebble pool with a small water feature.

And we sit there, in this magical paradise, happily talking about life, about cancer, and about everything until the early hours of the morning. It is a perfect still warm night. I think that if this were a movie, a film about happiness, then at this point the camera, filming above us would pull back and show our little patch of light, this suburban paradise in a dark terraced street; and pull back further over the rooftops and you would still be able to see our candles twinkling. And two very happy people.

CHAPTER 19

Hiding

The road to recovery is not a straight road. I have heard cancer referred to as a rollercoaster, as an analogy. And it's true, it is like that. Terrifying, 'I want to get off' one moment, then huge surges of elation when something good happens, followed by troughs of despair. Oh, and waiting in queues for your turn, lots of that. And I seem to be spending too long on the down bits of the rollercoaster.

Two months after my surgery and I feel well enough for a short walk. We pack our day bags with our lunch and drive over to Thurstaston, one of our favourite walks on the shining shore, the Dee estuary. We walk along the cliff top to the beach path, the seed pods of the gorse bushes are popping in the sun, I can hear them. Down the track to the wooden bridge in the valley, the valley that I think of as a New Zealand ravine; not because I have been to New Zealand but it looks like that part of the Lost Gardens of Heligan. It is lush and full of greenery, ferny and mossy. Then down the wooden stairs to the beach.

We sit on the beach on a blanket, the tide has just turned and is going out. We eat our lunch. And then I snooze, enjoying the feel of the sun on my face. Normally, we would continue along the beach and follow this walk another five miles, but today we head back up the wooden stairs to the cliff path and back home. I fall asleep in the car. That was a good day.

And then the rollercoaster does another loop. I would say that the Accident and Emergency department on a Monday evening is probably the last place most people would want to find themselves. And yet here I am, in the Royal Liverpool hospital. Having spent the whole weekend in pain, in bed, with gastroenteritis. Vomiting and diarrhoea for over 48 hours. I am too sick now for the GPs, my local doctors, to treat me and I have been sent here.

I am so familiar, too familiar I think, with this environment. The waiting, the lack of privacy, the nurses rushing about. But finally I am seen by a doctor. At last, after being here for five hours, I have an x-ray, and then get an intravenous pain killer and a saline drip. I am dehydrated from the vomiting and diarrhoea. They send me home when the drip is done, and I slide back into bed at 2 am while Ronnie boils water for me to drink when it has cooled.

How I dislike being a patient.

I feel sorry for myself. It's that skin peeled off sort of feeling. I used to have a life. I used to have things to do, that had meaning, be part of things. I spend too much time being a patient now, there is not enough time for me.

When I have recovered from this, we go to John Lewis and buy new orange towels for the bathroom. Feels like the most exciting thing I've done for months.

❧

I see Ken Graham for my follow-up from surgery. I tell him my result has exceeded my expectations. Because that is true. He is delighted. I know I am a work in progress, but I don't feel half-done, I feel much more than that. He says he is sorry to hear about the gastroenteritis, and wonders if the hefty doses of antibiotics post-surgery might have caused this. He apologises anyway.

I swim every week. Four widths. A full length would be impossible, even though I used to easily do 20. But it is progress.

I am standing outside the sauna looking at the pool. I have to stop myself crying, it feels, well, it feels normal. And how I hate that word, *normal*, who wants to be normal? I know I don't. But what I mean is that my life felt 'normal' again. Swimming, no false breast, like before. Before. Before. A word I will always use to mean before breast cancer.

And the first few times I go to the pool I have a forgetting feeling when I look in my bag. The feeling of not having my Been-a-Boob with me.

It was with great glee that I cut out the breast pockets in both my swimming costumes. It felt like a sort of triumph really. Now, after I have been swimming, I take my swimmie off and hang it up outside the shower. There is no heavy object in the breast pocket, distorting it, pulling it down out of shape. I would previously observe it, think it odd-looking, a garment containing a breast shape lump, hanging strangely on the hook. But I preferred it like that, that the false breast was part of the garment, it could never be part of me. I never felt like I owned it.

The deep deep joy of getting undressed in the shower, and not feeling that cringing sense of fear, fear not of my appearance, but of frightening children or shocking someone with my one-breastedness. A real sense of recovery. Recovery of self.

❧

Sometimes, when I think about the impact breast cancer had on my life I think about 'famous' women who had breast cancer. Still alive, Carly Simon, Jenni Murray, Kylie Minogue, Barbara Ehrenreich. And then I think about those who died, Linda McCartney, Dina Rabinovitch, Audre Lorde, Dusty Springfield. Died of breast cancer. And there will be more to follow, I know that.

The possibility of me dying of breast cancer was, well still is, a reality. Although what I write here is about recovery, the reality is that I am choosing to find recovery in what I have done. The physical stuff, the breast reconstruction surgeries, they do make me feel better. *Better* is an understatement. I have tried to express how deeply psychologically healing I have personally found this process. For me, yes just for me, I can only speak of myself. But, in fact, I am not safe forever, the hanging-over dread of recurrence is always around.

And I am exposed to the reality of breast cancer. Of what dying from breast cancer is really like. Not just from the knowledge that women *do* die, but from real experiences. I use an internet forum, for breast cancer women only, and not everyone is in the life after breast cancer bit. The bit that I am in now, the good bit, where I am recovering my sense of self, emotionally and physically, even if it turns out to be temporary. No, there are other women who have been dealt a much worse hand. They are living with secondary breast cancer. That dread word, secondaries. The 'mets' - metastasis - the spread of this disease. The metastasizing into other tumours, other cancer in other parts of the body. Bones, often; brain, liver and lungs as well. And skin too. It is all so shit.

There is a woman who posts on the forum who has a regional recurrence in her chest, several years after her mastectomy and chemotherapy. Skin mets, but growing into large tumours all over her chest wall, externally weeping and smelly, and internally pressing on various nerves, causing pain and immobility. Her arm is swollen with lymphoedema, another side effect of removing lymph nodes from the armpit, fluid is retained, so the arm and shoulder become swollen and painful. She knows she is dying.

She is very direct. I like her straightforward style of expression. She says she didn't know how difficult or uncomfortable she would be. And no we don't talk about that. No, because it's not pleasant. Pleasant? Is that a word to use about death?

Of course it's all very well for me to say I have looked at death, accepted it. Have I? I mean really? Do I hope, as maybe we all hope, that death will be swift, painless, easy? That we will be ready for it. Know that our life on earth is done. Or do we face the possibility of illness gradually reducing us to a painful mortal, suffering our last days, weeks or months on earth, reliant on others to care for us, feed us, keep us pain free? Is that fear worse than the fear of dying?

Well, I like this woman's way of talking about the disease. I find it refreshing. To be challenged and to think about these possibilities, the reality of dying. Of what it could *really* be like. For me, but for any woman who has a breast cancer diagnosis. Or has yet to have one. The refreshing woman acerbically suggests they should photograph her naked next to a smiling pink t-shirt wearing 'survivor'. Which one is the one we accept as the woman who had a breast cancer diagnosis?

Because you see, mostly I think we are hiding from the truth. By 'we' I mean society. It's like every media message we are given about breast cancer is a 'good' one. It's positive, this disease is treatable. We're still smiling, us women. We're not angry, oh no, of course not, that would be so unfeminine wouldn't it? Anger? No.

We're putting up some sort of front about it, much like, I feel, we hide behind the false breast. We cover it up, we say it's OK, when it isn't OK at all.

I mean, I know this has been said before, by Dina Rabinovitch, but if breast cancer, or something as threatening and disfiguring was happening to men, in these numbers, I think more would be being done to find the cause. This attack on our femininity, our breasts, our ovaries, our uteruses, are all seen as things that can be dispensed with.

And the numbers that Dina was talking about were, at that time, one in nine. One in nine women. Now, the current statistic for a woman's risk of breast cancer is one in eight in the USA and one in nine in the UK. That's lifetime risk over 85 years. And I actually think that's very high, especially given that 60 years ago the statistic was 'only' one in 20.[19]

But I have seen some cancer charities say that the one in eight figure is misleading, because it is lifetime risk, and breast cancer incidence increases sharply after age 70, which makes the figure seem higher. So, they say, a more 'realistic' statistic would be one in ten.

So a cancer charity is trying to dumb down the statistics. What's that all about? One in ten is still too many.

And of course a cure is all very well, but what about some real research into preventing this happening in the first place?

What happens to us, the women, in terms of breast cancer is, I feel, marginalised, of less importance than if it happened to men. But also I think that we don't make things harder, we don't challenge. We are for the most part, compliant. We accept breast cancer and its treatments. We deal with it, and we deal with it well. As Audre Lorde said, we are not a horde of raging angry women descending on government asking them to start researching the causes of breast cancer.[20]

But we should be.

Instead we are donning pink t-shirts to support our sisters, raising money for the cancer charities, who search for cures, more drugs. Yes I can see a cure is attractive once you have breast cancer, but what about prevention? Have we blinkered ourselves with pink-tinted glasses here? Pink, sickly pink, the universal colour of hope. Where wearing pink and the fluffy pink campaigns around breast cancer are the norm. The 'sugar-coating of disease', as Barbara Ehrenreich calls it.

How come breast cancer has risen to this status? To an almost glamorous level? Just how did breast cancer get to be so glamorous? I get sick of seeing all these images of smiling women proving that we can 'beat' breast cancer. That we can be 'survivors'. And I hate it. I do not want to be branded by breast cancer and wear pink t-shirts.

Women smiling through lost breasts, devastating effects of drugs and chemotherapy, women losing their most feminine identifiers, breasts and ovaries. But they are still smiling. They are survivors, they have fought, and beaten cancer. How I hate that terminology. The fighting and battling. These words we use for war.

And these women, these smiling women, they seem to say 'It's OK, because I have survived. So when it's your turn....' And here is the great unsaid - that your turn will come, because just look at the statistics - 'When it's your turn it will be OK,' these smiling women reassure you.

It is profoundly not OK at all.

I am hoovering today. That is progress. I do upstairs and Ronnie does downstairs. After I have finished I need to sit down, to rest. I am aching in my back, my shoulders, my arms. I tire so easily even though I am three months post-surgery, the sort of time when I was hoping to feel better again.

So as I am hoovering I am thinking about another woman on the internet forum. She wrote a thread titled: 'Breast cancer was the best thing that happened to me.' At first I think that this is maybe a cynical post. But it's not, it's serious.

She says that she knows that some people may be upset by these words. But she is expressing that her experience of breast cancer made her be her real self, her true self. That it changed her outlook on life. And I am glad for her, I am. But really, did it have to take breast cancer to do this? Don't women have enough opportunities to find their real selves? Isn't that what feminism was all about?

And I want to reply to this post, but I find I can't do it without sounding too angry. Or without sounding like, 'My breast cancer experience was worse than yours.' That's not what I mean. I remember another woman, a breast cancer patient, saying to me that she felt that she got off lightly, she 'only' had a lumpectomy, not mastectomy, and 'only' had tamoxifen, not chemotherapy. My response was, 'Well, none of us gets off lightly.' Because that's true. The sword of uncertainty that hovers has entered your life, and it will never leave.

To me, that uncertainty, plus all the other stuff of breast cancer, is definitely not the 'best thing' that happened to me. That would imply that I enjoyed it, that I would like it to happen again, or that someone else would enjoy it. When I first heard the expression 'cancer is a gift' I was gobsmacked. I mean. Seriously. A *gift*. What would you think of the person who gave you a gift like that? Valuing life more *is* a good thing, of course it is, but cancer is not a gift.

Because if you go through a challenging adverse situation, say breast cancer, and you come through feeling good about yourself, then the good bit is *you*, not the situation, that is the cancer. I do not think *good* is a word for cancer, neither is evil, it's just a disease. The effect it has can be devastating, can end in death. But in other cases the person may triumph, come through changed or more authentic, true to themselves. But it is the person who did that, not the cancer.

So, I think if we start calling cancer 'good' or the 'best thing' we run the risk of overlooking the damage that it can, and does, do. And if we start to view cancer as a 'good' thing, then we'll start to accept it. And if we accept it, then we'll never bother looking at the causes of cancer, to prevent the disease in the first place.

There are very clear arguments now about the cause of breast cancer which point to suspicions about environmental carcinogens present everywhere but invisible to us, and chemical carcinogens in the products we use all the time. We frequently hear about genetic links, but in fact there are maybe as few as 5% of breast cancers, and at most 10%, caused by a faulty gene.[16] So further research in genetics will help us identify women who are at risk. And what do we do then?

Then we tell young women, women in their 30s – in families where the faulty gene exists – that they are at high risk of breast cancer and possibly ovarian cancer. And they have to make excruciating decisions about prophylactic double mastectomies and oophorectomies.

And that still leaves about 90% of breast cancer with no obvious cause?

Martin J Walker wrote an article in 2000 called 'Your Money and Your Life' about the cancer industry.[21] He points out that the cancer establishment avoid 'awkward questions about what causes the disease', and that 'the motivation and funding for preventative cancer research has all but dried up.'

Barbara Ehrenreich points out that for the breast cancer movement to align ourselves with these suspicions about environment would link us with anti-corporate social movements. And it appears that the pink brigade are not prepared, or do not want to do that.

Is it somehow our duty to smile and show our sisters that it's not really that bad after all? To give them 'hope'.

Hope? What's that all about? Hoping you don't die after all?

I always wondered why those fields of daffodils are called 'Fields of Hope'. I mean, what does that mean, hope? And now that I have been a cancer patient I can quite categorically say that I think it's something dreamt up to put a veneer on cancer. I mean, what could be 'nicer' than a field of golden daffodils, bursting out in the beginning of spring, that lovely exciting new time of the year. And, by the way, the time of year I was diagnosed with breast cancer. What could there be not to like about that? Nothing, it's lovely, perfectly lovely. So why taint it with cancer?

I mean, we use these 'nice' symbols, the daffodils, the pink-ness, and you know - there's really not that much nice about cancer.

Breast cancer. And here's the reality. It's either unpleasant treatment for primary cancer, or prevention of recurrence, or it's the symptoms of the secondaries, and managing the pain of that. And dying.

And I can't think of anything good about it.

part **four**
Coming down the mountain

June 2010 - My Marlies Dekkers bra. Six weeks after DIEP surgery.
'I want a record of this, this lovely new shape I am becoming.'

CHAPTER 20

Salvage

notice a small lump in my abdomen, above my scar. It's hard to the touch. I ring the hospital, it's only a couple of weeks since I saw Ken Graham, but they arrange for me to be seen again. I am already in the hospital in a few days for my appointment at the scar management clinic, so Ken will come and see me then.

Am I worried? I suppose, yes, I am. I don't believe that somehow breast cancer has spread to my stomach, I've never heard of that anyway. But it's just that anything now has the potential to be *sinister*. And I don't like that. I am pissed off. Had enough of resting, of hospitals, of worrying, of ringing up for advice. I hate breast cancer with a vengeance.

So Ken is summoned whilst I am in the prosthetics room, and he appears at the door, his usual calm dignified self.

'Didn't expect to see you again so soon,' I say.

He smiles. His lovely gap-toothed smile. He says he needs to examine me so could they find a gown for me. He then leaves the room while I get changed. Ken comes back in, knocking on the door first, and does a very thorough slow examination of the lump. First with me standing up and then with me lying down. He doesn't say anything. I hate that, when the room is dead quiet with a doctor examining you. Always feels ominous.

Ken Graham ends his examination and then explains to me the two possibilities. One is a collection of fluid, the other is a weakness in the muscle, both would cause a bulge and both feel the same. The collection of fluid seems unlikely, it is very unusual for that to happen months after surgery, so if I were making a bet here, I think Ken thinks it's the muscle weakness. And that means more abdominal surgery. Ken very gently says, 'If it is that, then I will repair it.' And he makes a sewing motion with his hand. So, the bottom line is he doesn't know which one it is.

And the only way to tell is to have a scan. Ken fills in the form for an ultrasound request and I go away to wait for an appointment. But not that day, of course, no it will be in a week or so.

I am so fed up. Tired, so tired of the subject of breast cancer. Blame myself. I didn't have to do this surgery, and now I have a complication. This surgery complication, the investigations to find out. Two miserable weekends pass while I wait, yet again, for 'investigations'.

The consultant radiologist receives the ultrasound request but decides that a CT scan would be better, and so I am back in the big white machine. I have drunk two pints of water this morning, and I am given another jugful to drink.

In the machine room I am quickly ushered in and told to lie down. A young nurse approaches me and from behind my head says, 'When was your last period?' I had forgotten this, this checking that you are not pregnant when you have abdominal scanning. My answer? I have said, 'Two years ago.' I have said, 'I have no ovaries.' They always look surprised. And then they ask you to sign a form, remember I am lying on my back at this point. A piece of paper with nothing to lean on and a biro. Have you tried writing upside-down with a biro? Why don't they make this part of the procedure earlier, like when you arrive?

There is another woman now in the machine room, it is the same woman who did my CT scan before the DIEP. I recognise her and show her my surgery. I tell her how pleased I am. She is glad, happy for me that it worked out well. Then she disappears into the room where the staff avoid exposure to the x-rays.

Whirr, click. The disembodied voice telling me to breathe in and hold. And the scan is done, it's all over pretty quickly and off I go.

The next day I get the result by phone. It is a collection of fluid and I go back to the hospital to have it drained. This time Ken is in theatre so I see Mr Koshy, who helped on my operation. I have not seen him since before theatre back in May, four months ago, and I am very happy to show him my DIEP result. He is impressed and wants to send me to medical photography to record it.

But first the fluid collection needs to be dealt with. I lie on the bed and a very large needle attached to a large syringe is inserted through my abdominal scar and the fluid is drained off. This is done in several places across my stomach. It is such a relief when it is done, it feels so comfortable now. Had been feeling like I'd been walking round with a grapefruit in my stomach.

It is called an abdominal seroma. A pocket of serous fluid that collects after surgery. Sometimes they return. Hope mine doesn't.

I have done with the big white machines, the displays of neon green numbers that whir round and round. Needles and gowns. Enough.

We are in Mull again. Driving up north as we slip easily away from Glasgow and drive along the shores of Loch Lomond I am reminded how much I like this north adventure. It's a grey day but the water shines like silver and I can feel the tension in my chest melting. It is September now, and I have not been away for six months, since before my big surgery in May. Six months of surgery, rest, gastroenteritis, hospital, it seems to have not let up and was far more difficult than I thought it would be. My abdominal seroma did return within 24 hours, I ring the hospital and the nurse says to forget about it and enjoy my holiday.

The relief to be away. I barely have the energy to think about my next surgery which is provisionally planned for December, just three months away. I breathe easier here than I have done for months. I was so tense, anxious about my surgery. Letting go of that sensation is hard. Hard to believe that I am nearly through. And it is a good feeling.

The feeling that this will end. And all shall be well.

In Calgary Bay, the same place we stayed in March, we walk down to the beach. It is windy. The tide almost in, a high 'spring' tide. I love this place. Back in the loft we sleep deep and long. It is so quiet here. Even though the rain hammers on the window in brief squalls, but it is not city noise.

We walk on Mull. Langamull beach, Ulva, Dun Ara, Mornish Head. It is wild and deserted. We see eagles again. It is exactly what we need. I have my birthday here. Forty-six.

One day we only go for a short walk to the beach. It is stormy, the sand blowing across the beach, forming small temporary piles of sand covering clumps of seaweed. We go back home and read. I have my seaweed book, learn the name of the wracks and the big brown seaweeds. Laminaria, the big fronds you see on the beaches up here.

After a week in Mull we travel to Iona. We leave the car at Fionnaphort on Mull, and get the ferry across, the short crossing, but stepping onto a different island. We stay in a hostel at the far end of the island. We can walk down to the beach from the back door. The beach here is covered in red and pink seaweed. And the stones. I gasp when we get onto the beach. So beautiful. So many different colours, they look like jewels.

I sleep well. Dream of floating myself in baths of seaweed.

Today we walked across the whole island. Across the machir, and we walk again along the beautifully named 'Bay at the Back of the Ocean', from here the next land would be America. I grab some of the newly named seaweed, throwing it around in the wind.

We hunker in the sand dunes for our lunch and carry on to the south of the island, to St Columba's Bay. All big pebbles here, smooth and rounded, a thousand shades of grey, with other colours, a dull green, reds and orange. A wild sea. I sketch, and Ronnie films.

Time seems to pass slowly here. We have this day, this precious day, where time feels like elastic and it stretches to fill the feeling we have. And we are at peace. We only stay two nights here, but it is enough. We are ready to go home now. We have had the experience of 'away' and it has been good.

When we leave, it is a strange sensation stepping off the Iona ferry. It feels like we're re-entering civilisation, but it's in fact the far end of Mull, which is pretty remote by any standards.

I feel more like myself again. I don't feel like a breast cancer patient. I finally feel I am coming into my safe harbour.

R࿐ʘ

Back in Liverpool and I am feeling well. Yes, we walked most days while we were in Scotland. Had loads of time outside and we are rested.

The autumn has arrived. I am at the hospital every two weeks having my abdominal seroma drained. Very unusual I keep being told.

I am in a transitional place, sometimes in the hospital, but also in other-land. Yes, the space that is life after breast cancer.

I sometimes feel I am picking about in the debris. Debris that was my life, what's left of it, trying to salvage the good bits, or the bits I want.

I mean, all this treatment and the effect breast cancer has had on my life, and Ronnie's, on our lives. And yet, I still say, 'I'm lucky.' Because I am lucky. And that seems strange really, to go through all this, and for this to be the 'better' option. But it is.

In between hospital visits I go to Nottingham for the first day of my two-day bra making course, this one is the basic day. I will learn how to make a basic underwired bra. A further second day follows with more advanced techniques.

I have day trips to Delamere Forest with Bren and we hire mountain bikes and hunt for mushrooms. Cycling up and down hills, through bracken, under beech trees, the golden orange leaves like a carpet, the beech masts crunching under our wheels. Fantastic, exhilarating. My chest burns with exertion, what a great feeling.

I am still swimming. I go back to my yoga class. Then on one of my hospital visits, Ken Graham says they have set a date for my next surgery, at the end of November.

'You are a good man,' I tell him.

I am nearly there.

CHAPTER 21

Emerging

I haven't seen Alison Waghorn, my breast cancer surgeon, for over six months now. My October appointment is moved twice so it is November now and I last saw her in April, before my DIEP. In fact, apart from my visit to A&E for gastroenteritis, I've not been back to this hospital in Liverpool. So, I am looking forward to seeing her, to showing her the result of my surgery.

The nurse in clinic, Julie, is also excited when she sees me. As she shows me into the consultation room, she says, 'Oh Sarah, I was just looking at your file, you've had your DIEP now haven't you?'

'Yes, it's great.'

'Oh, well I haven't seen one before.'

'You're in for a treat then!' I say.

She gets a gown down off the shelf and puts it on the bed. Always unnecessary, I never bother with a gown with Alison. I take my jacket off, and am just about to take my tunic off, when Alison appears. She's laughing.

'Oh come on then, let's see!' she says.

Both Julie and Alison are stood in front of me as I remove my soft bra. I feel like saying 'Ta da!' But I don't need to say anything. Both of them are just staring open-mouthed at my new breast. They genuinely seem lost for words.

'That is the best nipple I've ever seen,' says Alison. She is openly impressed.

She then says, 'Wow, yes, well done Sarah, do you like it?'

Of course it's obvious that I am delighted, that it was all worthwhile.

Julie leaves us and then it is time for the 'proper' consultation. First, an examination. I lie on the bed and Alison carefully and thoroughly checks my left breast, expertly examining me with her hands. She asks, as she always does, if I have felt anything unusual. No. And then I tell her about the small hard lump underneath my reconstructed breast. Phoebe, Ken Graham's current registrar, is confident it is a very small area of fat necrosis, fat that has died and feels hard, but will soften in time. Alison agrees, but says that clinically you can't tell the difference between fat necrosis and tumour, as they both feel hard. So, she wants me to have it checked. I knew she would. She does everything so thoroughly, she's a cancer doctor. So that means ultrasound and needle aspiration. Just how great will that be?

I get dressed and we continue the consultation. I have few questions now, and I feel I have come a long way from the early days with my pages of notes and questions. I am moving away from that.

I tell Alison about my next surgery, now only two weeks away. My left breast will be reduced in size, and lifted slightly, to match my DIEP breast. The breast tissue that is removed will be sent for a biopsy. I am worried now it is actually happening. I hadn't realised until I ask the question, 'What if the tissue was cancerous?'

Alison thinks I should have a mammogram on my left breast before the surgery: 'Just in case,' she says. That it would be sensible. She says that I can come to one of her clinics and have the lump checked at the same time. I know what those clinics are. They are the rapid diagnosis clinics. The same one where I found out I had breast cancer. Horrible.

Alison can see from the look on my face that I am worried now. I wasn't worried before, or at least I have managed to pretend I wasn't worried. She has suggested a clinic appointment over a week away, the day before my surgery, which feels like a long time to wait. We are about to have a short break, a holiday, and I don't want to spoil it by worrying. Then Ronnie tells her I have been losing sleep. I didn't know he noticed me tossing and turning in the night, unable to forget about the hard lump in my breast.

'Right,' she says, 'that's it then, I'll get you in tomorrow. Just give Shirley a ring after eight o'clock tomorrow, and we'll sort it out.'

This is why I like Alison so much. She sorts things out.

Of course, the next morning when I ring Shirley, Alison's secretary, she knows all about this, and has an appointment for me at 1.30 pm.

A cruel trick, an unfair blow, just as you think the end is in sight. Back in the rapid diagnosis clinic. Just going in there triggers memories of diagnosis day, D-day as I always think of it. Why is this all so horribly, horribly, horrible?

Ronnie is working today, so Bren has come with me, although in this clinic the men wait outside so it's pretty much like being on your own anyway. Alison herself came out of her clinic downstairs, and brought me upstairs and through the doors to this clinic. So I am sitting there in a gown, with my clothes in a wire shopping basket. Just like diagnosis day. Although actually, the gown is much better. It is new and a soft blue fabric, but also it is roomy and actually crosses over at the front and ties properly. Perhaps my comments to the PCT, my healthcare provider, did actually change this? Remember on diagnosis day they had old flimsy gowns that barely covered you and I pinned mine closed with a brooch, but most of the women sat there clutching them across their breasts, looking terrified.

Alison strides back up the corridor and says they will do the ultrasound first as they have someone free.

So, here I am back in the ultrasound room, where I was on D-day. I am breathing very shallowly now, and I can taste fear in my mouth. Alison is so nice to me, so caring, she says she is going now but after my tests I will see her, in person, and she will tell me the results later today. She introduces me to the female doctor who is going to do this test and I immediately forget her name.

'OK?' Alison says. I nod, then remember, 'But the vessels?' I say.

'It's OK, she knows all about the vessels.'

The vessels are the blood vessels in my reconstructed breast. They have been carefully and slowly joined by Ken Graham using his expert micro-surgery skills to make sure the new breast has a good blood supply so it will stay alive. If they are damaged by a needle, then it could mean part of the breast would die.

And then I am left with the doctor and a nurse. I lie back on the bed and the doctor puts the probe on my breast. She easily locates the lump, and then begins the tricky business of working out a route to get the long needle into the lump, avoiding the vessels. She stares at the screen for a long time.

The needle is inserted, very slowly, the doctor carefully negotiates a clear path to the lump by looking at what she is doing on the screen. I hadn't looked at the aspiration equipment on diagnosis day, but I do this time. It's a long thin needle attached to a clear thin plastic piping about three feet long, attached to a syringe, which the nurse is holding.

I can barely breathe. It takes forever, putting the needle in.

The nurse is standing next to me, but does not hold my hand, like the nurse on D-day did. This nurse is waiting with the syringe to 'aspirate' when the doctor tells her to. My right hand is above my head, and I make a fist with my left hand, lying alongside my body on the bed. I would rather be anywhere else than here, anything would be better.

There are several attempts to aspirate, but the doctor says little fluid is coming out. Is that good? I don't know. Will they keep trying?

Then she is satisfied she has enough of a sample to send to the lab. As she squirts it out of the syringe into another container she says, in a confident voice, that it looks thick and oily, like fat. Can I breathe again yet?

Mammogram is next. Done very gently and skilfully by a lovely nurse. She asks if I had a skin-sparing mastectomy, that is a mastectomy where the breast tissue is removed but skin and nipple is kept, then reconstruction done immediately. In the dimly lit room she can't have seen the skin coloured Mepiform tape covering my scar across my breast, the special tape to help the scar heal. And she looks again when I tell her that my nipple is made of silicone. It is a huge compliment to my plastics team.

And then the waiting. I sit in the corridor, the waiting area in this clinic. All the women who are there are grim faced. After all, no-one wants to be here. I can hear a woman telling a frightened looking younger woman all about her first diagnosis with breast cancer. I just want to zone out, to disappear through the floor. I get my iPod out and put the headphones in, even though I don't need them to play Patience, the card game. It is mind numbing and I have found it a useful tool for waiting in hospital. I have also brought a flask of peppermint tea, so settle in for the wait.

Time passes. And then I am told I can get dressed. The nurse escorts me through the waiting room, Bren has got bored with waiting and gone down-stairs to the café. I follow the nurse down to the second floor. The nurse has my file clasped to her chest and I feel like grabbing it from her and looking at the results myself. I am shown straight away into a consultation room. She doesn't leave my file in the room with me, and then I wait for Alison.

The door flies open in the usual style. I can tell by Alison's face before she says anything that it is OK. Her lovely smile. She flops down in the seat next to me.

'Fat necrosis,' she says.

Huge relief. It *is* fat necrosis.

'And the mammogram?' I say.

She looks at the file, 'No significant change from last time.'

She looks at me, so tenderly. Then stands up, goes to the door.

'So have a great trip away.' And then she is gone.

A star indeed.

The next week we go away to Bath for a few days, as a pre-surgery treat. We walk right up Lansdown Road and look back down into the valley and all the sandstone buildings. Beautiful. I go to the spa. Twice. I relax. I reflect on the clinic incident. And I realise that last week was actually what 'living with cancer' means. It means the shadow is there, always, even if it hasn't been around for a while. And then, suddenly, all your plans will be disrupted.

Things can change in an instant. I hate that.

It does reinforce the desire to enjoy each day as it comes, because really, yes, really, you don't know what's in the next one. And there is no point worrying about it.

I cannot allow myself to worry about tomorrow, it's simply not possible anymore.

I am preparing for my next surgery, the revisional surgery. The surgery to make my 'old' breast match my 'new' one. But first I am going to Sheffield for the second day of my bra making course, the advanced day. I will learn how to make alterations, to get a perfect fit, to make lace cups, padded bras, a full band bra without wires, the technique I most want to learn.

As the train leaves the station I have an almost childlike sense of glee. This is exciting. For me, at least, it feels so 'normal' to be doing this, and it is a good feeling.

So much of my life has been, by necessity, forced, in that I have appointments to attend. Just yesterday, my pre-op appointment at Whiston. Hours of my life in hospital-land.

The sleeping allotments whizz past my window, still dark now in the morning, the darkling days as the earth turns to a stand still. And I feel some deep, deep peace. Tinged with excitement.

I had not consciously thought I was doing this, making up for the grief of losing my breast, my bras, by making new ones. I couldn't see forward to now, I didn't dare to really. I see that now.

In two days I will be back in theatre. Phew. Ready? Here I go again.

❦

I am back at Whiston this morning for revisional surgery. As instructed I have not eaten since the previous evening and only had a small drink of water when I got up today.

I have been at Whiston many times in the last few months because of my seroma, and I have seen Ken Graham on several occasions as well as his current registrar, Phoebe. But we have not actually discussed *exactly* what the revisional surgery will be.

So, it's eight o'clock in the morning and I am waiting, fully dressed, sat by my hospital bed, to see my surgeons. Phoebe comes to see me first. I like her, she is always wearing absolutely perfect eye make-up. Gorgeous shades of eye liner, gold and green, and she has lovely smiling eyes. Even though today she is going to be in surgery all day, she still has her perfect make-up on.

She has the consent form that Ken Graham has filled out. It says 'liposuction to flank,' but I explain to Phoebe that I thought it was lipofill, not liposuction. At the end of my mastectomy scar, under my arm, there is a flap of skin, a dog ear as they call them. I thought the plan was to fill this in so that it matches the other side.

Phoebe has not been involved in my previous surgery, she is a new registrar, new to me, so she says she will come back with Ken so we can clarify things.

This is the first time I have felt unclear about what is going to happen. I don't like the feeling. And I'm very thirsty.

Ken and Phoebe come back, and Ken starts to explain that they don't fill the dog ear, they actually remove it, and on the other side they do liposuction so that it matches, nice and flat.

He says, 'Women always complain about that bit of the breast, they say they want it out of the way.'

'Don't tell me what women want,' I snap. Ken sighs very deeply, and crouches down in front of me, kneeling on one knee.

My emotions run high at the best of times, but extremely high pre-surgery when I am also hungry and thirsty.

I go on, 'Did I misunderstand something?' I am nearly crying. 'When we talked about this in July I thought you said...' I lean forward, touch his knee, to emphasise what I thought *he* said.

Ken interrupts me, he can see this is a difficult situation.

'OK,' he says, 'look, I need to be in theatre now, so what I will do is change the order of surgery and you will be later on the list, but I will come back and we can have a longer discussion. We will sort this out, and we will do it today, I promise.'

'So can I have a drink of water?'

'No,' they say in unison.

He leaves with Phoebe following him. He is still very dignified.

I go and find Ronnie who is sitting in the day room. He is concerned, can see how upset I am. So I go to the desk on the ward and ask if they will ring Alison, my breast reconstruction nurse, and get her to come and see me. And then I burst into tears. Very gently the ward nurse calms me down, and soon I am sitting in the staff room, with Tina, the other breast reconstruction nurse, who has my file. Tina is back now, after her maternity leave, and Alison has a day off today. It is a very small room, in fact it's more like a cupboard full of files, but it's the only really private space on this ward. Ronnie comes too and we talk about my surgery.

I realise now, a bit late really, that although I did have a list of questions about this surgery, I never asked them, because I was always in clinic, and I kept thinking, 'Oh, I'll ask next time.' Then the last time I was here, I didn't see Ken Graham, so I didn't ask. So I am confused now. But actually when we talk about it, I realise that liposuction does make sense and will give a better cosmetic result, it's just not what I was expecting.

Also I try and explain that I like the droop of my breast, that I am worried that I will have my breast lifted too much, that it won't look like how I want it, rather how a surgeon might think a woman wants it to look. Tina sympathises and says that I will have the opportunity to discuss the surgery fully. At that point there is a knock on the door, and Ken appears. 'Oh, you are in here,' he says. He is in full surgeon kit, including the hat. I like him like that.

He sits down, and says, very calmly, 'OK Sarah, I thought about this, and I realised that we never talked about this and what you want. I am very sorry. It is my fault. I knew by the look you gave me that I had done the wrong thing. I'm sorry.' He pauses, looks at me, then says, 'So, Sarah, what do you want.'

This gives me the opportunity to explain that I don't want my breast reduced and lifted too high, I don't want it to look false or like a pair of young breasts on a middle aged woman. I want some droop. Ptosis is the medical term. I don't want my nipple to be too high up.

So, he very carefully explains to me that there is ptosis of the *breast*, and there is ptosis of the *nipple*.

'And you don't want droopy nipples Sarah, pointing down, they are no, no, no,' he shakes his head to emphasise this point, 'they are old lady nipples.' He looks at me, and says, 'But you are young.'

I am smiling now, I like this man so much.

He then asks if he can have a look. So I take off my top and vest and soft bra. I am sitting in front of him, facing him. I had not really ever properly looked at where I put my silicone nipple, and now I realise I put it on the lower part of my reconstructed breast, because then it lines up with my nipple of my droopier breast, it is visually in the same place. But it is pointing down.

'So,' I say, pointing to my silicone nipple, 'this is in the wrong place, it will be different afterwards.' Ken says, 'Well maybe an inch higher, try it, see what it looks like.' So I peel off my nipple and move it up on my breast. 'Here?' I ask. Ken leans forward and positions it centrally on the breast. There is no mirror in the room, so I ask Ronnie how it looks. He is nodding, yes it is right.

'And so,' continues Ken, and his pen magically appears, 'on this breast,' he is drawing on my left breast, 'the nipple position will be here, and we cut away this tissue.' And he shades in the area above my nipple.

'So I won't have old lady nipples,' I say. And we all laugh.

He needs to do some more drawing on me, but with me lying down, and there is no bed in this small room we are in. So I slip my top on, to go back to my bed on the ward. When I stand up he says, 'Oh Sarah,' and he puts his arm around my shoulders, 'when you gave me *that* look I thought you were going to fall out with me.'

I put my arm around his waist, and say, 'I will never fall out with you.'

We go back to the ward, he finishes his drawing and I sign the consent form. Situation recovered. Well done Ken.

On the other side of the anaesthetic I am feeling like an elephant has trampled on my chest, not that I actually know what that feels like. Also the recovery room is spinning round, thanks to the pain relief. I have had enough morphine.

I am shivering with cold, always like this after anaesthetic as the blood returns to the vital organs first. They bring blankets, they are warm, they have a special cupboard where they are heated. I didn't notice after my last surgery here.

I am soon back on the ward, and surprised how long I've been in theatre, a couple of hours, I thought it would be quicker. I spend a few hours in bed listlessly listening to my iPod. I've ordered a tuna salad for tea and by the time it arrives, before six which is tea-time in hospital, I am sitting up and greedily eat it, I am so hungry. I eat all the snacks I have brought in with me. Ronnie visits, doesn't stay long, I am tired.

Phoebe comes later, and sits on a low stool next to my bed. She, like Alison Waghorn, has managed the trick of looking stylish in surgery kit. She says she thinks I'll be very pleased with the result, everything has gone well. I am wrapped in what they call a binder. It is a piece of elastic, about 12 inches wide which is wrapped round my breasts and fastens at the front with velcro. It is extremely unattractive and it seems inappropriately unglamorous for my new breasts. This is why my chest feels so tight. When Phoebe removes it to check my wounds I can see my nipple is covered with gauze and so I don't get to see the final position just yet.

And later on, about nine o'clock that evening, I am of course visited by Ken Graham, still in the hospital checking on his patients, surgery finally over for the day. By now I have got up, changed into my lounge wear, navy cotton jersey camisole and trousers, and my pink and purple silk loose top, and happen to be standing up when he appears round the door of the ward. I am in the first bed by the door.

He looks surprised. But in a good way.

'You'll have to do more than that to keep me in bed,' I say. He says he is glad it has gone well. I know that if he stays any longer he will start apologising again.

I see him again the next morning, I am sitting on my bed with Ronnie, waiting to be discharged, I feel fine. He says it is a social visit, he doesn't want to see my surgery. I hug him and off we go.

Glad to be safely home, on my chaise longue with my iPod. Resting.

The binder has to stay on for ten days, I have not dared to remove it and have a look, only peeked down the front, yes my nipple is still there, covered in steri-strips. The overall shape looks very encouraging, although the bruising is going to be a spectacle.

I ask Ronnie to buy me dye for my white opaque thigh-length surgery stockings, which also must stay on for a few weeks to avoid blood clots. Tulip Red. Because the stockings are synthetic they do not dye a strong colour, but they come out a nice shade of pink, and I paint my toe nails to match. I will attempt to be glamorous at all times.

I am cutting the ribbon at my local pharmacy which has re-opened as a Boots. It feels very local, friendly and we spend some time chatting to the guests and customers. It is only four days since my surgery, but I had committed to doing this, and am glad to.

I am sitting down nearly ready to leave, standing up has been quite hard for me. A woman on crutches comes in with her prescription, hands it in and comes over to me. There are only two chairs and both are occupied. She says to me, 'Can I sit down.' It is not a question. It is a statement. She does not say, 'Please'. I am mildly offended but am so shocked I give up my chair.

I do not say that three days ago I was still in a hospital bed after my sixth trip to theatre. That I am bruised and aching, that I actually want to sit down. No. I don't. Because so often I've been shocked when people say, 'You can't tell.' So that's alright then is it?

Breast cancer can be like this, you don't look ill, but you feel maimed and emotionally depleted.

But I am making progress. The bruises are fading. Back at the hospital clinic the staff are telling me how great my surgery looks. The glamorous Phoebe is coveting my surgical stockings, thinks I have a special supply so I share my tip. She says she wears them when they do long surgery days. Maybe she will co-ordinate with her eyeliner.

I am still finding it difficult to adjust to these new breasts. They are very symmetrical, but they are different than the breasts I had before. As well as the symmetry I also see the scars, fully revealed now as Tina takes off the steri-strips. I have a single cut which starts at the edge of my left breast under my arm, and comes under the fold of my breast and then up to my nipple, and then around the nipple. I knew it was done like this, but somehow now seeing it on my own breast makes it feel invasive. I know also the scars will fade, in time.

But I can see by the way Phoebe and Tina smile at me they think I look great. Tina says the oophorectomy scar from my abdomen, now up on my new breast, makes it look more real somehow, sort of aged. She is right.

It was a grey day when we arrived at the hospital, as we leave it has turned into a proper winter day. Icy big plops of rain.

Sitting at the traffic lights back in Liverpool, windscreen wipers swishing. Red lights, car brake lights, buses. Swish, swish. Pause. We are silent in the car.

'Feels like an ending,' Ronnie had said in the lift in the car park.

Yes, strangely it does. Finished. Am I?

One of my big concerns now, and it seems such a small thing, but it's very important to me, is that my nipples don't match. My existing nipple is now perfectly round. Ken Graham has expertly, very neatly, cut round my nipple and stitched it back into place with extreme care. Previously it was a sort of diamond shape. Now my silicone nipple for the new breast, which was cast from this original nipple, is the wrong shape.

Why does this bother me so much? I remember at diagnosis asking if I could keep my nipple when I had the mastectomy. I received one of 'those' sort of looks from the nurse, but actually I was serious. To me nipples define my breasts. When I don't have my silicone nipple on my new breast, the brief time every week or so when I take it off to replace the glue, well at those times it doesn't feel like a breast anymore. It feels like a lump of fat stitched on my chest, albeit very skillfully.

At the hospital they refer me back to the prosthetics clinic to have a new cast made, but I will have to wait about three months for my nipple to settle into its final shape. So, standing in front of the mirror, I carefully cut my silicone nipple to match the shape of my post-surgery nipple. It will do, for now. The cut edge is not ideal, the making of a good prosthetic nipple involves carefully making a very thin edge which blends onto the skin. This cut edge is thicker and the nipple doesn't stay on as well, mildly infuriating to wake up in the morning and find it on my thigh.

I want to look my best. And this temporary nipple doesn't feel like my best. It is so important to me to look good naked, if it was only clothed that mattered then a false breast would do the job wouldn't it?

R⁓Ɛ

In the weeks after this latest surgery I feel so raw. So sort of strange. I feel worn out, just so emotional really. But I also have a draining physical feeling. The sheer effort of all this.

I can tell by the dark circles under my eyes that I am exhausted. Even though I have had so much sleep, I sleep well, ten hours at night and nap during the day. The anaesthetic effect, the healing taking so much energy. I ache. The aching is draining.

I know that this is a very long road. Seems obvious really.

I am just so tired and I feel like I have been thrown in a washing machine. What will hurt next?

⁓Ꭷჯ

During this recovery period I have started to do my photo albums, something I've always done, promptly at the end of each year. Well, 2006 didn't get finished and now we are nearly in 2010. I am behind.

It is interesting to see the year before diagnosis, 2006. I see the camping trips we made that summer; the trip to Cornwall where we didn't camp so I could indulge in plant shopping and fill the car with plants; a trip to the Lost Gardens of Heligan, one of my favourite places on earth.

I see myself as I was 'before', working on a film, setting up my camera equipment, I look confident, able.

I see myself selling my beloved 2CV, for a mere £80; the passport photos done for a new passport for our trip to Amsterdam for our wedding anniversary, but which never happened as we were in 'results' clinic.

And when I get to 2007, my diagnosis year, I realise that I can re-frame the year by choosing the images that don't tell of a time of pain, of sorrow and hurt, but joy and life. Not disappointment and shock. Not me looking fierce and determined in Harley Street or any of those places I sought medical opinion.

So, instead, I choose images of the baby swans in the park; a fern unfurling; the fun time we had in Blackpool, despite the drug side effects I am having fun. Ellie starting to walk, supporting herself using the push chair. Was she really that small?

Life does continue. Different, but continuing. I have reclaimed that year. A good feeling.

⁂

Me and Ronnie go on one of our favourite walks in Liverpool. Five miles across golf courses, parks and footpaths. I am only three weeks post-surgery. An achievement and I am pleased with myself. It was good to be out.

Late December now. The year coming to the end, the earth turning so slowly I can nearly hear it creak.

I suppose it was a good time to have surgery, the darkling days so I can feel 'cocooned'. I am enjoying the quiet time. So I am doing some painting, just for the pleasure of it, with water colours, enjoying the flow of water, the blending of colours on the paper. Teach myself to bind books by hand, enjoying the feel of the linen thread, the stitching of paper. Got my sewing machine, now serviced and ready to start making my bras, now I have finished my courses.

This surgery, I found the emotional impact much bigger than expected. Yes, it does look great, the final result of the surgery, but this is such a long journey, and now it's nearly ended I'm glad; but it's a really complex set of emotions that I am experiencing. Not least, looking at the void that was my life, that I will re-enter in 2010.

It's normal, apparently, for cancer patients to experience a difficult time at the end of treatment. And I hadn't quite realised that this is, effectively, my 'end of treatment' time. I've had so many 'I'm nearly there' moments in the last three years, that I didn't really know when the last moment would be. I expected something different. Some kind of 'Hallelujah!' moment, an epiphany, that I would wake one morning to a triumphal choral song, angels gathered round my bed singing.

And it's a bit of an anti-climax, not the celebration I was expecting. Such a long slog, that sort of peters out now.

It's a celebration. It is. This 'end' feeling. But also I feel, more than ever, angry. So angry I spent the last three years doing this. And yet, I don't want to take away from how good I look now, at least to myself in the mirror.

I didn't want to do any of this at all. And now that it is ending I feel rage and anger. About what I lost. I channel my energy into tidying and clearing. My knicker drawer is sorted out, post-surgery big knickers thrown away, the net curtains get washed, tiles and grout in the shower are scrubbed, the bathroom cupboard cleared out.

It's like emerging.

CHAPTER 22

An ending

ew Year's eve. Today we have been on another of our favourite walks to the shining shore on the Wirral. The estuary is full of wading birds in the mud. We walk the cliff path which drops down to the shore, passing the gorse bushes. Remember walking here late last summer, hearing their seed pods popping open in the heat.

I am excited by the thought of 2010. I am ready. To look forward again. A new year is a new start.

When we talk about what we are looking forward to this year, we both say the same thing.

Camping.

Camping and no surgery.

The new year brings snow, the most snow I have ever seen here, and the country is forced into stillness by a thick white blanket. The snow turns into ice on the pavements. Hard packed lumps of grey ice. And an opportunity for me to speak on national TV turns up.

An article from Barbara Ehrenreich's new book has been published in the Guardian. It is called, 'Smile! You've got cancer'. It is a refreshing, honest article challenging the positive thinking approach to illness.[22]

Sky News has picked up on this article and decide to have a live discussion about it. They find me through the internet forum I use, where they ask if anyone would like to take part in a live discussion. I am ready to do this. I have a lot to say.

It happens very quickly, one evening I ring the producer to say I am interested, and three days later the satellite van turns up at our house to do an outside broadcast from my chaise longue.

The people in the discussion are the oncologist Karol Sikora, the doctor I consulted in Harley Street as it happens; a young woman who is a breast cancer patient; and me. Karol Sikora is on satellite from his home in Beaconsfield, the other woman is in the TV studio in London, and I am in our living room in Liverpool with a massive camera pointing at me and wearing an earpiece. I cannot see the others, only hear them.

'So,' I say to Guy, my cameraman, 'I can't swear on live TV, right?'

'Yes, right,' he says and smiles at me.

The night before I thought about what I want to say. I want to talk about prevention. That is my agenda. So prevention yes, and I have four points to make. One: cancer is not a gift. Two: anger and pink culture. Three: the one in eight statistic.[23] Four: conned, the fallacy of the 'all clear'. They all contain prevention as well.

I have posted on the forum to ask what colour clothes I should wear. We decide on red.

The presenter starts with me, first asking how I am, which gives me an opportunity to praise my NHS team. And then he asks me what I think about a cancer patient, saying that cancer was the best thing that happened to him. He is quoting the cycling champion Lance Armstrong, who calls himself a cancer survivor, not a cancer victim.

So, cancer is the best thing?

I say that I do not like the way we have adopted this idea that cancer is a gift, it's not. That no-one would want my 'gift', that the treatments I and other women have been through are gruelling and gruesome. And I have felt that women are somehow expected to put the pink t-shirt on and smile and say it's OK, but we should be more angry. And we should be asking *why* breast cancer is happening to so many women, and increasingly younger women.

My first and second points made.

The interviewer then turns to my 'opposite' in the debate here, the other breast cancer woman. I don't know what she looks like at this point, but I hear her saying that having cancer does change your life, and although the experience is not a gift, it might inspire you to do things you'd never done before, and to stop wasting time. So it could be a gift. About positive thinking she says that it is 'somewhat' important, that if you smile, then you will feel better. But as well, you have to take positive action to help yourself and not just think positively.

The interviewer then says that he is not being flippant, but asks Karol Sikora, 'Can wearing a pink ribbon help your body beat cancer?'

'No, obviously, it doesn't have any effect on the biology of the disease,' he says.

He then presents a well-balanced argument for the medical treatment of cancer, not positive thought. And also that all patients are individual and deal differently with a cancer diagnosis. And there is no right or wrong way to 'cope' with cancer.

The interviewer questions whether the pink ribbon might make you feel supported when you think of all the other women wearing one.

Karol Sikora says it's one way of coping. And that patients can support each other through self-help groups, and counselling as well. But really the complete uncertainty is actually very difficult for cancer patients to live with. Will the cancer return? Will I die?

The interviewer seems fairly determined to bring in the pink stuff, and says he doesn't want to call them the 'pink ribbon brigade', but then asks if I found the 'overwhelmingly positive people' a bit too much?

I say that it is individual, just as Karol Sikora has said, we all have individual responses. And I demand the right to deal with this disease in my way, in an individual way. And that doesn't mean being forced into wearing a pink t-shirt or a pink ribbon. If women get support from doing that, then that's fine, but you shouldn't feel shunned if you don't want to wear one.

The interviewer interrupts me, picks up on the word 'shunned'. He seems surprised. 'So,' he asks, 'if you want to not participate in that pink stuff is that what happens, you are shunned?'

I am briefly caught off guard. Shunned? Did I feel shunned? I immediately think about the pink t-shirt, the giving back. That I could not wear pink and feel good about breast cancer. Because why wouldn't you think from the media presentation of breast cancer that we're in a happy pink club together? And I also realise that I am on live TV at this moment. Having been asked a question, 14 million viewers waiting for me to reply.

'Well, yes, I did feel shunned,' I say. And that is true. And I say I think it is unfair that this issue should divide women, when if we stick together more we might have more voice and be able to actually ask the question of why are we all getting breast cancer and why there isn't research looking at prevention, rather than cures? And I recognise here that I have been helped by modern medicine, of course when we have a disease we want a cure. But much better would be not to have the disease in the first place.

But I do not want to be diverted here by the pink question. I want to get the statistics in. And, I say, one in eight is the current statistic for a woman's lifetime risk of breast cancer. Sixty years ago, the lifetime risk was one in 20.[24] That's a big increase. And that's just not acceptable. Point three.

While I'm at it I carry on and say we've conned ourselves in some way, that we call this a treatable disease. But in fact breast cancer can and does recur, and we never get the 'all clear', and it seems unfair to allow the possibility of this disease for the other women that come after me. That is if we don't look at preventing it. Point four.

The presenter is quite clearly taken aback. He says he is alarmed by the figures. He has obviously not heard that statistic before. He works in the media, and they're very good at not putting out the bad news on this one. He asks the other woman, the younger woman, what she thinks about this.

I can't hear her very well in my earpiece, it is only afterwards when I watch the recording that I see her smiling and chirpily flicking her newly-washed hair. She is saying that there are lots of things individuals can do, that we don't live in a 'nanny state' where we should expect the government to have answers. 'People need to eat healthily and stop smoking,' she says. I am furious, I have heard this all before, blame the patients, blame us.

I hadn't put environmental carcinogens on my list of points but they are on there now. But I don't know what the protocol is on satellite. Do I interrupt? It would seem rude.

Karol Sikora gets the final contribution, he says again that learning to cope with uncertainty is very difficult for cancer patients. And also that, speaking as a doctor, telling a patient that the cancer has returned is very difficult, that a recurrence is likely to mean that the disease is fatal at some point in the future. Everyone has to die, even though we don't want to, and cancer forces us to look at that.

I suppose at least he has brought death into a discussion about cancer.

And then the interviewer closes the piece. I get a call from the producer telling me that this was due to be a five-minute piece, but they ran for 11 because it was an interesting debate.

Afterwards I receive lots of posts from my fellow forum users, telling me how well I did. How I raised good points, points we rarely see raised about breast cancer. Am I, as a solo voice, able to even put a dint, well a scratch would do, on the shield of pink that surrounds breast cancer?

❧

I wrote earlier about a woman on the forum with secondary breast cancer. The woman who was so honest and matter of fact about her experience of the disease, and I liked her honesty. She has died. And, typical of her really, she wrote a last post before she died, which was put up after her death. And the words of the dead seem to carry more weight somehow. Loud opinionated Jane, loud even after death.

She writes that her experience of breast cancer was not 'positive or uplifting'. And she hopes that some younger women, after they have had their treatment, will want to get involved in cancer campaigning. A different sort of campaigning than we have now, not the fundraising at 'pink pampering parties', and appearances in fashion shows. Not the 'airbrushing of this disease into some designer must-have condition'.

I like the fact that she has chosen her words so well, recognised that these events are deeply deeply entrenched in this whole breast cancer culture. She is being cynical, implying that they don't actually change anything. That they project a stereotype of what a 'survivor' looks like.

After all, fashion shows. What's that all about? Jane is a woman who says she would have attended a Miss World event as a protester, so this parading of femininity would not be for her. And she has written before about these pink fashion shows, these fundraising events where the models on the catwalks have all had or have breast cancer. The publicity for these events talks about the models in glowing, soppy terms, saying that 'their courage and strength literally shines through'. What is the purpose of these events then? To prove to us, all us women who may get this crappy disease, that it's not that bad really?

The women who participate seem to like them though. Although of course many women do like the opportunity to wear posh clothes, to have professional hair and make-up done. But it's the message behind this that upsets some of us. Jane refers to the central London offices of a national breast cancer charity, and the photos on the walls of the previous models, all smiling. And she says you can't miss the point that 'ultra feminine, attractive, youthful and happy' is how you're supposed to look after breast cancer. And I'm all for us looking our best, I mean that's what I've tried to do, but I find this parading distasteful. I dislike the way it gives a message to the world which seems to say, 'You can't tell.' Audre Lorde calls this a 'conspiracy on the part of Cancer Inc' for women to appear 'no different from before' and show the world that 'nothing has happened to challenge her'.[25]

Of course we are different. But different seems to equal unusual. We are not prepared to be visibly different.

But breast cancer is not the only cancer is it? What about the others? Ovarian, pancreatic, bowel. Jane says she doesn't think people with colostomy bags get asked to walk the catwalk.

As Audre Lorde also says, breast cancer and breast surgery have been depicted as though they are simply cosmetic problems.[26] They clearly are not, and breast cancer is *cancer*, and it can and does kill. That's why Jane, in her message after her death, is asking for campaigners.

She says that in the future the cancer campaigners will have rallied round, and that it will be a 'radical route' that will challenge governments and charities. That we won't be 'smiling sweetly' about the statistics, that we will have become angry that too many women die of this disease.[27]

She says that although now we are afraid of breast cancer she believes that in 40 years we won't be, that few women will get the disease and no-one will die of it.

But I don't know who she thinks these campaigners are? Who is going to take this radical approach, ask the difficult questions? I wonder if it's 'us', by us I mean those of us who had a breast cancer diagnosis? I don't see a huge response to her post. No, there is not a call to arms, a response where this dead woman has galvanised us. Did she think she would? I'm not sure. We're weary and worn out.

We, the lucky ones, who have escaped death, at least for now, do we want to use up our energy trying to stop breast cancer happening? Or are we too tired? Well I know I am. I am bored, sick of the subject of breast cancer. And yet, even as I write that, I feel a surge of anger and know that I have not spoken my last word about it yet.

And I wonder about this anger, this feeling I always return to when I think about breast cancer. It's my instinctive reaction to the whole mainstream culture that I have been exposed to, where we are not encouraged to be angry. Instead we are given 'tips' for getting through our treatments, mostly about keeping up appearances. And I feel so angry that we are even expected to continue to look just the same when we are facing the trials of surgery, the aftermath of sledge hammer drugs. It's this whole sense of 'coping' that seems too lame, too pithy, for what treatment for breast cancer actually entails.

I feel that there is a danger that we are accepting the increasingly high incidence of breast cancer and thinking of it as a treatable disease. Mastectomy is *not* a cure for cancer. Having a mastectomy will *not* guarantee you stay cancer free, in fact no breast cancer treatments can claim they have cured you, ever. Mastectomy does *not* guarantee you won't die. And whilst a mastectomy may be an important part of treating a woman for breast cancer, it can have devastating emotional impact on how a woman feels, as well as dealing with a life-threatening disease.

We should not be accepting breast cancer in this way. We should be putting more energy into getting research about the causes of breast cancer so we can reverse this increasing statistic.

I was angry to have part of my body cut off. Yes, I was, and I still am. And at its worst it has felt primitive and mutilating. However, I am pragmatic, I accept it, it saved my life, at least I hope it has. But it's not something I think we should just be accepting as the norm, instead of trying to stop it happening in the future. So, to me, this whole pink culture seems to be about making it 'OK' and 'acceptable' to have breast cancer, and is part of the silencing that I feel is being done to women.

What we have now in our society is definitely a much more acceptable culture where we can mention breast cancer. I was not old enough 40 years ago to know what it must have been like, an almost unmentionable disease. The word 'cancer' like a death threat, to be spoken as a whisper or not even spoken at all. So it is better that we can talk about breast cancer.

But when we speak of breast cancer now, for the most part it's much too nice, too accepting, too glossy, too pink; not enough anger. Am I repeating myself?

And so we come to the end of breast cancer. Through. After. Over. Or is it? On a good day I'd say so. Other days I remind myself that I am living in remission. That's what this is, a remission that may last for the rest of my life. Or may not. That's how breast cancer behaves. Not what they tell you on diagnosis day, now three years in the past. That I will live with breast cancer forever.

So do I feel I am living in borrowed time? No, I feel I only know the present moment, and there is no space and no time for trivia or anything superficial.

It's just the fact that we call this disease treatable. Permanent fear and 49 inches of scars does not seem like treatable to me. I mean I don't live in permanent fear, but it is often there, can return at unexpected moments. Everyone who has had a breast cancer diagnosis knows what it is like to feel an ache in your lower back or hip, and immediately think it's secondary breast cancer in your bones. Or some other symptom, a cough that could be secondary breast cancer in your lungs, an unexplained headache. Always the worry that it is the dreaded secondary breast cancer. Will that ever go? And I know my scars will fade, but they will never go.

My sense of 're-entry' feels difficult. It feels hard to accept the ending, to go back. Because I don't want to feel I am going back, I want to feel I am going forward. I ring Julie, my counsellor, and ask if I can see her again, just for a while. Julie was my weekly refuge in the weeks and months after mastectomy. I don't even remember when I stopped seeing her, only that it was when it felt right for me, maybe even after a year.

I find this luxury, the luxury of talking about myself, deeply therapeutic. I think, with hindsight, that counselling, at the point of need, has been as valuable as many of my NHS medical treatments. But I feel sad that it seems to be outside their remit, or certainly in my case I was never offered emotional support at this level.

Julie knows everything I have been through. I even went back to see Julie before I made the reconstruction decision, she knows me so well that I knew she would be able to see if I was not sure about making such a big step.

It is a wise counsel.

And now I am well, I am doing what women do. Running for charity. But I am not doing it in *that* way. That is, running for a pink charity. Not one of those searching for this elusive 'cure'. I don't believe we will find a cure for cancer, or not anytime soon. It is not in the interests of those who have the power in our society. Not government, but big pharma, yes those of corporate greed, where patients equal profit. Am I cynical to think that sick people are very profitable for pharmaceutical companies?

This is not my original thinking. Plenty of people have said this before me. Martin J Walker is deeply suspicious about the cancer charities, calling them 'footsoldiers for the chemical industry'.[21]

No, I will be running for the charity Yes to Life. They gave me choice. They helped me take control of my treatment. I know, and they know, that they can't guarantee a happy ending, a positive result. But in dealing with my cancer I can be proactive, questioning, can feel that I am making the right decisions, for me; so that whatever the outcome I will not regret what I did. That even if I die, then I can die well. A strange concept I know, dying well; but I do not want to die with regrets and doubts about what I chose to do. And I always knew that I wanted to have the best quality of life while I was dealing with the cancer, and Yes to Life have enabled me to do that.

But three years of surgery and treatment has left its mark on me physically of course. And although there have been pockets of time, windows where I have been able to do physical activity, it is always punctuated with surgery or treatment. And recovery. So although I know I want to run the Liverpool Women's 10K in May, it feels like a big challenge. I have not run a 10K, which is just over six miles, for four years now. The last one I ran in 70 minutes, although when younger I ran one in 42 minutes. It all feels a long way from my current fitness level.

My surgical team will not let me start physical activity until six weeks after my last surgery, which is the first week in January. That then gives me 17 weeks before the run.

My first challenge, though, even before I start to run, is a sports bra. Yes, I still have the red front fastening bra I found which worked with my one breast. I try it on now with two breasts and it completely squashes my lovely but hard-gained surgical result against my left breast into an uncomfortable, unattractive lump. I want something that will show off my lovely new breasts, that will look like I do have two breasts. So over the Christmas break I order a selection of bras from my favourite internet supplier. I don't even know what size I am now. Funny feeling. To not know my bra size.

I measure on the tape as a 42E, but it soon becomes clear that I am in fact a 40D. I used to be a 38FF. I have discussed my requirements with my sports bra supplier and at one point I am in possession of over £300 worth of sports bras. They are confident that we will find something, but it might take a bit of trial and error. They are right, and eventually I have two delightful sports bras, totally supportive and very comfortable.

Emboldened by this new discovery, that I am a 40D, I then go shopping for an everyday bra. After breast surgery it is not recommended that you wear an underwired bra, certainly at first while you are healing. So I have found crop tops and soft bras and support vests to wear during my surgery recovery periods.

There are conflicting opinions about whether or not underwired bras should be avoided with breast reconstruction. Indeed there have been claims that there may be a link between bras and breast cancer caused by reduced lymph gland circulation. No medical studies support these claims.

Now that I have done my bra making course I know that it is ill-fitting bras that are problematic and dig in and press on delicate breast tissue. I have certainly had bras, both underwired and not, that are not my friends after several hours' wear and I have been delighted to remove them.

So, I'm not sure what's best, but I am going to stick to non-underwired bras for now. There is a limited selection for me to try. I spend an unsatisfactory time in the wrong shop huffing and puffing and trying on 12 bras and finding nothing and come home. A few days later my energy has returned and I go back to another shop and find success, although limited to only black and white. It is a great moment when I come to the top of the stairs and call Ronnie out from the living room to see me wearing a bra.

My new life, with bras. Again.

❧

Through a friend of Ronnie's I meet the delightful Karen, who is a running coach. We meet up and I tell her about my goal, the 10K.

So we start in January, and every week, on a Thursday, we train together. Well, she trains me. Varied exercises, not just running. From my short one-minute runs followed by two minutes' walking, I am soon running five minutes non-stop, doing push-ups and tricep dips. My strength returning. A good feeling.

Karen sets me homework which I eagerly do, pushing myself. The old me returning. I know that I have a lot to catch up, if my five-minute runs are going to turn into a 10K, about 70 minutes non-stop. But I am so determined. And I am so glad to have found Karen. She is lovely, glamorous, smiling and beautiful. I like her so much.

And around the same time I find a tai chi class, something I always wanted to do. Movement. I easily learn the movements, find a small group of friendly people who don't know I had breast cancer.

New people are in my life. Most of the old people aren't.

It is sleety and I go out for my run. I am on the path in the park, the slush is soft, but not slippy. I time my five-minute interval around three sides of a grass block, two football pitches. I draw a line in the slush at the end, and then start back from that line to the tree, which was my starting marker.

I can see my first foot prints in the slush going the other way. I can see that my stride now is slightly wider, I am over-taking my backwards prints, so when I get to the marker it is not yet five minutes, so I run on. Then I repeat the interval, not looking at my watch or counting my steps this time, I am just running. I start back again, a fourth set of prints, now a blur in the slush, but I can see them, I know it was me running back and forth here. I shout out, 'Come on.' And as I near the end I increase my stride, that familiar feel of ease, of increased velocity, but it feels slower as the foot strikes are further apart.

I remember this.

I remember how I would easily run like this. It becomes a meditation now, I am moving beyond the pain, the hurt of this last three years. My body is forgetting, slipping back into itself. The fear, tension, trauma, all those limiting feelings are starting to release.

At last.

I have been back to Whiston and had a new nipple cast made. In fact I have been twice. My nipple is still healing, the suture line that goes round it still visible but gradually changing and fading. The first nipple cast didn't match properly, so I'm back.

With infinite patience Gina at Whiston carefully observes me, after she has made the mould from my nipple. She mixes the colours, yes there is more than one colour in a nipple. It is all done with great sensitivity. She puts the palette in the fridge with my name on and will make the nipples later. This whole thing is quite a time-consuming process, so I take this opportunity to talk to Gina about surgical nipples.

A surgical nipple is made by cutting the skin on the reconstruction and twisting it to form a nipple bud. Or the surgeon can take skin from another place, like the earlobe or labia. It is usually done with a local anaesthetic, rather than a general. When the minor surgery has healed the nipple colour is then tattooed onto the skin to recreate the areola. This is usually done over two or three sessions to get a natural shaded tattoo, rather than a flat solid colour. Gina shows me photographs. I am encouraged, yes it would mean I never have to peel off my nipple and clean it. I am not seeing Ken Graham until later in the summer, and he has said we can discuss it then. At the moment, I am glad to be hospital-free, or at least less-hospital anyway. No rush.

My lovely new nipples, one to wear, and one spare, arrive in the post. Yes, that is better. A small thing, but my prosthetics team understand how important this is.

I also receive a newsletter from one of Britain's big breast cancer charities. It drips pink. It is printed in shades of pink, purple, lilac, lavender. Yes, it is feminine. And I look through this and I read the fundraising stories, and I see that there are people all over the country holding pink days in their offices or places of work, baking cakes and doing raffles while no doubt wearing pink garments. Yes, there are pictures too. And oh, how I hate it.

I see the 'girls' wearing pink swimming caps, swimming in a triathlon. 'Let's hear it for the girls!' All these women in pink t-shirts, and pink hats some of them, smiling, having fun, a great day out. Cycling, walking, trekking. Healthy activities.

Words like 'tireless' and 'dedication' punctuate the pithy lame text. Exclamation marks! How great! How much fun!

Yes, there are serious articles too about 'taskforces' and secondary breast cancer, about how they are 'moving forward' with their plans to develop services. All their support services, support for women who have a breast cancer diagnosis. And a book about chemotherapy chirpily reviewed, saying the side effects are not as bad as we expect.

And I don't see the word *prevention* anywhere in this newsletter. I see *managing*, and *coping*, and I am so angry.

They report that a major supermarket has raised over £1million last year for them, from product sales and employee fundraising. And in total over £20million for various breast cancer charities. Do they say that there has been, at last, a serious backlash and offence taken about the title of this campaign, primarily by breast cancer women? Tickled pink. Yeah, right. That just about sums me up, or any woman hearing she has a life threatening disease and may lose several parts of her body. Oh, or die. As well.

These trinkets you can buy too, like the jewel bracelet, pink of course. Sickening. The 'exclusive' pink heart pin badges from a high street clothes retailer. Why? It is January now so it would appear that this is not now restricted to October after all. Well, of course not, business is business isn't it?

A double page spread with information sessions, short courses, practical help, telephone support groups. Half an hour online on a Wednesday morning for secondary breast cancer. Is that enough? I see a lingerie evening in Liverpool. I already know how sickening this will be. I know it will be all about, 'You can't tell.' This 'socially sanctioned' cover up, that's what Audre Lorde called the prosthesis. Another way of 'keeping women with breast cancer silent', she says. I call it a cover-up, and I hate it.

I don't see the word anger. I don't see the word lonely. Or isolation or fear.

And I think, 'Oh, am I being oversensitive here? Am I wrong?' These women in the photos, are they the ones who had breast cancer or are they supporting 'us'. But no, often these other women are not breast cancer patients, often they are 'supporters'. This pink culture is so big, so seductive, it draws women in on the periphery, sisters, mothers, friends, all 'helping' find a cure for this disease that we are smiling about.

Is it some sort of banal way of protecting themselves, of being part of this happy cheerful sisterly movement where you'll never feel alone, where your pink-wearing friends will always be there for you?

People believing, and why would you not, but believing that the plethora of charities out there will actually 'win the war on cancer'. Their words repeated again and again: to improve and research 'diagnosis, treatment, prevention and cure'. These four words carry equal weight. Prevention is slipped in there between treatment and cure. But surely, surely that is the main research we should be looking at?

These pink charities, who produce these newsletters, who have all these thousands of people raising money for them. Why? Because it doesn't make breast cancer seem quite so bad when you are wearing a pink wig?

This whole pink thing. I feel so repulsed by it all. Am I wrong?

I ask, but I don't think I am.

It seems to me that we have whole-heartedly swallowed this pink culture, in fact this 'cult' as Barbara Ehrenreich describes it, from America.

The pink ribbon for breast cancer, which is now so ubiquitous, originated in America. But if you look at the history of the pink ribbon, you will see that the original breast cancer ribbons were not pink, they were peach. They were made by Charlotte Haley at her home. And she made them as a statement, a statement about cancer prevention in the USA. Because in 1990 out of 1.8 billion US dollars for cancer research only 5% of the cancer budget was spent on prevention. 'Help us wake up our legislators and America by wearing this ribbon,' the card sold with them said.

They were popular, they spread quickly.

But then, then what happened? A magazine editor and a cosmetics company ask if they can use the idea and work with Charlotte to develop a ribbon for National Breast Cancer Awareness Month in October. She says no, that they will become too commercialised. And that is not what she wants. This woman, this individual, who - by the way - has breast cancer, as does her daughter. Who makes the peach-coloured ribbons for prevention; she was right.

So the corporates, the big giants, they consult with their lawyers and then they make a new ribbon. It is pink. Apparently pink is 'soothing comforting and healing'. And the rest, as they say, is history.[28]

And now the pink ribbon and the pink colour is an international symbol for breast cancer awareness.

Even before the pink thing, the pinkwashing of breast cancer, October had been established as National Breast Cancer Awareness Month. This idea was founded in 1985 by AstraZeneca, an international pharmaceutical company. The main aim of National Breast Cancer Awareness Month was to promote mammograms as the most effective 'weapon' against breast cancer. The terminology of war used yet again, a *weapon*. And why is this weapon so effective? Well it results in higher detection rates, which results in higher sales of both tamoxifen, and also now Arimidex, two of the most popular anti-hormone breast cancer drugs. Do you know who manufactures these? AstraZeneca.[12]

❦

I see a whole swallowing of this approach to breast cancer. And it is coated in pink, just as Barbara Ehrenreich says, a sugar-coating, like a pill we have swallowed, the nasty vile tasting centre disguised by the pink shiny sugar coating.

And now it seems that there are no limits to the October month of breast awareness. Pink is here all year. The running season will kick off with the pink charities using life-affirming words to sell places on fundraising events, where you run or walk, or now even cycle. And you and your sisters, these ever increasing band of women who are all so happy to be doing this, having great days out and creating pinkwashed memories, you are all part of finding that all elusive *cure*. And yet so many women want to do this, to take part. They feel they are doing *something*, without being in a protest. Remember those marches, the banners, the trips to London, the campaigning for political causes, for feminist causes? I do not see it happening in the breast cancer world.

And the clever thing also about the selling of the pink products is that it aligns the businesses that support this as 'pro-women' rather than feminist doesn't it? So they are female friendly, they *care*, do they? Or is it as Charlotte Haley thought it would happen, a commercialisation? That breast cancer is guided by commercial interests, not female interests?[29]

There are too many unanswered questions.

And in my reflections on breast cancer, my rage against pink, I quote again and again Lorde and Ehrenreich. They are my guides. My angry sisters in spirit. So, two angry women in 30 years? Is that all? Both had breast cancer. Lorde died of it. She said, 'When we speak we are afraid our words will not be heard or welcomed. But when we are silent, we are still afraid. So it is better to speak.'[30]

And I am speaking now. I find it impossible to stay silent.

Bren and I resume our fire-food ritual at the allotment. Trying to invent ever more imaginative meals to cook on the fire. We both rise to the challenge, to find three-course meals that can be cooked on an open fire. Baked eggs in ramekins, cod cooked with tomatoes in foil, baked bananas with dark chocolate melted inside them, delicious with soya ice cream.

The snowdrops are here. Emerging under the red stems of the dogwood.

Why?

In the chemotherapy corridors the sense of desperation, the epidemic, all these people with cancer and no-one's asking why?

I have a memory of the chemotherapy corridors. Three years ago, and I am a newly diagnosed cancer patient. I am waiting to see the oncologist. To be told what I will be given for my treatment following my surgery.

There are so many of us, too many, and there is not enough space. So although this is a relatively new cancer unit, a fairly modern building, that has been designed for the purpose, there is not enough room to put us all. All of us people with cancer. So we are sitting in chairs lining the corridors. The indignity. I did not feel it at the time. I feel it now.

And as I sat there, in that corridor, waiting for hours that day, the clinic running over, too much demand on the oncologist, I am cheerily greeted by a woman pushing a supermarket trolley towards me. In the trolley there are some cuddly toys, a teddy bear Easter egg. It is surreal. And then the woman asks if I would like to buy a raffle ticket. Had it happened now I would probably have sworn at her. But then, because I was in shock and I was only a few weeks into becoming a patient, I just say no. She tells me that they are raising money for the cancer unit, this place that I am in. So her inference by telling me this, and by me refusing to buy a raffle ticket, is that I am not supporting the cancer unit that is about to treat me. But, you see, I have already supported it. It is an NHS facility, I have paid my tax all my life. So I have paid for this, for everything, the doctors, the buildings.

Selling raffle tickets to cancer patients. People who are sick. Why? If there is not enough money then raffling some Easter eggs is not how it's going to change. If there's not enough money for my health services, then that's a government issue.

We cannot continue to sustain treating people for cancer at this level. It has to stop. Our health system cannot manage increasing numbers of us. It is time for a serious look at prevention. Which, by the way, is also a government issue.

⁊⊱

As a statistic I am not that unusual. Breast cancer being what it is, now in the early 21st century, a one in nine chance of breast cancer in a woman's lifetime in the UK. One in nine is a woman's risk over an 85-year lifetime for breast cancer. Sixty years ago, the lifetime risk was one in 20.[24] That's a big increase.

Breast cancer incidence has continued to increase steadily from the 1940s until 1996, when it reached one in 12, and then increasing in the following five years to one in nine.

And if it carries on like this then in 40 years' time it could be one in four. And that's just not acceptable, but it suggests that what we have here is an epidemic. And if it were happening to men, in these numbers, then I think something would be being done to stop it.

This is definitely the trip no-one wanted. The game no-one wanted to play. The club no-one wants to be in. Breast cancer. Government and doctors measure 'success statistics' in terms of number of lives saved or deaths prevented. They do not see, or choose not to see, the broken hearts and lives and the devastation of breast cancer.

The emotional impact is overlooked.

A breast cancer diagnosis is for life. Even the most successful treatments do not guarantee a 100% cancer-free survival. We have conned ourselves into thinking this is a treatable disease, that it will go away after treatment.

No breast cancer patient gets the 'all clear'. Breast cancer can, and does, recur at any time, regardless of how many years have passed since an initial diagnosis. That fear can be very difficult to come to terms with for many women, the fear of recurrence, I know all about that. So, that's why, we need to look at prevention, not more and more cures. We are hiding from the truth.

Women are not expressing their anger about this so it's not on any agenda to prevent it.

Women band together for breast cancer. Which is good. A 'faint feeling of belonging' and a 'dilute sisterhood' is how Barbara Ehrenreich describes it. But, in my experience, they are not angry. Too obedient. Feminism, the 'F' word, it seems that it is a dirty word now. That anger and feminine don't go together. Being a feminist is seen as 'bad'. Angry is bad. That would make me very very bad then.

Barbara Ehrenreich says that the lack of anger she found in the American breast cancer culture made her feel isolated, no-one was questioning *why* so many women get this disease. The same happens here in the UK. We have a massive pink culture around breast cancer. And we are bombarded with images of women smiling their way through what is a devastating illness. Who is asking the questions? Surely there's a big enough movement, the pink movement, that they could be really putting pressure on government, to be asking the questions? But they are not.

So this is why I am enraged about pink. That's how they control us is it? Quiet and smiling. And I wonder whether this is a failure of feminism? Why not just chain me back up to the kitchen sink? Then I won't be able to get near the places I can have my say: speak on TV, or write a book.

I try and dredge something out of all this. Something good. Perhaps you read this and think it is an extraordinary journey? Or maybe you felt like you needed to come up for air sometimes? Because that's what it felt like to me. Just a relentless ongoing series of medical interventions, and emotional highs and lows. A three-year hole in my life. And increasing anger. As the American journalist Molly Ivins said about breast cancer, it is 'massive amounts of no fun'.[31]

And I would rather it had not happened. At all. Any of it.

In trying to find something good I'd like to say something really positive and heartwarming about how everyone rallied round and helped me and

Ronnie. Or everyone I knew in my previous life. But, sorry to disappoint you dear reader, this was not how it was. It did not happen like that. If you've read this far then you know that this story doesn't contain many characters, mainly Ronnie, and Bren. Oh, and a large cast of medical staff: surgeons, doctors, nurses.

Some people, some, rallied round. A few. Most didn't. And smartly disappeared out of my life. Sarah having a life crisis, was not, after all, interesting enough for them. Sarah, alive and interesting, was what they wanted, was it? I don't know. Because they didn't, for the most part, stay around to be asked.

Often, when I have met someone, told them about what has happened to me, I am not trying to shock them or frighten them. I am just being honest. I am very open and direct, I know that. But I don't know how to express my experience without being completely honest. And I can see the looks on their faces and it's like they are thinking, 'I am really glad this hasn't happened to me.'

I wonder how will we get people to think about cancer prevention? In my experience, they don't want to think about it, the dreaded 'C' word. They are just so glad it hasn't happened to them. And crossing their fingers and hoping it won't? Maybe. Fear, so much fear. I touch it all the time. People back away from me. I am only trying to be myself. To tell the truth. What else can I do?

Dina Rabinovitch didn't live to do anything about this. Nor did Audre Lorde. The baton is lying on the ground. Left there by Audre Lorde I think. The feminist baton, the one I felt I didn't want, that I somehow had to protect myself. That I am not the one to break this silence. But I am too angry. Yes, I see this baton now, and I want to pick that up. This is mine. It burns my hand. Makes me want to grip it even tighter.

I am not prepared to join in this collusion of silence, of covering up. I want my words to be heard.

I am not ready to make nice.

Notes

1 *page iv*

'I had known the pain, and survived it. It only remained for me to give it a voice, to share it for use, that the pain not be wasted.'

When I read this in the introduction of Audre Lorde's book, *The Cancer Journals,* it was like an arrow that pierced my heart. That someone else had recognised and given voice to the pain, the fear and the loss; that I was not alone with my emotions.

2 *page 47*

'Parabens are a class of chemicals widely used as preservatives in the cosmetic and pharmaceutical industries.'

http://en.wikipedia.org/wiki/Paraben

'They are becoming increasingly controversial, however, because they have been found in high concentrations in breast cancer tumours.'

Harvey PW, Everett DJ (2004). 'Significance of the detection of esters of p-hydroxybenzoic acid (parabens) in human breast tumours.'
Journal of Applied Toxicology 24 (1): 1–4

3 *page 62*

'The reduction in breast cancer mortality rates is likely to have several different causes including screening, increasing specialisation of care and the widespread adoption of tamoxifen treatment since 1992.'

Cancer Research UK website cancer statistics

4 *page 62*

Janet Edwards, *Choosing to Heal*
(Watkins Publishing, 2007) p97

5 *page 62*

'Goserelin (Zoladex) offers an effective, well-tolerated alternative to CMF (chemotherapy) in premenopausal patients with ER-positive and node-positive early breast cancer.'
Conclusion of the ZEBRA study 2002.
http://jco.ascopubs.org/cgi/content/full/20/24/4628

6 *page 67*

My Iscador doctor pointed me to this website as the best source of information about Iscador and other mistletoe-based therapies.

www.mistel-therapie.de/mistletoe.html

7 *page 67*

'With more than 100 clinical studies of different quality and several hundred preclinical laboratory studies dedicated to its use mistletoe therapy is one of the scientifically most thoroughly researched methods of complementary medicine.'

http://allgemein.mistel-therapie.de/index.php5?page=49&lang=1

8 *page 76*

I am deeply grateful to Audre Lorde and her writing in *The Cancer Journals,* for expressing her feelings about the false breast. I use the term 'the false breast' objectively and do not use a personal prefix, ie my false breast. It is not mine, and it is not a breast.

9 *page 81*

Janet Cockburn's story can be found here.
www.janacsportswear.ca/mystory.htm

In the UK the Been-a-Boob can be bought from Less Bounce. www.lessbounce.com

10 *page 84*

'The Sacred Space Foundation is a charity providing peaceful and confidential rest and recuperation facilities. It helps those suffering from the extremes of stress, burnout, emotional exhaustion or "spiritual crisis" that have severely shaken their sense of meaning and direction in life.'

www.scaredspace.org.uk/

11 *page 148*

'All over the world women who are survivors in every sense of the word are demonstrating their 'can do' attitude as they take part in dragon boat racing.'

Pool of Life website: www.pooloflife.net/

This is used on the Pool of Life website, but also used in shorter form at another cancer dragon boating club: www.paddlersforlife.co.uk/more%20about%20us.htm

The expression is also widely used on many American websites about dragon boating and breast cancer.

12 *pages 156, 249*

Wikipedia: 'AstraZeneca, which manufactures breast cancer drugs Arimidex and Tamoxifen, founded the National Breast Cancer Awareness Month in the year 1985. The aim of the NBCAM from the start has been to promote mammography as the most effective weapon in the fight against breast cancer.' The citation for this is the NBCAM website: www.nbcam.org/about_faq.cfm

13 *page 156*

Libby Brooks: Let's not pinkwash proper discussion about this disease. *Guardian*, 2 October 2008. www.guardian.co.uk/commentisfree/2008/oct/02/cancer.women

14 *page 156*

Barbara Ehrenreich: Welcome to Cancerland. *Harper's*, November 2001.

15 *page 158*

'Many of the established risk factors for breast cancer – such as earlier menarche, later menopause, childlessness, and delayed childbearing – are ones women cannot change. And established risk factors do not account for all breast cancer cases. We simply do not know as much as we should.

Many people are now looking at our increasingly polluted environment as a possible culprit. Breast cancer incidence in the United States has risen since World War II, when industry began pumping out pesticides, plastics, solvents, and other chemicals, leaving residues in our air, water, and soil. Laboratory studies suggest that many of these chemicals may cause breast tumours, hasten their growth, or leave mammary glands more vulnerable to carcinogens.'

www.silentspring.org

Silent Spring is a nonprofit research organisation dedicated to identifying the links between the environment and women's health, especially breast cancer. They focus primarily on chemicals in everyday products that cause mammary tumors in animals and those that can make breast cancer cells grow in a laboratory.

16 *pages 158, 211*

'About 5% to 10% of breast cancer cases are thought to be hereditary, resulting directly from gene defects (called mutations) inherited from a parent.'

www.cancer.org/Cancer/BreastCancer/DetailedGuide/breast-cancer-risk-factors

'To date, most inherited cases of breast cancer have been associated with two genes: BRCA1, which stands for BReast CAncer gene one, and BRCA2, or BReast CAncer gene two.

'The function of these genes is to keep breast cells growing normally and to prevent any cancer cell growth. But when these genes contain abnormalities, or mutations, they are associated with an increased breast cancer risk. Abnormal BRCA1 and BRCA2 genes may account for up to 10% of all breast cancers.

'Women diagnosed with breast cancer who have an abnormal BRCA1 or BRCA2 gene often have a family history of breast cancer, ovarian cancer, or both. But it's also important to remember that most women with breast cancer have no family history of the disease.'

http://www.breastcancer.org/risk/genetic/

17 *page 158*

'Breast cancer – an environmental disease: the case for primary prevention' report by UK Working Group on the Primary Prevention of Breast Cancer 2005. Available online at www.nomorebreastcancer.org.uk

18 *page 158*

The statistics I quote at the conference in 2008 are based on my own calculations. I am not a mathematician or statistician, but I have made the 40-year projection using the actual increase in the period from 1996 to 2001:

'The chance of a woman contracting the disease in her lifetime rose from 1 in 12 to 1 in 9 in the five-year period 1996-2001.'

Sources: Cancer Research UK & Office of National Statistics (ONS) 2003

In addition an article on C4 news 30 May 2008 predicts that in 2024 the incidence of breast cancer will be 1 in 7, so it is an estimate of taking that further to 2048.
www.channel4.com/news/articles/society/health/more+women+face+breast+cancer+risk/2265107

19 *page 209*

'The lifetime risk of being diagnosed with breast cancer in women is 1 in 9.'
www.nomorebreastcancer.org.uk

'It has been estimated that the lifetime risk of developing breast cancer is 1 in 9 for women in the UK. These were calculated on February 2009 using incidence and mortality data for 2001-2005.'
Cancer Research UK

20 *page 209*

What Audre Lorde says is, 'What would happen if an army of one-breasted women descended upon Congress and demanded that the use of carcinogenic, fat-stored hormones in beef-feed be outlawed?'

She wrote this in 1980. I find it staggering that 30 years later it is still not happening, either in the USA or in the UK.

21 *pages 211, 243*

Martin J Walker: Your Money and Your Life? - cancer research in the UK. *Ecologist*, Vol 30, No 7, October 2000, pp24-8
online: findarticles.com/p/articles/mi_m2465/is_7_30/ai_66457048/

I found part of this article quoted in Janet Edward's book *Choosing to Heal*, in the chapter on the politics of breast cancer where she writes about the 'money-spinning cancer industry'. p125

22 *page 235*

Barbara Ehrenreich: Smile! You've got cancer.
Guardian, 2 January 2010.
www.guardian.co.uk/lifeandstyle/2010/jan/02/cancer-positive-thinking-barbara-ehrenreich

23 *page 236*

'One in eight women will develop breast cancer' statistic is the lifetime risk calculation in the USA, from the Breast Cancer Action website.
www.bcaction.org/index.php?page=statistics-and-general-facts#Q4

24 *pages 238, 252*

'In the 1940s, a woman's lifetime risk of breast cancer was one in 22' is from the Breast Cancer Action website.
www.bcaction.org/index.php?page=statistics-and-general-facts#Q2

Given that the risk has gradually increased since then I have estimated that in 1950 the risk was one in 20.

25 *page 240*

Audre Lorde uses this expression 'Cancer Inc' so skilfully to describe the sense of bigger cancer industry where the patient is simply part of being expected to behave in a particular way; that is obediently.

26 *page 240*

Audre Lorde, *The Cancer Journals.*

27 *page 240*

'Breast cancer is the major cancer affecting women and the most common cancer in the UK. It kills more than 1,000 women every month. With a steady rise in new cases year on year – from 21,446 in 1979 to 41,000 in 2001 – the chance of a woman contracting the disease in her lifetime rose from 1 in 12 to 1 in 9 in the five-year period 1996-2001. Earlier and improved detection accounts for only a limited number of cases in this rising trend. Breast cancer is the most commonly diagnosed cancer in women under 35. Over 1,400 women between the ages of 35-39 are diagnosed each year. The highest rate of incidence occurs in women in the 50-74 age group. In any one year, breast cancer can affect

almost a quarter of a million women in the UK.
For example, in 2001 there were 41,000 new
diagnoses, 15,000 deaths and 172,000 women
living with diagnoses made in the previous ten-
year period.'

Sources: Cancer Research UK & Office of
National Statistics (ONS) 2003

28 *page 248*

I am indebted to Samantha King for the history
of the pink ribbon.
Samantha King, Pink Ribbons, Inc, pp xxiv-xxv

29 *page 249*

The expression 'pro-women' as opposed to
feminist is an observation made by Samantha
King, as is the observation of selling pink products
being for commerical interests not female
interests.

Samantha King, Pink Ribbons, Inc

30 *page 250*

Audre Lorde

'When we speak we are afraid our words will not
be heard or welcomed. But when we are silent,
we are still afraid. So it is better to speak.'

http://www.brainyquote.com/quotes/authors/
a/audre_lorde_3.html

31 *page 253*

Molly Ivins quote is from Wikipedia, and the
reference is given as: *Time* magazine, 'Who Needs
Breasts, Anyway?', Feb 18, 2002. Retrieved
February 1, 2007.

Back cover

'In the UK in 2007 almost 45,700 women
were diagnosed with breast cancer, that's around
125 women a day.'

Cancer Research UK. info.cancerresearchuk.org

Book list

The Boudica Within: Elaine Sassoon (The Erskine Press, 2007)

Elaine Sassoon is a plastic sugeon specialising in breast reconstruction. This book features 23 of her patients and shows their breast reconstruction surgeries.

The Cancer Journals, Special Edition: Audre Lorde: (Aunt Lute Books, Spinster's Ink 1980 is the first edition)

Written in 1980 following Audre Lorde's breast cancer diagnosis and mastectomy in 1979. She questions the silencing and invisibility that she experiences around breast cancer, and writes openly about facing the possibility of her death. She also makes very clear observations as a woman dealing with the loss of her breast. Thirty years later this still reads like a breath of fresh air and the pages are alive with her anger.

The Frontier Cancer Medicine Guide: Professor Karol Sikora with Patricia Peat (Health Creation Ltd, 2003)

This small book is an exceptionally clear and straightforward guide with questions to ask your medical team to help you make treatment choices. I found this invaluable.

Pink Ribbons, Inc. Breast Cancer and the Politics of Philanthropy: Samantha King (University of Minnesota Press, 2006)

A fascinating read about the pink culture in the USA.

Recovering from Breast Surgery: Diana Stumm (Hunter House, 1995)

A great small book full of practical exercises for after breast surgery of all kinds.

The Secret History of the War on Cancer: Devra Davis (Basic Books, 2007)

A superbly researched and brilliantly written history of the United States' so called 'war on cancer', which started out as a mission to find, treat and cure the disease, but avoided dealing with its basic causes, due to the self interests of industry, tobacco and pharmaceutical companies. Devra Davies is a Nobel prize-winning Professor of Epidemiology and as she says, 'I know what cancer looks like and I know what cancer smells like.' She also knows more about the causes of cancer than any other scientist Ronnie or I have come across. This book could quite literally change the world.

Smile or Die, How Positive Thinking Fooled America & The World: Barbara Ehrenreich (Granta Publications, 2009)

A deeply wise book about the cult of positive thinking that, particularly in the United States, has resulted in immense social pressure to conform to the idea that all misfortunes are 'opportunities'. As well as looking at her own experiences of breast cancer and the pink industry, she also looks at how the addiction to 'putting on a happy face' has caused chaos throughout society and even played its part in the economic destructions of the last few years.

Take off your party dress: Dina Rabinovitch (Pocket Books, 2007)

This is a moving personal breast cancer story.

A Visible Wound: Julie Friedeberger (Element Books Ltd, 1996)

Drawing on her own experience of breast cancer, addressing key issues such as fear of death and coming to terms with mastectomy, and the false breast.

Websites

a sense of place
www.asenseofplace.com

We do creative things.

We're all about making great films and also working in unique ways with organisations and individual entrepreneurs on creating futures full of positive social change.

Being Sarah
www.beingsarah.com

Sarah's website, current news and lots of links to useful resources for breast cancer patients.

Breast cancer pals (bcpals)
bcpals.org.uk/forums/

This is an internet forum based in the UK, and only for women who have experience of breast cancer, unlike other forums that are public. It is used by an exceptionally friendly and helpful group of women.

Cancer Options
www.canceroptions.co.uk/

Cancer Options is a consultancy led by Patricia Peat where you can obtain advice and information for different cancer treatments and therapies.

Health Creation
www.healthcreation.co.uk/

Dr Rosy Daniel, Integrated Medicine Consultant, and a team of Health Creation mentors offer consultations to help you make informed decisions about treatment.

Jennifer Abod - Audre Lorde documentary
www.jenniferabod.com/

Jennifer Abod produced a DVD documentary, The Edge of Each Other's Battles: The Vision of Audre Lorde. It is a tribute to Audre Lorde's legacy of politics and poetry. It is available from her website.

Karen Choudhary
www.karenchoudhary.com

Karen is an energetic and motivational fitness coach who has a passion for coaching women with dreams of running, especially beginners and returners. She works creatively with women and men from all backgrounds delivering dynamic confidence building and exercise programmes that can seriously change your life.

Odyssey
www.odyssey.org.uk

Odyssey is a charity which enhances the quality of life for people being treated for cancer through imaginative programmes of challenging and dramatic activities using the outdoors. They are free for cancer patients. I went on a six-day holiday in Scotland in September 2008. It was brilliant.

Sacred Space Foundation
www.sacredspace.org.uk

The Sacred Space Foundation is a charity providing peaceful and confidential rest and recuperation facilities. It helps those suffering from the extremes of stress, burnout, emotional exhaustion or 'spiritual crisis' that have severely shaken their sense of meaning and direction in life.

Yes to Life
www.yestolife.org.uk/

Yes To Life are a charity set up to help cancer patients with information and in obtaining advice, and also funding for non-toxic treatments for cancer.

Index

Numbers indicated in **bold** denote a mention in the reference and links section.

Thanks

During the three years I have written about here I have been cared for by numerous medical professionals, for the most part in the National Health Service. I am deeply grateful to all of them. And I am grateful that the NHS exists. Thank you Nye Bevan and the post-war Labour government for that.

I thank my brilliant and amazing surgeons. In particular the best surgeon and doctor I know, Alison Waghorn. She will say she's just doing her job, but she's doing much more than that. Alison - thank you so much for your care and your honesty.

Ken Graham, my main plastic surgeon, has gently and quietly performed a series of miracles. He also does his work as though there is nothing else he would rather be doing. He wants to make things better. I thank him deeply, Ken you are a good man. And he also chooses fantastic surgeons to work with: Rowan - your patient-doctor style is so refreshing; Phoebe - you are so glamorous even in surgeon kit; and Mr Koshy - we didn't get to first name terms but you were great on my big day, thank you all.

Dr Rosy Daniel always knew exactly the right things to say, and reminded me that my spirit would guide me. Thank you lovely Rosy.

Stephen Wright helped me when I was vulnerable and afraid, and guided me into my safe harbour. Thank you Stephen, you are a gem.

Patricia Peat at Cancer Options, and Dr Chris Etheridge, thank you both for your support and opinions as I made my treatment choices.

Dr Nielsen, quiet, reticent Hugh, a good doctor. Thank you for your ongoing support and for prescribing Iscador, and giving me the information about it I needed for this book.

June 2007 – with Alison Waghorn in clinic at the Royal, Liverpool.
'She has done everything I asked her. She is a star.'

July 2009 – with Ken Graham in clinic at St Helens hospital.
'He wants everything to be alright for me. He really does.'

Shirley Cottenden, Alison Waghorn's assistant, for super responsive emails and down to earth efficiency. Thank you.

Karol Sikora, for honest and straightforward opinions, I thank you.

I am very grateful to Elaine Sassoon for publishing her book of breast reconstructive surgery and inspiring me with the possibility of a good surgical result. I am also really thankful that the women in her book were brave enough to show, so honestly, their surgeries. You all helped me to feel something deep and exciting, and I thank you all for that.

Anna Beckingham in Norwich, you took the time to meet with me and also showed me your surgery result. This meant a lot to me so thank you.

Tina Gallagher and Alison Goulden, the breast reconstruction nurses at Whiston hospital, thank you for your infinite patience and care. Gina Woolley at Whiston hospital has made me several superb silicone nipples, with the same infinite patience and care, thank you as well. And thanks to Jane MacPhail at Whiston hospital for your scar management expertise. Everyone who works at the dressings clinic at Whiston hospital has been a joy, thank you, I've spent too long in there but you made it a better experience.

Robin Daly at Yes to Life always answered my emails, and never refused a funding request. Thank you Robin. And everyone at Yes to Life, you are brilliant.

My friends on my Odyssey adventure in Argyll, thank you for the amazing experience at exactly the time I really needed it, a great confidence boost.

Louise Cooke pointed me in Rosy's direction, thank you for that Louise, and also for supplying my numerous supplements throughout my recovery, oh, and for the counting backwards in sevens trick.

Julie Templeton, my wise and sensitive counsellor, has helped me as I shaped my thoughts and opinions and found a voice for my pain. Thank you Julie.

Kate Anderson, my brilliant acupuncturist, who reminded me when my spirit was thirsty for nourishment. Thank you Kate.

Mohan, my lovely yoga teacher, generous in spirit and makes me smile when I think of him as a monk on a moped. Thank you for the breathing and relaxation. Namaste.

Dennis Donnelly, my intuitive osteopath, continues to share a deep empathy with me, thanks Dennis I appreciate our times together.

Thanks to my lovely new friends at tai chi: Mike, Daryl, June and Pam, you have all been so welcoming. Thanks for showing me the moves, and especially the hugs.

My cyber forum friends, the women who mostly I haven't met in person, thank you for your kind words and hand holding when most needed. You always understand.

Sheila Davies, a cyber friend I know for real, thank you for supporting me at the times when I needed to be totally honest.

Michelle Pye of English Couture, thanks for the brilliant, inspiring and amazing bra and knicker making courses.

Anne Morris, everyone needs a good accountant, but you are more than an accountant, thank you. And thanks to your team at Macfarlane and co, especially Maxine Dunn.

Sue Wilde, everyone needs good financial advice, and you've provided that and more through a difficult financial time. Thanks.

Jeanette Pilsbury, my champion in the Liverpool Primary Care Trust, thanks for listening.

Our lunch places, Greendays on Lark Lane, the Everyman Bistro, Leaf Teashop and the Neighbourhood; places that lighten up dark days, thanks for the atmosphere and great food.

And I am glad that I found some angry women to help me sharpen my opinions. Audre Lorde, whose words are so deep and have resonated so much for me. Dina Rabinovitch, for expressing the truth about breast cancer. Libby Brooks, for the pinkwashing article. And thank you to Barbara Ehrenreich for so freely giving me permission to quote you, and for helping me feel brave enough to express my opinions.

And even though I have written that there are not many people in my story, I remind myself that in fact there were lots of other people who were around but don't appear in print. Too many people to mention by name; but those of you who followed my story, read my website, sent me emails, prayed for me, thought about me, sent me money - thank you all for your genuine care. Often the small things touched me just when I needed it and the kindness of others, sometimes strangers, has both surprised and moved me. Thank you.

Karen Choudhary and Gemma Murphy both read the draft and gave me honest opinions; thank you both. In particular thanks Karen for the superlative coaching and the continuing fun and conversation, as well as taking the photo of me and Ronnie. Thank you Gemma for the ace hair cuts and the lovely conversations we have in the salon.

Thanks to David Parrish, for interesting conversations and creative sound business advice, and also for introducing me to Fiona Shaw. Thanks Dave.

Fiona Shaw at Wordscapes always gave the right advice at the right moments, is an eagle-eyed editor, made sure this book got published, and that I didn't over-rant, thank you. Ken Ashcroft has lovingly designed the most beautiful cover and text styling, and made sure this book got to look as good as I wanted it to, thanks.

Thanks to Ellie, age 18 months to three and a half years during this book, and with us most Mondays during this time. She reminded me about playing and total joy. She also came with us to Whiston hospital many times and Ken Graham gave her a bag of jelly babies.

Greenbank Lane allotments, where I have my garden on plot 44, a place of refuge for me, thank you for this very special place.

Brendan Byrne, for just being there all the way through and for being with me in my garden, thanks mate.

And finally 'thank you' doesn't seem quite enough for the one person who knows about everything in this book, and some more: my beloved partner, husband, best friend, soul mate - Ronnie Hughes. He who cared, and cares, so deeply for me. I love you and I am truly grateful. Grow old with me.

A note about the author

Sarah Horton is not just a breast cancer patient, although being one has taken up most of three years of her life. She is an artist, a film-maker, a knitter, a gardener, a quilter, and a runner. *Being Sarah* is her first book.

Sarah lives with her husband Ronnie Hughes. She and Ronnie have run their own business together, *a sense of place,* since 1996. They do creative things.

She divides her time between her home and her allotment, both in south Liverpool.